2.46

"The first farmer was the first man, and all historic
nobility rests on possession and use of land."
—EMERSON

LIPPINCOTT'S
FARM MANUALS

EDITED BY
KARY C. DAVIS, PH.D.

PROFESSOR OF AGRICULTURE, KNAPP SCHOOL OF COUNTRY LIFE, GEORGE
PEABODY COLLEGE FOR TEACHERS, NASHVILLE, TENNESSEE.

AGRICULTURAL MECHANICS
BY ROBERT H. SMITH

LIPPINCOTT'S FARM MANUALS

EDITED BY K. C. DAVIS, Ph.D.

AGRICULTURAL MECHANICS

BY

ROBERT H. SMITH

MEMBER AMERICAN SOCIETY OF AGRICULTURAL ENGINEERS.
INSTRUCTOR IN FARM ENGINEERING AND MECHANICS,
NEW YORK STATE SCHOOL OF AGRICULTURE
AT THE ST. LAWRENCE UNIVERSITY,
CANTON, N. Y.

"If vain our toil,
We ought to blame the culture, not the soil."
POPE—*Essay on Man.*

CHICAGO   PHILADELPHIA
J. B. LIPPINCOTT COMPANY

PREFACE

RECENT developments in agriculture and agricultural education have created a need for specialized instruction in farm shop work. As many of the teachers of vocational agriculture are too busy with teaching and community work, and as others are limited in their own shop training, it has been the purpose of the author to prepare a shop book so clear in its illustrations and in its instructive matter as to fully warrant the placing of the book in the hands of each student. It should not require a great deal of attention on the part of the instructor.

The modern farm carries a wide variety of equipment. The effectiveness of this equipment and the opportunity of conserving labor by its use depend upon its handling and care—a certain degree of mechanical ability is essential to successful operation.

This ability must be possessed by the farmer. But few farms are large enough to support a professional repairman, while their isolation prevents securing the services of a workman from town for making the every-day minor repairs.

In this book the attempt is made to present a course of instruction adapted to these conditions. The aim is not to make of the reader a plumber, carpenter, blacksmith, harness-maker, tinner, or painter, but rather to give him such essentials of these and other trades as will enable him to make satisfactory, practical repairs of farm equipment and to construct such new devices as will assist him in his work.

Instruction is given largely by the project method. Many devices for use in the farm shop, the dairy, the poultry-house, and other departments of farm activity are grouped under appropriate heads and used for this purpose.

This grouping of the projects permits the selection of a course adapted to the region served by the school, while the careful job analysis of each project permits the shop work to be carried on with the minimum amount of attention from the busy instructor and thus gives opportunity for student selection and individual work, taking the " project " out of the class of the hated " exercise " and making of it something desired and connected with the boy's farm enterprise and his experience.

Several methods of having the classes pursue the work are suggested:

1. In direct correlation with the particular farm project which the student is pursuing at the time—doing such work and making the things which will contribute to the success of his major enterprise. By this plan the shop work may parallel his home project work in agriculture.

2. If courses are more fixed in length and in term or season, mid-winter is probably best for most of the shop work. Students may follow more or less uniform work, all well adapted to the farms of the region.

3. If classes are not too large, the courses offered in the school should be very flexible. The needs of each student and the conditions of each home farm may be more fully considered and met by the work assigned to members of the class.

The projects have been gathered from many sources during the author's teaching experience and are in use in his classes. They have been selected, not only for the tool processes involved, but also because of the practicability of products and their use about the farm when completed.

Throughout the book emphasis is laid on utility, strength, and good construction rather than on exterior finish. Due to this and the fact that all of the devices are clearly illustrated and accompanied by a careful analysis of their construction, the book should be of value to farm-owners and operators as well as to students.

The author wishes to acknowledge with gratitude the many helps he has received from manufacturers, farmers, and others in the preparation of this manuscript.

OCTOBER, 1924.   ROBERT H. SMITH.

CONTENTS

JOBS ARRANGED BY FARM ENTERPRISES

Crops

Dairy Cattle

ix

Farm Buildings

Farm Machinery

Farm Shop

Horses

Household

Poultry

Surveying

Swine

AGRICULTURAL MECHANICS

CHAPTER I

THE FARM SHOP. INTERIOR ARRANGEMENT, TOOL EQUIPMENT, SELECTION OF TOOLS, POWER FOR THE SHOP, SUPPLIES

Necessity of a Shop on a Modern Farm.—The operation of a modern farm has become, to a large extent, a problem of engineering and mechanics. Farm buildings of the present time are costly structures that must have expert attention to be maintained with minimum deterioration. Crops are planted, cultivated, and harvested by the aid of machinery. Not only is the heavy, brutal work of the farm at present done by machinery, but tasks, such as milking, that have long been considered distinctly manual work, are now done mechanically. The efficient care and operation of the farm equipment, the necessary repairs and alterations to the buildings, as well as the design and construction of new devices to aid in the farm work, make a tool equipment and skill in its use essential to the successful operation of the farm.

The Farm Shop.—No definite design can be given for a shop to fit all cases; it must be made to meet the needs of the farm it is built to serve, and may range in size from a small space about a bench in an already existing out-building to a fully equipped machine-shop (Fig. 1). In general it is best to have a separate room or building devoted to this work, and as nearly as may be, it should meet the following requirements:

1. It should be convenient of access and well lighted by windows placed in the sides.
2. The walls should be tight and warm and provision made for heating.
3. It should have a wide entrance-door and a clear floor-space large enough to permit working about machinery brought in for repairs.
4. An overhead loft, reached by inside stairs and provided with an outside gable door through which long material may be passed, should be provided for the storage of lumber used in making repairs. A convenient way of storing this material is on racks built along the sides and down the center of the loft (Fig. 2).
5. Where running water is available a sloping concrete floor provided with a drain, makes it possible to clean vehicles and other farm equipment in comfort during cold weather.

1

FIG. 1.—Exterior of an inexpensive farm shop.

FIG. 2.—Rack for storing lumber. Home-made power sawing outfit in the foreground.

The importance of lighting and heating should not be over-looked, as most of the shop work will be done during winter and on rainy summer days when outside work is not possible. A portion of the tool-shed partitioned off and fitted up as described makes an ideal shop: it is convenient to the machinery to be cared for and can usually be constructed at a less cost than can a separate building.

Tool Equipment.—Farm shop work is largely in the nature of repairs. Such new devices as are made require ruggedness and good construction rather than exterior finish, and these facts should be kept in mind when selecting the tool equipment.

The tools selected should be strong, rugged, and made of the best materials. Their value should lie in strength and quality rather than in superficial finish. To secure a tool equipment of this kind buy well-known brands only, selecting each item singly, starting with the ones absolutely essential and adding to these as experience is gained in their use.

The following tool equipment for woodworking is suggested for the farm shop. The tools marked with a star are considered essential and should form a nucleus about which the others may be gathered.

List of Woodworking and Miscellaneous Tools for the Farm Shop.

* 1 26″ rip saw, 6 points per inch.
* 1 26″ cutting-off saw, 8 points per inch.
* 1 carpenters' steel framing square.
* 1 bell face, adze eye nail hammer.
* 1 ratchet bit brace, 12″ sweep.
* 1 set of auger bits, ¼″ to 1″ inclusive by sixteenths.
* 4 socket firmer chisels, ¼″, ½″, 1″ and 1½″.
* 1 18″ iron bottom fore plane. (optional) 1 16″ iron bottom jack plane.
* 1 mallet, made in the shop.
* 1 wood vise, screw purchased, remainder made in the shop.
* 2 screw-drivers, one large, one small.
* 1 carborundum medium grit sharpening stone.

1 10″ drawing knife.	1 8″ try square.
1 10″ sliding tee bevel.	1 24″ carpenter's level.
1 9″ smoothing plane.	1 6″ block plane.
1 pair 10″ side cutting pliers.	1 snail head countersink.
1 expansive bit.	1 adze.
1 wrecking bar.	1 putty knife.
1 12″ half-round wood rasp.	3 nail sets, assorted sizes.
1 carpenters' broad hatchet.	1 10″ rectangular file.
1 saw set.	1 compass saw.
1 glass cutter.	1 pair 8″ dividers.
1 10″ flat file.	1 10′ to 12′ straight edge.
1 6″ slim taper file.	1 set Syracuse twist drills.
1 auger bit file.	1 slip for sharpening gouges.
1 chalk and line.	1 plumb bob.

2 gouges, ½″ and 1″.

Interior Arrangement.—A convenient arrangement for a small shop is shown in the floor-plan (Fig. 3). The wall-space over the benches is painted a light color and a hook or other support arranged for holding each tool. When the tools are in place an

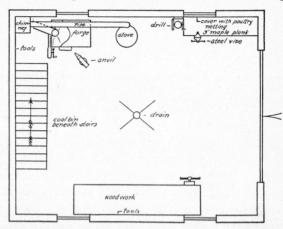

FIG. 3.—Floor-plan for farm shop. Size 16 x 20. When room is limited steel vise and drill press may be attached to woodworking bench.

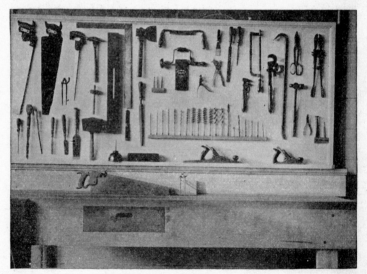

FIG. 4.—Tool board over bench with saw and dividers removed, showing silhouette behind.

outline is drawn around each and the silhouette blocked in with black (Fig. 4), making the place for each tool apparent. As a further protection against loss all tools should be marked with the owner's name. This can be done with a steel stamp or the name may be etched on with hydrochloric acid by coating the place to be marked with hot wax, scratching the name through the wax coating with a needle, applying the acid, and cleaning the tool up thoroughly after the action has been allowed to continue for a few

Fig. 5.—Power sawing outfit for ripping, cross-cutting, mitering, and grooving; made in the farm shop.

minutes. Painting the handles a distinctive color is another means of keeping the tool-kit intact.

The forge can be placed in one corner and a cinder or concrete floor should be provided about it to lessen the fire risk. The forge tools can be arranged on the wall about it in the way already described for the woodworking tools. The space beneath the stairs is utilized as a coal-bin. Heating a long iron in the middle is possible by extending the end through the window.

Power for the Shop.—A three-horse power gasoline engine furnishes ample power for driving a 12-inch circular saw, and if first belted to a line shaft can be used for other work as well. An outfit of this size (Fig. 5) will rip stock 3½ inches in thickness, and if the work is reversed can be used for heavier material.

Supplies.—The following list of supplies is suggested:

Lumber for the replacement of eveners and other wood parts of implements.

A limited assortment of round, square, and flat iron bars.

Spare parts for farm machines that are subject to rapid wear or frequent breakage.

Bolts, nuts, washers, spring cotters, rivets, nails, staples, wire, buckles, rings, hame fittings, faucet washers, pipe fittings, belt lacing, paints, oil, glass, and putty.

Storage of Supplies.—Machine parts, together with spare shovels, hoes, and forks are best cared for by hanging on the wall (Fig. 6). Small articles should be kept in separate containers. Separate storage permits instant location of the needed bolt or washer when making a repair and makes it easy to maintain the stock by purchase as it becomes depleted through use. Rectangular bread tins, obtainable at any five and ten cent store, make excellent containers for this purpose. The tins are marked by soldering or wiring one of the articles contained to the end and are placed on shelves near the bench. The labeled ends of the tins serve as an index of the supplies and make the location of any item easy. Boxes, approximately 3½″ deep, 6″ wide, and 12″ long, made in the shop, can be used in the same way or a storage cabinet similar to the one shown in figure 114, can be made for the purpose. This should be built to fit the existing space. Paints, oil, and putty are best stored in the original cans to prevent oxidation and hardening of the surface.

QUESTIONS AND EXERCISES

1. Draw a plan of one of the best farm shops you have seen.
2. Draw a floor-plan, changing the above to meet the needs of your particular place.
3. Calculate the cost of material required to build the shop building for your place.
4. From the list of tools given select those most necessary for shop work on your own place.
5. Obtain prices for the purchase of such a list of tools.
6. What articles of equipment for the shop can be made? Calculate the cost of supplies necessary to make them.
7. Where would you wish your shop to be located? Would you wish it to have doors and floor-space sufficient to admit mowers, binders, and other heavy farm machinery for repairs? Give arguments for and against this.

CHAPTER II

TOOLS, THEIR ADJUSTMENT, USE, AND CARE

THE present chapter describes briefly how to care for and adjust the principal tools of the farm shop. It is essential that tools

FIG. 6.—Farm shop interior, showing method of storing field tools.

be kept keen and in the best possible adjustment if good work is to be done with them (Fig. 6).

Planes designed for smoothing are the principal ones used. They are made in five models as shown in figure 7.

The jointer plane is from 20 inches to 28 inches long with a 2½-inch cutting blade or bit. It is heavy and sturdy in construction and is designed for straightening edges and surfaces.

7

The fore plane is similar to the jointer but is shorter, being about 18 inches long. Because of its shorter length and greater convenience it is used on smaller work. For the farm shop this plane can take the place of the jointer in the plane equipment.

The jack plane is from 14 inches to 16 inches long. It is designed for pre-surfacing rough lumber that is afterward to be finished with the smoothing plane. When used for this purpose the cutting edge should be ground to a broad curve rather than a straight line. It is frequently used in place of the jointer or fore plane, and when kept for this purpose the edge should have a slight curvature only.

The smoothing plane is a short, broad plane about 9 inches

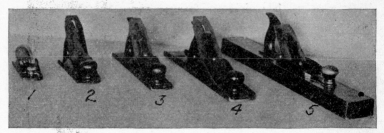

Fig. 7.—Five models of common planes: 1, block plane; 2, smoothing plane; 3, jack plane; 4, fore plane; 5, jointer.

long. It is used to give a smooth surface to the work after the inequalities have been leveled with one of the longer planes.

The block plane is about 6 inches long. It is designed for planing across the end grain of wood. Ordinarily this plane should be but little used. Although convenient for occasional use, the smoothing plane, if properly set, will do most of the work required of it.

Parts of the Plane.—The accompanying illustration (Fig. 8) and explanation of the different parts aids in understanding the plane and its proper adjustment.

The plane iron or bit is the cutting edge of the plane. It should be ground to the proper shape (Fig. 9), whetted keen, and adjusted to cut a thin shaving over its entire width.

The plane iron cap (2) has three uses: it provides a spring tension for holding the plane iron tightly to its seat; it permits lowering the cutting edge as it is worn away through use; and its curved shape at the lower end breaks the shaving as it is pared

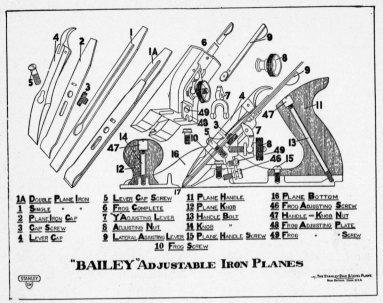

FIG. 8.—Parts of the plane and their relation to each other.

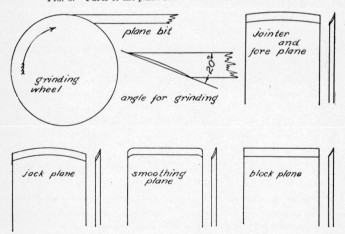

FIG. 9.—Proper angle for grinding plane irons, with shape of edge for different types of planes shown somewhat exaggerated.

from the wood, thus tending to prevent splintering. It should be sharp at the lower edge and should fit tightly to the plane bit. It is aided in breaking the shaving by the forward edge of the throat (17), and it is sometimes desirable to move the frog (6), which carries the cutting and adjusting mechanism, forward, closing the throat somewhat and bringing the cutting edge nearer the bearing edge (17).

The adjusting nut (8) is used to move the cutting edge up or down for a thicker or thinner shaving, turning it to the right or to the left as the case requires. It acts through the " Y " adjusting lever (7).

The lateral adjusting lever (9) is used to bring the cutting edge parallel to the width of the bottom surface of the plane by swinging it sidewise. The under side of the plane is called the sole, the forward end being termed the toe, while the part back of the handle is called the heel.

The lever cap (4) clamps the cutting mechanism in place through the action of the cam lever at the top. The lever cap screw (5) serves as a fulcrum and should be tightened until the lever works snugly and the plane bit is held securely.

Sharpening the Plane.—Plane irons are sharpened by grinding, whetting, and stropping. The grinding may be done either on a high-speed dry grinding-wheel, or on the regular grindstone. Hold the plane iron against the grinding-wheel as shown in figure 9, forming a bevel of from 20 to 25 degrees. Be careful to retain the original angle of bevel.

Whetting and stropping a plane iron is necessary to smooth up the rough edge left by grinding. A good artificial stone of medium fine grit is used for this purpose. Because of the use of oil to float off the steel particles removed by whetting, it is called

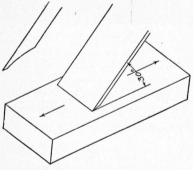

an oil-stone. A good grade of light, non-gumming oil should be used and the stone kept clean and covered when not in use (Fig. 10).

Tests for Keenness.—A rough test for keenness is to hold the edge to the light. If dull, it will appear as a fine bright line, due to its rounded condition. If keen, it will be invisible. A surer test is to draw

FIG. 10.—Position of plane iron when whetting.

the thumb lightly over the edge to be tested (Fig. 11). The thumb will slip over a dull edge, while a sharp one will catch in the cuticle. Care must be exercised in doing this or a bad cut may result. After whetting a plane iron the parts should be wiped free from grit before reassembling (Fig. 12). Test the plane on a piece of waste wood and, if necessary, adjust until it cuts properly.

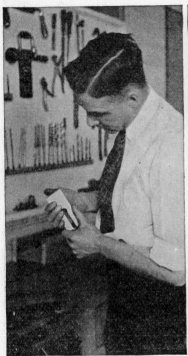

FIG. 11.—Testing an edge for keenness.   FIG. 12.—Adjusting plane for thickness of shaving.

The proper thickness of shaving will vary with the work being done. Where the purpose is to reduce in size, a comparatively thick shaving may be taken. Where it is desired to smooth the work only, the plane should be set to cut lightly. A properly whetted and adjusted plane will pare a thin shaving, which will come from the throat in curls (Fig. 13).

Precautions to Prevent Dulling.—To avoid unnecessary dulling, form the habit of placing the plane on its side when not in use, keeping the edge from contact with the gritty bench-top. A drop of light machine oil applied occasionally to the moving parts of the plane keeps them working easily and free from rust.

Troubles and Remedies.—When a good plane, properly whetted and adjusted, fails to do satisfactory work there is usually some

FIG. 13.—A properly adjusted plane will engage the wood easily and pare a thin shaving which will come from the throat in curls.

FIG. 14.—Smoothing up the nose and heel of plane with file.

easily removable cause that is making the trouble. Some of the most common troubles are outlined here with means of correcting them.

  1. *Choking* is caused by shavings catching beneath the lower edge of the cap iron and lever cap, which should be filed smooth. Wet or pitchy lumber will frequently cause clogging. Keep the plane keen and clean frequently.

  2. *Chattering* is caused by the springing of the cutting mechanism, if set too deep, clogged with wood, or if material is knotty.

  3. *Ridges* or *Marks* on *Finished Work* are of two kinds, raised or sunken. The common causes are nicks in the blade, high corners on the blade, and roughness on heel or toe of the plane, which may be smoothed by filing (Fig. 14).

Other Edged Tools.—The sharpening of chisels, slicks, hand axes, draw knives, and other tools having a similar bevel is much the same as for plane irons. The angle of bevel is approximately the same—about 30 degrees— and should vary with the work for which the tool is being fitted. For heavy mortising in hard, knotty wood a chisel should have a blunter bevel than when fitted for paring or other light work. The extremely thin edge produced by the long bevel is not strong enough to stand up under heavy work. When whetting the draw knife it is more convenient to hold it rigidly and move the oil-stone over it. (Fig. 15).

Fig. 15.—Whetting a draw knife.

Hand Saws.—The saw equipment will consist of a rip saw, a cutting-off saw, and a compass saw. The first two mentioned are

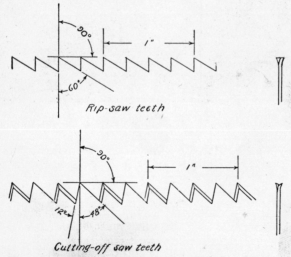

Fig. 16.—Shape of rip and cutting-off saw teeth with method of measuring points per inch.

alike in general appearance but are differentiated by the shape of their teeth (Fig. 16). The compass saw has a much narrower blade than the others, which permits it to be passed through a small opening and to be turned easily when cutting a curved outline. A saw is designated by its length and the number of points per inch, which will be found stamped on the blade near the handle. It will be noted that there is one more point per inch than there are teeth (Fig. 16).

Fitting the Saws.—The points of the teeth must be in an even line from the heel to the point of the saw, sharp, even, and of the proper shape. This line should not be straight, but should be slightly curved, giving what is termed "breast" or "crown" to the saw. A thin stiff blade is necessary for easy cutting.

Jointing is the first step in saw-fitting (Fig. 17). A file is run lengthwise of the saw blade with its face at right angles to the side

Fig. 17.—Jointing a saw.

of the saw and the teeth dressed to a uniform height. Jointing should be carried no further than required to get this result, as it makes more filing necessary. The original crown of the saw should be preserved when jointing. If it has been destroyed by previous filings it should be restored somewhat at this time. The crown should be restored gradually, adding a little more curvature each time the saw is jointed until the original shape is restored. A saw that is kept in good condition will require but a few light strokes of the file to bring the points of the teeth to an even line.

Setting.—After the saw is jointed it should be set (Fig. 18) by bending the points of the teeth alternately to the right and left, making the edge of the saw slightly wider than the back and permitting it to run freely in the cut. A good saw has its back ground thinner than the toothed edge and requires but little set. Put the set in the points of the teeth only, and set each tooth equally. Setting at the bases of the teeth results in a hard running saw and may

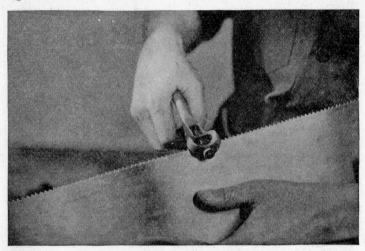

Fig. 18.—Setting saw with lever set.

distort or crack the blade. If the saw is kept in good condition a single setting will do for two or more filings, a sharp saw requiring much less set than one that is dull. More set is required for wet or green lumber than for dry material.

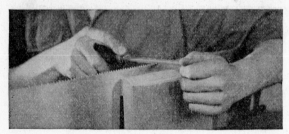

Fig. 19.—Filing a saw.

Filing the teeth to a point or edge is the third operation in saw-fitting. Due to the shape of the teeth the cutting-off saw and rip saw are filed differently.

Filing the Rip Saw.—Place the saw in the clamp, securely fastened breast-high in a good light (Fig. 19). Use a file to fit the work; usually a 5-inch or 6-inch slim taper file will give good results on saws of this size. Grasp the file-handle firmly in the right hand and support the tip of the file between the thumb and fingers of the left hand (Fig. 19). Hold the file level and file straight across at right angles to the edge of the saw in such a way that the face of the tooth will be vertical (Fig. 20). If the teeth show unevenness in size crowd the file against the larger ones to make them uniform. Use the file its full length and release the pressure on the return stroke, as it cuts only in a forward direction. Filing may be begun at either the heel or point of the saw, filing each alternate tooth,

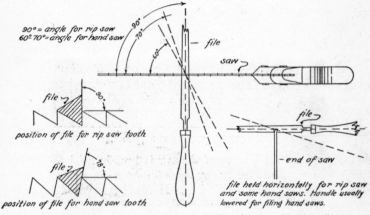

Fig. 20.—Shape of teeth and positions of file in filing rip saw and cutting-off saw.

then reversing and filing the other side. A noted saw-manufacturer recommends filing from the point of the saw against the cutting edge of the teeth turned toward the filer by setting. Filing " against the set " in this way prevents the formation of the " feather edge," so likely to be produced when filing is done from the back of the tooth " with the set." If the saw is securely clamped close to the edge there will be little trouble from chattering. The proper shape of the rip saw tooth is shown in figures 16 and 20.

Filing the Hand Saw.—The teeth of this saw, being designed for cutting across the grain, differ in shape from those of the rip saw. The angle at the point remains 60 degrees, but the whole tooth is tipped backward so that the front stands at an angle of about 12 degrees with the vertical (Fig. 16). This makes the back of the tooth meet the edge of the saw quicker and results in a deeper tooth for a given number of points per inch. The face of the tooth is also given some bevel, the exact amount depending upon the work for which the saw is being fitted. A bevel suitable for general use is formed by holding the file across the edge of the saw at an angle from 60 to 70 degrees with the length of the blade (Fig. 20). The handle of the file should be lowered slightly; it forms a little deeper tooth and tends to prevent chattering. More bevel is given for soft woods than for hard dry material. After filing, the saw should be examined and any of the teeth showing " tops," indicating that they have not yet been brought to a point, should be carefully pointed up. Discontinue filing as soon as a point has been reached, or the tooth will be made too short.

Side-filing.—Place the saw-blade flat on the bench-top and with a flat file or oil-stone rub lightly on the sides of the teeth

FIG. 21.—Side-filing a saw to even up set.

(Fig. 21). Side-filing must not be overdone or the saw will bind or pinch in the cut. A properly fitted hand saw, when the sight is directed along the toothed edge from heel to point, should show a groove down which a fine needle might be slid the length of the blade.

The compass saw is designed for sawing curves and for working in places where the regular saw-blade would be too wide. It is given a wide set to permit it to be turned readily in the cut. As it cuts both lengthwise and crosswise of the grain its teeth are a compromise between those of the cutting-off saw and those of the rip saw, having little bevel and with the face of the tooth nearly vertical.

The steel square is a tool used in laying out and assembling work, and must be kept a right angle if satisfactory work is to be done with it. Using it as a scraper to remove dirt or concrete from

2

lumber results in wear and inaccuracy. A fall may open or close
the angle slightly, making the square inaccurate. Should this hap-
pen, it may be returned to its original shape by placing it on an
anvil and peening lightly near
the outside or inside corner as
the case requires (Fig. 22).

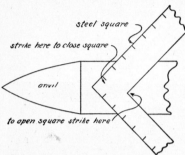

FIG. 22.–Peening a square to restore accuracy.

The level is used in building, its purpose being to insure
that work is placed "level," or
parallel with the horizon; or
"plumb," which is at right angles to a level surface. It acts by
the pull of gravity, the necessary
parts being a glass tube filled
nearly full with ether or other
non-freezing liquid and a stock for carrying this bubble tube. The
bubble tube is mounted in such a way that the lower edge of the
stock is level when the bubble stands in the middle. When placed
on an inclined surface the bubble floats to the higher end of the
tube. To cause it to stand in the center of the tube when the work
has finally been made level the tube is curved.

Testing and Adjusting the Level.—The level is frequently
made inaccurate by careless handling. If the bubble changes posi-

FIG. 23.—Testing and adjusting a level. The bubble should stay in the same position when
the level is reversed.

tion when the level is changed end for end on a solid plane surface
it shows that the level is out of adjustment. In all the better levels
the bubble tube is supported in a frame that may be adjusted by
means of a screw (Fig. 23).

Selecting a Level.—A good carpenters' level with a wood stock made up from several pieces glued together makes a satisfactory tool for farm use. This construction tends to prevent warping. A machinist's level with a metal frame is more accurate, but is also more easily broken.

Auger bits are used for boring practically all holes in wood from ¼ inch in diameter up. The type with the solid-center stem

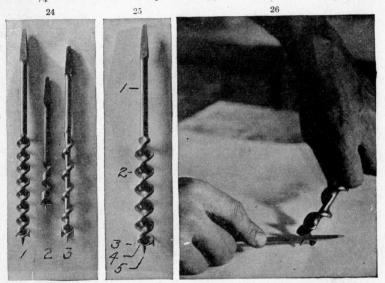

Fig. 24.—Common types of auger bits: 1, Russell-Jenning's pattern; 2, Ford pattern; 3, Irwin pattern.

Fig. 25.—Parts of the auger bit: 1, shank; 2, twist; 3, scoring nibs or nickers; 4, cutting lips; 5, spur.

Fig. 26.—Sharpening an auger bit. The cutting edges are filed on the inside.

gives good service in farm use where strength is a consideration (Fig. 24). The auger bit has five parts (Fig. 25).

Sharpening the auger bit is best done with a small file made for that purpose, although a small triangular file can be used (Fig. 26).

Prevention of Rust.—A small quantity of "Kant-Rust," "Three-in-one," or other acid-free, light mineral oil applied occasionally to the polished surfaces of tools with a soft cloth will keep them in their original condition. Should rust develop through neglect, rub with fine emery cloth and apply oil. Satisfactory work cannot be done with dull, rusty tools.

Selection of Files for Saw Filing.—The following table, adapted from Disston's *Tool Manual,* gives the correct size and type of file for fitting hand saws.

Files for Saw Filing

Kind of saw	Points per inch	Kind of file	Size of file
Cutting-off	5–5½	triangular	6″ regular taper
Cutting-off	6–9	triangular	6″ slim taper
Cutting-off	10–11	triangular	6″ extra slim taper
Rip-saw	4	triangular	6″ regular taper
Rip-saw	4½–6	triangular	4½″ regular taper

QUESTIONS AND EXERCISES

1. Describe the different types of planes that you have seen in use.
2. Study types and sizes of planes in tool catalogues and determine which you would select for home use. Give reasons for the selection made.
3. Devise a simple tool-rest for use with your grindstone which will help in securing the proper bevel when grinding your planes.
4. How would you use a dry grinding wheel to prevent overheating tools ground upon it?
5. If an oil-stone becomes glazed so that it does not cut properly what would be the probable effect of washing it with kerosene oil?
6. What would be the probable effect of using a heavy oil on a stone that cuts too rapidly?
7. From a good tool catalogue select a steel square for farm use and give reasons for the selection made.
8. When a plane bothers by shavings clogging in the throat what are the possible causes? How may the condition be remedied?
9. Study types of auger bits in a tool catalogue and make a selection for farm-shop use. What qualities did you consider in making this selection and why?
10. Explain how an auger bit is sharpened.
11. Explain the difference between a cutting-off saw tooth and a rip-saw tooth. What part of the tooth cuts in each case?
12. Where should the set be placed? What is the objection to bending the tooth at the base in setting?
13. Under what conditions would you consider it best to attempt to file your own saws? Under what conditions would it be best to have them fitted by a professional filer?
14. Explain how a level can be tested and adjusted.
15. What can be done to prevent and remove rust in caring for tools?

CHAPTER III

BASIC TOOL OPERATIONS

EVERY piece of shopwork, whether it be repairing or new construction, is a combination of such basic tool operations as planing, ripping, boring, etc. For example, the fitting of a board to a rectangular opening involves the operations of squaring, cutting to length, and ripping to the correct width. Jointing and smoothplaning may be necessary also if the piece is to be closely fitted.

Laying Out Work.—It is seldom that a board is found whose edges are exactly parallel. For this reason all work should be laid out from one edge, one face, and one end, called respectively the

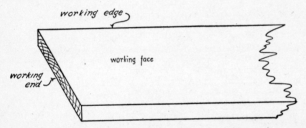

FIG. 27.—Working face, working edge, and working end.

working edge, the working face, and the working end (Fig. 27). Study processes of making these very true in figures 28, 29, 30, 31, and 32.

Gauging.—Set the gauge the required distance from the point. (1) Measure this distance with the rule as shown in figure 33, for due to wear the graduations on the beam cannot always be trusted. (2) Roll the gauge slightly, so that the point engages the wood lightly at an angle, and push it from one end of the work to the other (Fig. 34), keeping the gauge-head crowded against the working edge. (3) Rough-gauging may be done with the rule and pencil as shown in figure 35.

Rip-sawing.—Hold the work with the knee as shown in figure 36. Keep the saw at an angle of about 45 degrees and cut with long, easy sweeps. Use little pressure; crowding will cause the saw

21

FIG. 28.—Smooth-planing a piece of stock to establish a working face.
FIG. 29.—Jointing edge of stock to establish working edge. Note method of holding down nose of plane when it is being run onto stock.
FIG. 30.—Testing with try square to see that edge is kept at right angles with working face.
FIG. 31.—Testing straightness of edge by sighting.

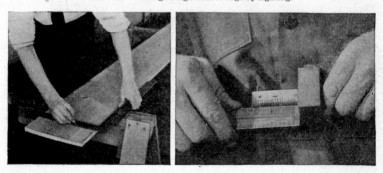

FIG. 32.—Squaring the end of a board, establishing a working end.

FIG. 33.—Setting gauge with rule.

to " run " to one side. Saw in the waste wood about ⅛ inch outside the line to provide material for jointing. Tests should be made fre-

Fig. 34.—Use of gauge. It is crowded against the edge of the board and pulled or pushed along to form mark.

Fig. 35.—Rough-gauging with rule and pencil. The rule and pencil are held as shown and drawn along the edge of the board.

quently with the try square as shown in figure 37 to insure that the edge is kept square.

Sawing across the grain is done with the cutting-off saw. It should be held as shown in figure 38, and the cut made in the waste wood, touching the line but not cutting into it.

Fig. 36.—Method of holding work while rip-sawing.

Fig. 37.—Using the try square to maintain a vertical saw cut.

Fig. 38.—Using the cutting-off saw.

Using the Compass Saw.—Where it is desired to follow a curved line the edge of the saw should be held at right angles to the

FIG. 39.—Using the compass saw.

face of the work (Fig. 39). If held at an angle as directed for the other saws it will undercut and make it impossible to obtain a square edge.

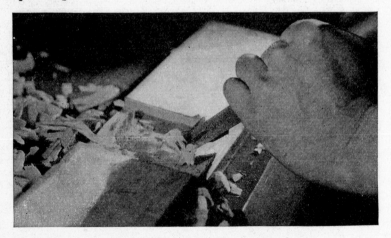

FIG. 40.—Rough-paring with chisel, beveled edge down.

Using the Chisel.—The chisel is used in two general ways: (1) with the mallet, as in beating out a mortise; (2) with the hand, as when paring a surface.

For rough paring and the rapid removal of wood, hold the chisel as shown in figure 40, with the bevel down and the edge obliquely across the work. It is guided with the left hand and forced through the wood with the right, using blows with the palm of the hand if

FIG. 41.—Smooth-paring with chisel. Chisel held flat with beveled edge uppermost.

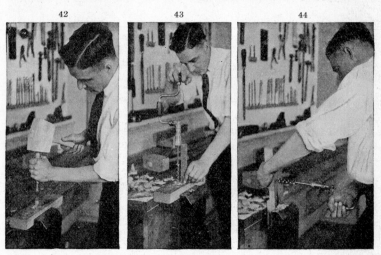

FIG. 42.—Beating out a mortise.
FIG. 43.—Using try square to insure boring hole at right angles to face of stock.
FIG. 44.—Through boring, using hand back of material to detect point of bit when it comes through to avoid splintering.

necessary. Where a true flat surface is required the chisel is used with the bevel up and laid flat, or nearly so, on the work (Fig. 41).

The wood is first scored by cutting parallel grooves across it with the corner of the chisel and the waste material then pared out. To prevent splintering keep the chisel keen and work from both edges toward the center.

Remove all the material possible by boring when making a mortise. A through mortise is laid out and worked from both sides to insure accurate work. Hold the chisel as shown in figure 42, with the bevel toward the opening made by boring.

Boring in wood should be done carefully. (1) Unless at an angle the hole should be made perpendicular to the surface by means of a try square (Fig. 43). Practice gives a sense of perpendicularity that should be cultivated. (2) When boring through material place the hand back of the work and start the bit from the opposite side as soon as the lead screw pricks through (Fig. 44). This will prevent splintering. A piece of waste material clamped back of the work can be used for the same purpose. (3) Continue turning in the forward direction when pulling the bit out. This cleans the chips from the hole.

Hewing.—In rough construction wane-edged boards are frequently straightened with the hand-axe. A guide line is made with the chalk line or straight edge, and the axe first used at an abrupt angle, making cuts at intervals of two to four inches along the edge of the work nearly to the line. It is then used more nearly parallel to the line and the waste wood removed (Fig. 45).

Fig. 45.—Hewing with hand axe. The board is first "scored" to prevent splitting and then hewed to the line.

Scribing, Laying Out Work with the Dividers.—The dividers are used in "scribing" an edge to fit against an irregular surface. The board to be fitted is temporarily fastened in position with its edge against the surface it is to fit when finished. The dividers are set with the points separated by a slightly greater distance than the width of the greatest opening between the parts to be fitted and are drawn along the length of the board, one leg bearing against the irregular surface and the other point tracing a parallel line on the board (Fig. 46).

When using the dividers to lay off a distance in a given number of equal parts set them as closely as possible on the square (Fig.

47), making the final close adjustment with the nut on the side. Step off the distance along a straight line, and should it not come out exact the first time change the space of the divider points an amount proportionate to the error, and space the line again.

Fig. 46.—"Scribing" a board with the dividers to fit against an irregular surface. One leg follows the surface to be fitted while the other traces a corresponding mark on the board.

Fig. 47.—Setting dividers. Making final close adjustment by means of thumb-screw.

Leveling and Plumbing.—The following precautions should be observed when using the level. (1) See that it rests fairly on the work. Where the surface is irregular, a long straight edge with parallel edges may be placed against it and the level held on this. This provides a representative bearing for the level. A level line may be carried a considerable distance by first setting a row of stakes and marking from one to another with the level and straight edge. (2) Where a level line is to be carried any distance the level should be turned end for end at each alternate application. This tends to correct inaccuracies in the level and prevents them from becoming cumulative. (3) Handle the level carefully at all times. When necessary to tap the work being leveled to bring it to position the level should be raised and not allowed to receive the jar of the hammer blow.

Using the Plumb Bob and Line.—In building it is often necessary to locate a point on the ceiling directly over another on

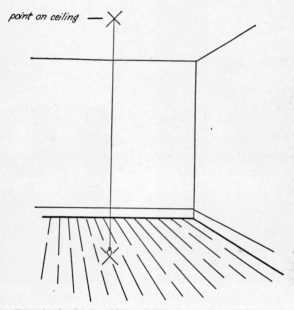

point on ceiling — ✕

FIG. 48.—Using the plumb bob and line to transfer a point from the floor to the ceiling.

the floor, or *vice versa*. This is best done with the plumb bob and line. Suspend the bob from the ceiling, using line enough to permit it to swing just clear of the floor (Fig. 48) and move it about until the point of the bob comes to rest just over the desired point on the floor. Mark the point where the line touches the ceiling. To transfer a point from the ceiling to the floor suspend the bob from the point on the ceiling and mark the point on the floor where the bob comes to rest. The points are best marked by two lines crossing at an angle, the intersection being directly over the point. See that the bob swings clear and is protected from the wind.

The sliding tee bevel is used for laying out work at any angle other than a right angle. It is set in one of three ways: (1) By fitting it to an angle already cut. (2) By juxtaposition over a draw-

ing. (3) By means of the steel square. Practically any angle can be obtained from the square. The bevel is held against it as shown in figure 49, and set to the angle desired. The numbers shown in figure 50 will give the angles listed on the diagonal lines. The blade of the bevel must cut the graduations exactly on the edge of the square.

FIG. 49.—Setting sliding tee bevel from square.

Striking a Line.—The chalk line is used to secure a straight guide line. It is fastened at one end by means of a scratch awl or

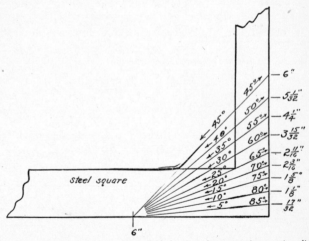

FIG. 50.—Figures to be used on tongue and blade of steel square when setting sliding tee bevel to approximate angles shown.

nail, and is "chalked" by having a piece of colored chalk rubbed over it as it is unwound. It is then stretched taut, lifted a little

Fig. 51.—"Striking" a line.

in the center and permitted to snap, transferring the chalk to the board (Fig. 51). When putting the first course of shingles on a roof the line is itself used as a guide.

Use of Miter Box.—Where many small pieces have to be cut to a uniform length or angle a miter box is a great convenience and time saver. A practical miter box can be made as shown in figure 110. Figure 50 shows the method of using the steel square for laying out cuts of any desired angle when making the box.

The spoke shave is convenient for smoothing curved surfaces. It is in effect a short plane and can be either pushed or pulled. To secure smooth work keep the edge keen and adjust to cut a thin shaving.

The wood rasp is used for smoothing the inside of small openings and irregular surfaces. The usual shapes are half-round and flat. The wood rasp should not be used on plane surfaces.

Use of Wrenches.—Many farm repairs are made through the use of bolts. A good monkey wrench is one of the most convenient wrenches as it can be made to fit most of the bolts used. To avoid springing the jaws place the wrench on the nut with the open side away from the body when the wrench is to be pulled, and toward the body when it is to be pushed. Other adjustable wrenches should be used with the adjustable jaw away from the body when the wrench is to be pulled and toward the body when it is to be pushed. Keep the adjusting screw clean and well oiled and the jaws adjusted closely to the nut upon which the wrench is being used. Do not use the wrench as a hammer. Rusted nuts can sometimes be loosened by holding a heavy iron against one corner and hitting the diagonally opposite corner with a hammer in the direction to loosen it.

THOUGHT QUESTIONS

1. Tell of a shop job that has been done on your place and list the total operations necessary.

2. What objection is there to laying out work indiscriminately from both sides of a board? How can this trouble be overcome?

3. How would you secure a smooth and even surface on a piece of lumber?

4. Why is a long sole provided on the jointer plane? What objection is there to letting this plane ride diagonally across the edge when jointing a board?

5. What precautions should be taken in setting and using the gauge? How can a rule be used as a gauge?

6. What difficulties have you encountered in using the rip saw and how have they been overcome?

7. How should the compass saw be held when cutting out a milking-stool top?

8. Explain how the chisel is used in (a) rough paring, (b) smooth paring, (c) beating out a mortise.

9. How can you prevent splintering the under side of a board when boring through it?

10. If you turn a bit backward when pulling it from the hole what will be the effect?

11. Under what conditions would you use a hand-axe to straighten the edge of a board?

12. For what purposes other than scribing can the dividers be used?

13. If a bubble tube were out of adjustment sufficiently to cause one end of the level stock to stand $\frac{1}{32}$-inch high when the bubble stood in the middle of the tube what would be the effect upon a line to which the level was applied 32 times without changing ends? What would be the effect if the level was reversed at each alternate application?

14. Can you suggest a way in which a plumb bob and line could be used as a level?

15. If you were placing a small watering-trough and had no level how could you secure a level setting?

16. Can you suggest a method of applying the chalk to the line that will prevent cutting it up?

17. What would be the effect on the mark made if the line were pulled to one side in striking?

18. Suggest a method of striking a line stretched between two points 30 feet apart.

CHAPTER IV

GEOMETRICAL CONSTRUCTION USED IN FARM CARPENTRY

DURING the building and repairs common about the farm, many geometrical problems, such as the determination of a roof pitch or rafter length, come up for solution and must be solved with a certain degree of exactness.

The steel square is the principal tool used in laying out work, and although very simple is capable of doing a wide variety of work. The form most commonly used consists of a "blade" 24 inches long and 2 inches wide, with a "tongue" 16 inches long and 1½ inches wide affixed to it at right angles, forming a single L-shaped piece of steel.

Measuring.—The edges of the square carry every graduation commonly used, and in addition a 1/100 scale. One side has the inches divided into twelve equal parts each, a system of graduation useful when laying out work to scale.

Determining Rafter Lengths and Cuts.—A rafter is one of the parallel timbers composing the framework of a roof extending

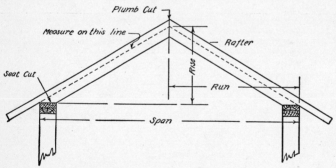

FIG. 52.—Diagram of common gable roof.

from the plate to the ridge. On the common gable roof (Fig. 52), rafters are used in pairs, meeting each other at the ridge by an oblique cut and seating on the plate in the same manner. The cut at the top, being vertical, is called the "plumb cut," while the joint at the plate is called the "seat cut."

3

The width of the building from outside to outside of the plate is called the " span," half of the span being called the " run," while the vertical distance from the plate to the ridge is known as the " rise."

The slope of a roof is known as the " pitch " and is expressed in a fractional form, the rise being used as the numerator while the span is used as the denominator. A roof 24 feet wide, with a rise of 6 feet, would be called a ¼ pitch roof, $^6/_{24}$ being equal to ¼. A

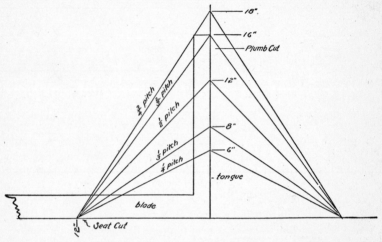

Fig. 53.—Roof pitches and figures on tongue and blade of square used to obtain "plumb" and "seat" cuts. Apply square as shown in Fig. 54 as many times as there are feet in the "run" to secure rafter length.

half-pitch roof, one in which the rise is equal to ½ the span, is frequently referred to as a " square pitch," the rafters forming a right angle at the ridge. The common roof pitches, together with the necessary measurements to be taken on the square to obtain the proper angles and lengths for the rafters, are shown in figure 53.

The rise and run of a roof form the imaginary base and altitude of a right triangle of which the rafter is the hypotenuse. This fact is used in laying out the roof. A certain proportion of the rise, usually one-twelfth, is taken on the tongue of the square and the same proportion of the run is taken on the blade. When these points are connected by a diagonal line, the length of the line will represent the same proportion of the length of the rafter. The triangles formed by the square and the rafter are similar.

In practice the rafter length is obtained as follows:

Rule.—Take as many inches on the tongue of the square as there are feet in the rise of the roof and as many inches on the blade of the square as there are feet in the run. Hold the square so that the points so selected just touch the edge of the rafter, or a line gauged 2 inches from

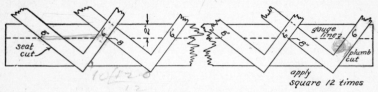

Fig. 54.—Method of using steel square in laying out rafters.

its upper edge, and apply it as indicated in figure 54 twelve times. This will give the correct length of the rafter, as well as the cut at both the top and bottom. Figure 54 shows a rafter being laid out for a roof 16 feet wide with a six-foot rise.

The rafter as commonly used is left projecting beyond the plate to form a framework for the eaves. The thickness of this projection is usually two inches. To avoid mistakes it is best to gauge a line lengthwise of the rafter at this distance from the top edge and apply the square, in laying out the rafter, to this line rather than to the edge.

For a slant or shed roof the method is the same, but the whole width of the building is taken on the blade, while the vertical distance between the front and rear plates is taken on the tongue.

Laying Out Braces.—The square has a brace measure which gives the lengths of braces commonly used in framing. The table

Fig. 55.—Section of blade of steel square showing brace measure table.

(Fig. 55) is arranged with the numbers representing the rise and run printed one over the other, while the length of the brace appears at their right; $\frac{36}{36}$ 50.91 meaning that with a rise and run of 36 inches each, the length of the diagonal or brace would be 50.91 inches.

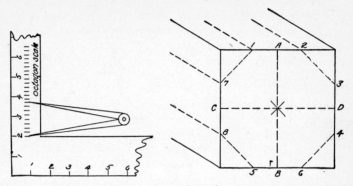

Fig. 56.—Laying out an eight-sided stick by means of the octagon scale.

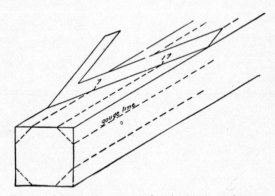

Fig. 57.—Laying out an octagonal stick with the steel square.

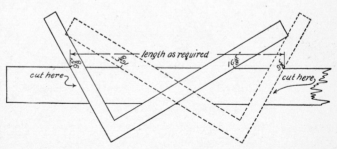

Fig. 58.—Using steel square to lay out cuts for six-sided figure. Other regular figures can be laid out in a similar manner by use of "table of cuts for regular polygons."   Page 37.

Octagon or "eight square" scale is found on the side of the tongue opposite the brace measure table. Figure 56 suggests its use. Another method often used in laying out an eight-sided stick is to lay the blade of the square or a two-foot rule diagonally across the stick as shown in figure 57, marking at the points 7 inches and 17 inches.

Securing Angle Cuts for Common Polygons.—By using the square as indicated in figure 58 the cuts for making the common regular polygons can be obtained. A regular polygon of any size can be laid out by making the length of the side to suit, the angle of cut remaining the same whatever the size may be.

Table of cuts for Regular Polygons

Number of sides	Fig. on blade	Fig. on tongue	Degrees
3	6–$^{15}/_{16}$ inches	12 inches	30
4	12 inches	12 inches	45
5	18 inches	13–$\frac{1}{8}$ inches	54
6	16–$\frac{5}{8}$ inches	9–$\frac{5}{8}$ inches	60
7	17–$\frac{7}{8}$ inches	8–$\frac{5}{8}$ inches	64–$^{2}/_{7}$
8	18 inches	7–$\frac{1}{2}$ inches	67–$\frac{1}{2}$
9	16–$\frac{3}{4}$ inches	6–$\frac{1}{8}$ inches	70
10	18 inches	5–$\frac{7}{8}$ inches	72

Laying off Angles with the Steel Square.—The square can be used for laying off the most common angles by using the figures as shown in figure 50. The cuts on the blade and tongue are indicated

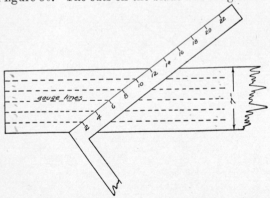

Fig. 59.—Dividing a board into equal strips with steel square.

on the diagonal line. The blade of the sliding tee bevel can be set at the angle desired and used as a guide in laying out the work.

Dividing a Board into Strips of Equal Width.—The square is laid diagonally across the material, using a portion of the blade that is exactly divisible by the number of strips desired. The method of doing this is shown clearly in figure 59, where a 7-inch board is being divided into six equal strips.

The Essex board measure table found on the blade of the square provides a quick method of determining the number of board

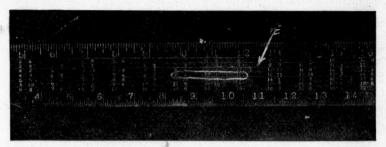

Fig. 60.—Use of Essex board measure table.

feet contained in a given piece of lumber. To use it, find in the column beneath 12, the width of the board in inches. Glance along the edge of the blade until the length of the board is found in the edge graduations. Directly beneath the number representing the

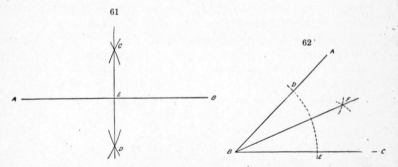

Fig. 61.—Bisection of a straight line. Use *A* and *B* as centers and strike arcs intersecting at *C* and *D*.

Fig. 62.—Bisection of an angle. Use *B* as a center and describe an arc cutting the side of an angle at *D* and *E*. With these points as centers describe arcs intersecting at *F*.

length, and in the same horizontal space with the width of the board, will be found the number of board feet in the board being measured (Fig. 60). The table is computed on a basis of 1-inch material, and where lumber is more than one inch in thickness the result as shown by the table must be multiplied by the thickness of the

material used to obtain the correct result. Lumber less than one
inch thick is considered as one-inch material.

Geometrical Constructions Useful in Farm Carpentry.—It
is often desirable to erect perpendiculars or lay out regular polygons when making things for the farm. Some of the more common
constructions follow. They can be laid out with the dividers, or in
cases where a larger figure is desired, they can be laid out on a

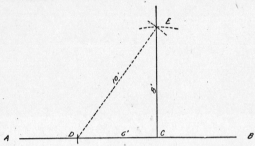

Fig. 63.—Erecting a perpendicular by 6-8-10 method. *D* is located six feet from *C*, and with
the radii shown arcs are struck intersecting at *E*. *C-E* is then perpendicular to *A-B*.

convenient barn-floor, using a piece of stovepipe wire or light strip
of wood of the proper length as a radius. A nail can be fastened at
one end to serve as a center, while a loop or hole can be provided at
the other to take the point of a pencil.

Bisecting a Line and Angles.—These steps are indicated in
figures 61 and 62.

**To Erect a Perpendicular at a Given Point on a Given
Straight Line.**—Study the steps indicated in figure 63. This is
called the 6-8-10 method, and is
based on the fact that any triangle
constructed with its sides in the proportion of 6, 8, and 10 will have a
right angle opposite the long side.

**At a Given Point on a Given
Straight Line to Construct an
Angle Equal to a Given Angle.**—
Figure 64 shows the necessary steps.

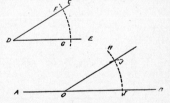

Fig. 64.—Constructing an angle equal
to a given angle.

Make the radii O H and I J equal or in proportion to the radii
D F and G F in the original angle.

To Inscribe a Regular Pentagon in a Given Circle.—(Fig.
65.) Let A-C-B-D be the given circle. Draw the diameter A-B,

and bisect it as described under "Bisection of Straight Line" (Fig. 61) to secure the diameter C-D at right angles to it. Bisect one of the radii, as O-B, at I. With I as a center and a radius C-I

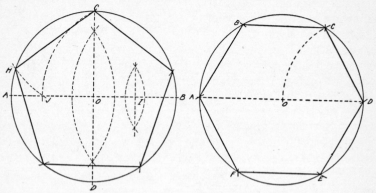

FIG. 65.—Method of inscribing a regular   ·FIG. 66.—Method of inscribing a regular
five-sided figure in a circle.   hexagon.

draw the arc C-J, intersecting A-B at J. With C as a center and a radius C-J describe the arc J-H, cutting the circumference at H. The chord C-H is one side of the figure, and if stepped around the circumference will complete the pentagon.

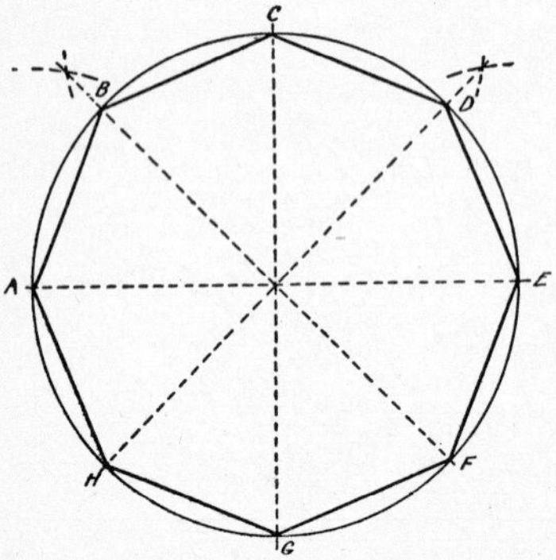

To Inscribe a Regular Hexagon.—(Fig. 66.) Let A-B-C-D-E-F be the given circle. If the radius is not known, secure it by means of intersecting diameters. Set the dividers at the radius of the circle and step it off around the circumference. It will go just six times.

To Inscribe a Regular Octagon.—(Fig. 67.) Let A-B-C-D-E-F-G-H be the given circle.

FIG. 67.—Method of inscribing a regular
octagon in a circle.

Draw a diameter, as A-E, and a second diameter, as G-C, at right angles to it. Bisect one of the four equal arcs, as A-C. A diameter, B-F, drawn through this bisection will bisect the opposite arc. In the same way bisect the two remaining arcs. Straight lines con-

necting the ends of the diameters will make a regular
eight-sided figure.

**To Inscribe a Regular
Polygon of Any Number of
Sides in a Given Circle.—**
(Fig. 68.) Let the circumference about the center O represent the given circle, and
through O draw the two diameters at right angles to each
other. Divide the horizontal
diameter D-E into as many
equal parts as the polygon is
to have sides (in this case
seven). Prolong the radius O-
A and make the extension F-A
equal to ¾ O-A. From F
draw a line through point 2,
cutting the circumference at

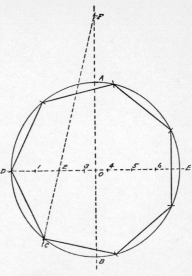

Fig. 68.—Method of laying out a regular figure
having any number of equal sides.

C. The chord C-D will be one side of the proposed polygon, and
may be stepped off about the circumference.

Constructing an Ellipse.—(Fig. 69.)   An ellipse of desired
width and length can be very accurately constructed with a piece

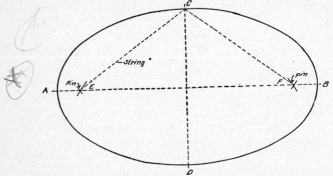

Fig. 69.—Construction of ellipse by means of string and pins.

of string and two tacks or pins.   Draw the major axis A-B and the
minor axis C-D at right angles to and bisecting each other.   With

one-half of the major axis as a radius and the point D as a center describe arcs intersecting the major axis at E and F. The points E and F now serve as locations for the pins. Fasten the string securely to one pin, and placing the pencil upright at C, pass the string about it, and drawing it up taut, give it two or three turns about the pin at F. Hold the string at F, and with the pencil describe an arc which will represent the upper half of the ellipse. The lower half is obtained in the same manner. Care must be taken in doing this to keep the string taut, to see that it does not slip, and to see that it is kept down at the point of the pencil where it serves as a guide.

QUESTIONS AND EXERCISES

1. Why is a system of graduation where the inch is divided into twelfths better adapted to laying out work to scale than where it is divided into sixteenths?
2. Lay out a rafter for a half-pitch gable roof with a 24' span.
3. Lay out a rafter for shed-roofed building sixteen feet wide with ¼ pitch.
4. With the steel square contruct an octagon within a 10" square.
5. Lay out a girt for an octagonal silo 6 feet on a side.
6. Explain how to use the steel square to divide a 5" board into three equal strips.
7. By means of the Essex board measure table find the number of board feet in a plank 2½" x 8" x 14' long.
8. Assuming it is desired to build a concrete silo 16' in outside diameter, can you suggest a method of laying out the frame for the outside form full size on the barn-floor? Make a sketch of your method of laying it out.
9. Explain how you would lay out an elliptical flower bed 10 feet long and 5 feet wide.
10. How could the 6-8-10 method of constructing a right angle (Fig. 63) be used in squaring up the foundation of a building?
11. What other dimensions could be used for the sides of the triangle when laying out a right angle?
12. What are the longest dimensions that could be used for the sides of the triangle when constructing a right angle by the 6-8-10 method if a 100-foot steel tape were used as a measuring instrument?
13. What advantage is there in using the greatest distance possible when laying out a right angle by this method?
14. After a rectangular foundation has been laid out by the 6-8-10 method, what test can be applied to check the accuracy of the work?

CHAPTER V

MECHANICAL DRAWING—BLUE-PRINT READING

ASIDE from the mechanic and the builder, no man should be more vitally interested in mechanical drawing than the farmer. It is essential to his best progress.

It enables him to plan and arrange his buildings to the best advantage, to estimate their cost, and to lay out his farm for the most economical and efficient handling. It places the plans of others

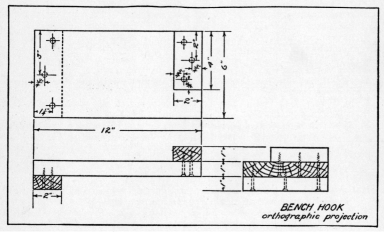

FIG. 70.—Drawing of bench hook in orthographic projection.

at his disposal, and aids in selecting machinery and equipment from catalogues. It is a universal language, enabling one man to transmit his mechanical ideas to others with the greatest possible clearness and the least effort.

A working drawing is one that depicts an object as it really is, not necessarily as it appears. While made as simply as possible, on it will be found the shape and size of every part necessary to construction. Drawings of a simple object in orthographic, isometric, and oblique projection are shown in figures 70 to 72. A study of these drawings will show the essential differences.

43

Orthographic projection is used when it is desired to give complete information about the object. Three views, the plan, front view, and side view, are usually shown. The plan shows the

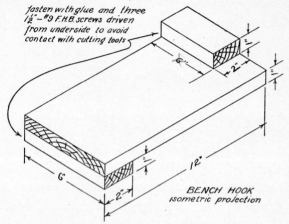

fasten with glue and three
1½"-#9 F.H.B. screws driven
from underside to avoid
contact with cutting tools

6"

2"

12"

6"

2"

BENCH HOOK
isometric projection

Fig. 71.—Drawing of bench hook in isometric projection.

object as it appears when viewed directly from above. The front view shows the object as it would appear if the eye of the observer were directly in front of it and equally distant from all parts, while

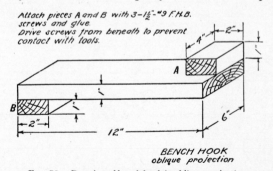

Attach pieces A and B with 3-1½"-#9 F.H.B.
screws and glue.
Drive screws from beneath to prevent
contact with tools.

4"　2"

A

B

2"

12"

6"

BENCH HOOK
oblique projection

Fig. 72.—Drawing of bench hook in oblique projection.

the side view shows it as it would appear if viewed from the side. The side view shown is usually the one at the right. In some cases, where the nature of the work seems to demand it, both the right and left sides are shown, as well as a view of the object looking upward from the bottom.

These views are arranged as shown in figure 70. This arrangement can best be understood by assuming that the object to be drawn is placed in a glass box, the corners of which are hinged to permit opening (Fig. 73). By looking down through the top of

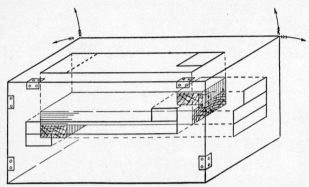

Fig. 73.—Bench hook enclosed in imaginary glass box with sides and ends hinged to open outward, showing method of arranging views in orthographic projection.

the box the outline of the object can be traced on the glass, and in the same manner, by looking directly into the front and side of the box, respectively, the front view and side view can be traced. When

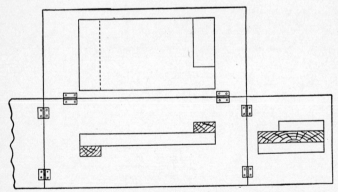

Fig. 74.—Plane of projection, the position taken by the views when the glass box is opened.

the box is opened up on the hinged corners the views will take the positions shown in figure 74. The position assumed by the imaginary glass box when opened up is termed the plane of projection, and is represented by the surface of the paper when drawing.

When about to make a drawing of an object study it to determine which view will include the most essential measurements. A view should be selected with as much of its surface either parallel

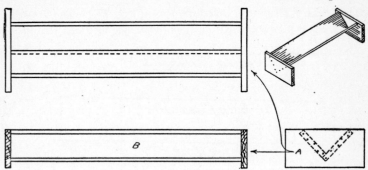

Fig. 75.—Illustration of rules of orthographic projection. Orthographic projection of V-trough, showing foreshortening of inclined surfaces, representation of surfaces perpendicular to the plane of projection and representation of surfaces parallel to plane of projection.

or perpendicular to the projection plane as possible, as the first to be made. The limiting lines of oblique surfaces are obtained by

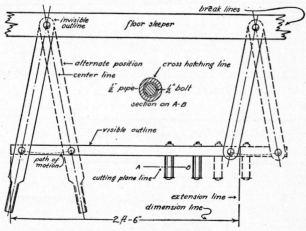

Fig. 76.—Belt-shifter, showing application of alphabet of lines.

projection from other views where they appear in their true size (Fig. 75).

Alphabet of Lines.—As all surfaces are represented in the same plane, without light or shade, various lines are used to designate different things, making the drawing more clear and readable. Some of the more common lines and their uses are shown in figures 76 and 77.

Necessary Drawing Instruments.—(Fig. 78.) The drawing board is a soft pine board with a smooth surface to which the draw-

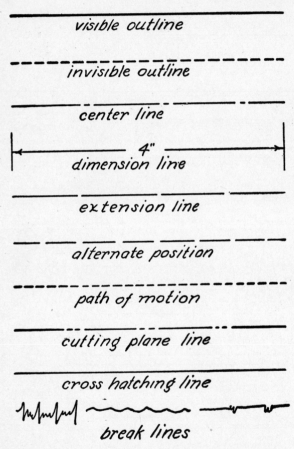

visible outline

invisible outline

center line

4"

dimension line

extension line

alternate position

path of motion

cutting plane line

cross hatching line

break lines

Fig. 77.—Alphabet of principal lines used in mechanical drawing.

ing paper may be fastened with thumb-tacks. It should have cleats across the back to prevent warping, and the left-hand end should be straight to form a working edge against which the head of the tee

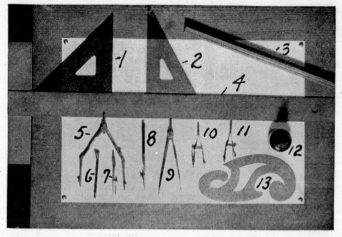

FIG. 78.—Common drawing instruments: 1, forty-five degree triangle; 2, sixty degree triangle; 3, triangular scale; 4, tee square; 5, compasses with pencil-point attached; 6, lengthening bar for compasses; 7, pen-point for compasses; 8, straight line pen or ruling pen; 9, dividers; 10, bow pencil; 11, bow pen; 12, India drawing ink; 13, irregular curve.

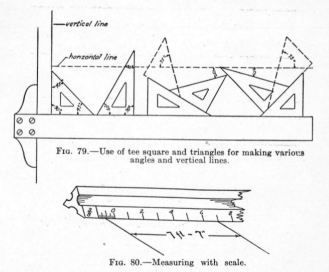

FIG. 79.—Use of tee square and triangles for making various angles and vertical lines.

FIG. 80.—Measuring with scale.

square can be held. A convenient size for a drawing board is 18 x 24 inches.

Other tools are a tee square, two triangles (Fig. 79), compasses, scale (Fig. 80), and a hard pencil.

Laying Out a Drawing.—The first steps in laying out a drawing are to decide what views will be required to show the object clearly and to determine their size. For example, if an object 10 feet wide and 20 feet long is to be drawn in a space 5½ x 10½ inches it is obvious that it will be necessary to use a scale no greater than ½ inch = 1 foot. The above computation may be made by the following rule:

> *Rule.*—Multiply the scale used, expressed as a fraction, by the length of the object to be drawn in feet. The result will equal the actual length of the drawing in inches.

A rough plan sheet with dimensioned rectangles roughly blocked out on it in the approximate position that the views will

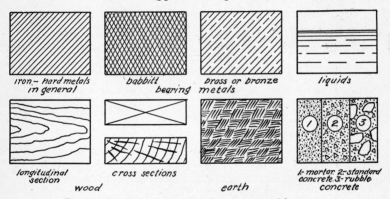

iron,- hard metals   babbitt   brass or bronze   liquids
   in general   bearing   metals

longitudinal   cross sections   1- mortar. 2-standard
section   concrete.3-rubble
         wood   earth   concrete

Fig. 81.—Standard cross-sections of common materials.

occupy is a great aid in laying out a drawing. It represents the space required and serves as a guide from which to work.

Conventional Breaks and Symbols.—Many symbols, frequently called "conventions," are used to represent different

Fig. 82.—Hammer-handle with shape indicated by means of turned sections.

materials. Each trade usually has its own, making the list too long to be included here. There are, however, certain practices that are mentioned.

Figure 81 shows various conventions used to represent different materials in section. An example of a turned section is shown in figure 82. The use of break lines is shown in figure 83.

4

Dimensioning.—The value of a drawing lies largely in the accuracy, completeness, and convenience of its dimensions. Where

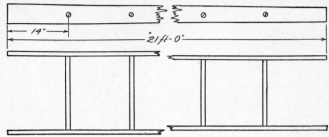

the space permits, dimension figures are placed in a break in the dimension line, as at A, figure 84; but where the space to be dimen-

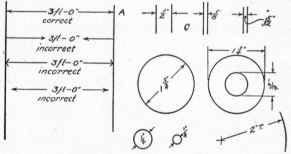

FIG. 84.—Common methods of dimensioning.

sioned is small, the methods shown at C are used for the sake of clearness. Strive to make the work simple, legible, and clear.

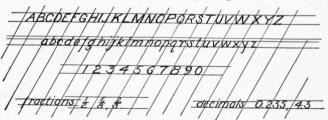

FIG. 85.—Alphabet, with guide lines used in printing.

Titles and Lettering.—The title and explanatory notes on a drawing should be printed with a simple form of lettering. The

Engineering News style of lettering shown in figure 85 is neat, legible, and rapidly made.

Isometric and oblique projection drawings are made in an inclined position so that three faces of the object, usually the top, front, and right side, are shown. This type of drawing is useful where only a general idea of an object with the principal dimensions is required.

The isometric drawing has three axes about which the picture is made; one is vertical and the other two each form an angle of 30 degrees with the horizontal. This skeleton is shown in figure 86. In oblique projection (Fig. 87) one axis is vertical, one horizontal, and

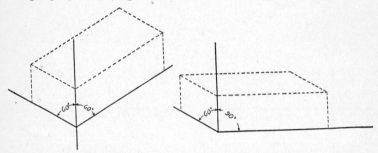

FIG. 86.—Isometric axes with relation to object drawn.   FIG. 87.—Oblique projection axes with relation to object drawn.

the other inclined at any angle desired, although 30 degrees is commonly used because of convenience. This method of projection permits one side of the object to be drawn in its true shape. To avoid the appearance of excessive thickness, apparent in oblique drawings, all measurements that extend away from the observer may be divided by two, and when so made drawings are termed cabinet projections. When making an oblique drawing choose for the horizontal view that side of the object containing circles and irregular work that would be difficult to draw in an inclined position.

Sketching.—Frequently a clear pencil sketch, approximating closely the shape of the object, and provided with the necessary dimensions, is all that is needed. Make as many views as are required to show the work clearly, place them in the proper relation to each other, and provide them with sufficient explanatory notes and dimensions to make them clear.

Reading Drawings and Blue-prints.—The title should first be examined, giving an idea of purpose of the drawing. Next examine the plan, front and side views of the assembly in the effort to get at the general shape of the object shown, trying to visualize the three views combined as a whole.

After the use and general shape of the object as a whole and the shape, relation, and purpose of its parts have been determined, the dimensions may be examined. Constant study of the explanatory notes on the drawing is also necessary to read it properly. The most important point, however, is to see the object complete in the mind's eye by study of the title and assembly views. With this picture before one it is easy to decipher the shape and size of the various parts and their relation to each other.

QUESTIONS AND EXERCISES

1. In what ways can you profit by a knowledge of mechanical drawing?
2. Do you know of any case where trouble might have been avoided in building if a working drawing had been prepared and used?
3. What kind of working drawings are most commonly found in farm papers and bulletins?
4. What would be the simplest way of explaining to a friend by letter the method of making a new trap nest?
5. What is the purpose of a " section " ? A " turned section " ?
6. Explain how to determine the proper scale to use when placing a drawing on a sheet of given size.
7. How can you construct a drawing board for your own use?
8. How can a large scale be used in making a drawing of a 30-foot ladder and still keep the drawing on a small sheet?
9. In what ways do orthographic, isometric, and oblique drawings differ? In what ways is the oblique drawing superior to the isometric?
10. Explain how to read a working drawing.
11. Make a dimensioned sketch of a wagon box or other device on the home farm that it is desired to duplicate or improve upon in the shop. The sketch should include all necessary dimensions and sufficient detail to permit construction from the sketches.
12. Design a rack to attach to the stable wall for holding four (or some other desired number) milking stools of the type shown in figure 120. Make a dimensioned sketch and submit it to the instructor for approval.
13. Submit a dimensioned isometric sketch of a medicine cabinet for the stable or other device for farm use. Show all detail and dimensions necessary for actual construction.
14. Make a working drawing of a window screen or screen door to fit a given opening. Use the largest scale possible, dimension fully, and show detail of corner construction and cross section.
15. Design and make a working sketch of a simple file for storing your bulletins and trade literature in available form. Make all views necessary, and show all dimensions, the materials used, and details of joints together with longitudinal or cross sections where needed.

CHAPTER VI

SELECTION, USE, AND CARE OF LUMBER

CERTAIN qualities of lightness, stiffness, strength, and heat insulation are possessed by lumber in a marked degree. It lends itself readily to a wide variety of decorative treatments, is easily worked, can be obtained in numerous grades and varieties, and has a secondhand value. These qualities of convenience, adaptability, and economy make it of great value in making farm alterations and repairs.

Manner of Growth.—Practically all of the lumber used on the farm is cut from trees of the exogenous group, which increase their girth by adding a new layer of wood fiber around their trunk, beneath the bark, each year. This new growth is called the "annual ring" (Fig. 88).

Heart-wood and Sap-wood.—As growth progresses in the stem the inner wood, known as "heart-wood," turns darker in color, and becomes stiffer and stronger. It contains less moisture, warps and shrinks less, and is more resistant to decay than "sap-wood," which is the outer, lighter-colored portion cut from the same tree.

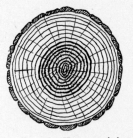

FIG. 88.—Heart-wood in center, sap-wood around it. Rings and medullary rays clearly shown.

The sap-wood of hickory is valuable because of its toughness, while that of basswood is desired because of its light color.

Medullary Rays.—Radiating outward from the pith of the tree are the "pith rays," or "medullary rays." These rays vary greatly in appearance with the species of wood, being almost invisible in some of the pines and standing out very clearly in the oaks, making the peculiar flake in quarter-sawed oak. With the annual rings, they help in giving each wood its characteristic grain. Both the rings and the rays have much to do with the successful drying of wood.

Sawing.—Two general methods of sawing are in use: termed "slash sawing" and "quarter sawing" (Figs. 89 and 90).

Much of the lumber used for furniture-making is "quarter sawed," as it shrinks and warps but little, and in some woods, as oak, it presents a beautiful grain. The flakes in quarter-sawed oak

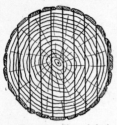

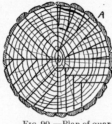

are due to the medullary rays being uncovered by a saw-cut parallel to their face.

FIG. 89.—Plan of slash sawing of lumber from a log.

FIG. 90.—Plan of quarter sawing of a log at *A*. Modified plans also shown.

Shrinkage.—Practically all shrinkage is in a direction parallel with the annual rings. This is termed tangential shrinkage, and is about twice as great as radial shrinkage, which takes place from the center of the log outward, along the medullary rays. There is practically no change in length when drying. A board cut from the center of a log will shrink little in width, the principal shrinkage being in thickness, and there will be little tendency to warp or check.

The boards cut from the outer part of the log have the annual rings extending across them in a direction more or less parallel with their face and will shrink excessively when dry-

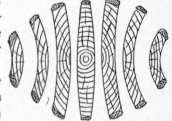

FIG. 91.—Shrinkage of lumber and shapes assumed in drying.

ing (Fig. 91). This is due both to the position of the rings and to the high water content.

Seasoning.—A tree when cut contains from 20 to 60 per cent of water, the amount depending upon the variety, the age of the tree, the season when cut, and other factors. This surplus moisture must be driven off, the process being termed seasoning. Seasoning of lumber is very important, as it makes it stronger, stiffer, and lighter, more nearly permanent in size and shape, and more resistant to decay. It is accomplished by two general methods: (1) air-drying and (2) kiln-drying.

In air-drying the lumber is piled so that the air can circulate freely through it, and is left for a period of time varying from

Fig. 92.—Typical coniferous stand, showing long, straight, cylindrical trunks suitable for long-length lumber. (U. S. Forest Service.)

three months to two years or more. Lumber dried in this way will have the moisture content reduced to that of the outside air, *i. e.,* 12 to 15 per cent, and is suitable for outside work, framing, and rough interior alterations.

Selection of Wood for Special Purposes

Wood	Type of use	Example
Spruce Hemlock Southern pine	Used where length, strength, stiffness, and comparative cheapness are desired.	Building frames, sheathing, rough floors, etc.
White pine Basswood Poplar	Used where a smooth working surface that will hold paint or enamel well is required.	Exterior and inside trim in buildings, wagon-boxes, and crates.
Cedar Cypress	Used where a decay-resisting wood is necessary.	Fence-posts, sills, e t c. Cedar used extensively for shingles.
Hickory White ash Rock elm White oak Maple Southern pine	Used where strength, hardness, and wear-resisting qualities are needed.	Eveners, tool and implement handles, repairs to farm machines, inside finish and floors.

For interior finish or other work where shrinkage must be eliminated, the lumber is kiln-dried by being piled loosely in a highly heated room, through which a hot blast of air with controlled moisture content is kept circulating. Air-dried lumber can be thoroughly seasoned by this method in a period of time varying with the nature, thickness, and condition of the wood. In general, soft woods require from two to four days for each inch in thickness, while hard woods need from two to three times as long.

Small pieces of lumber can be seasoned for shop use by storing them in a heated room in such a way that the air can circulate readily about them, making sure that the pieces are so supported that there is no opportunity for them to warp or bend in drying. Lumber stored in an attic through the summer is usually sufficiently dry for all farm repairs. Where stock is dried rapidly the ends should be sealed by an application of thick paint or oil to prevent checking.

FIG. 93.—Forest of deciduous or broad-leaved trees. As a class these trees do not grow to as great a height without large branches and do not furnish as straight and cylindrical trunks as do the coniferous trees. (Prof. Laurance Lee, New York College of Forestry, Syracuse University, Syracuse, N. Y.)

FIG. 94.—A well-made lumber-pile with protecting roof. (The *Rural New Yorker*, New York City.)

Piling Lumber.—The lumber-pile should be made on well-drained ground and placed upon supports sufficiently high to permit a good circulation of air beneath it. The courses are separated

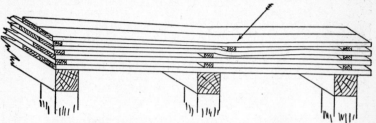

Fig. 95.—Distortion of lumber by improper piling due to weight above.

by sticks to permit air circulation, and these must be kept directly over each other or bending will result (Figs. 94 and 95).

Measuring Lumber.—Both the width and thickness are considered when measuring lumber, the " board foot " being the unit used. It is equivalent to the amount of material contained in a piece of board 1 foot long by 1 foot wide by 1 inch in thickness

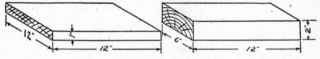

Fig. 96.—Examples of board foot.

(Fig. 96). Lumber is usually bought by the 1000 (written **M**), which is equal to 1000 feet board measure. The contents of a board or a stick of timber, in board feet, are obtained by the following rule: Multiply the length in feet by the width in feet by the thickness in inches. In the case of 1-inch boards 12 feet long, the number of board feet is equal to the width of the board in inches; a 1-inch board, 12 feet long and 6 inches wide, containing 6 board feet. Lumber, such as siding, and ceiling which is less than 1 inch thick is sold as though it were 1 inch thick.

The following table provides a way for quickly determining the contents in board feet of the usual sizes of lumber.

Find the length of the piece of lumber at the top of the table and the nominal size in the column at the left. Where the vertical and horizontal columns intersect, the contents of the piece is found in board feet.

Board Measure Table

Nominal thickness and width in inches	Length in feet								
	4	6	8	10	12	14	16	18	20
1 x 2	⅔	1	1⅓	1⅔	2	2⅓	2⅔	3	3⅓
1 x 3	1	1½	2	2½	3	3½	4	4½	5
1 x 4	1⅓	2	2⅔	3⅓	4	4⅔	5⅓	6	6⅔
1 x 5	1⅔	2½	3⅓	4⅙	5	5⅚	6⅔	7½	8⅓
1 x 6	2	3	4	5	6	7	8	9	10
1 x 7	2⅓	3½	4⅔	5⅚	7	8⅙	9⅓	10½	11⅔
1 x 8	2⅔	4	5⅓	6⅔	8	9⅓	10⅔	12	13⅓
1 x 9	3	4½	6	7½	9	10½	12	13½	15
1 x 10	3⅓	5	6⅔	8⅓	10	11⅔	13⅓	15	16⅔
1 x 11	3⅔	5½	7⅓	9⅙	11	12⅚	14⅔	16½	18⅓
1 x 12	4	6	8	10	12	14	16	18	20
2 x 4	2⅔	4	5⅓	6⅔	8	9⅓	10⅔	12	13⅓
2 x 6	4	6	8	10	12	14	16	18	20
2 x 8	5⅓	8	10⅔	13⅓	16	18⅔	21⅓	24	26⅔
2 x 10	6⅔	10	13⅓	16⅔	20	23⅓	26⅔	30	33⅓
2 x 12	8	12	16	20	24	28	32	36	40
3 x 4	4	6	8	10	12	14	16	18	20
3 x 6	6	9	12	15	18	21	24	27	30
3 x 8	8	12	16	20	24	28	32	36	40
3 x 10	10	15	20	25	30	35	40	45	50
3 x 12	12	18	24	30	36	42	48	54	60
4 x 4	5⅓	8	10⅔	13⅓	16	18⅔	21⅓	24	26⅔
4 x 6	8	12	16	20	24	28	32	36	40
4 x 8	10⅔	16	21⅓	26⅔	32	37⅓	42⅔	48	53⅓
4 x 10	13⅓	20	26⅔	33⅓	40	46⅔	53⅓	60	66⅔
4 x 12	16	24	32	40	48	56	64	72	80
6 x 6	12	18	24	30	36	42	48	54	60
6 x 8	16	24	32	40	48	56	64	72	80
8 x 8	21⅓	32	42⅔	53⅓	64	74⅔	85⅓	96	106⅔
8 x 10	26⅔	40	53⅓	66⅔	80	93⅓	106⅔	120	133⅓
10 x 10	33⅓	50	66⅔	83⅓	100	116⅔	133⅓	150	166⅔

QUESTIONS AND EXERCISES

1. Give some of the properties of lumber that make it of value in farm construction and repair work.
2. When building a silo why would you prefer to get "heart-wood" staves?
3. What are some conditions where sap-wood would be preferable? Why?
4. Why does lumber split or "check" at the ends when dried rapidly and what can be done to lessen this?
5. Explain why quarter sawing is preferable in most cases to slash sawing.
6. What woods are used in the framework of your barn? the sheathing? siding? shingles?
7. What woods are used for floors and inside trim in your house?
8. What wood would you select for an evener, a ladder, a wagon-box?
9. Can you suggest a good arrangement for a farm lumber-pile? How should it stand to permit the prevailing winds to blow through it most readily? Would the presence of weeds and bushes affect it?
10. What are the contents in board feet of each of the following for each foot in length: 2" x 4", 2" x 6", 2" x 8"?

CHAPTER VII

FASTENINGS FOR WOOD

THE chief fasteners used in the construction and repair work of the farm are nails, screws, bolts, rivets, corrugated fasteners, and glue. These are made in a great variety, permitting the choice of a type suited to the work and the character of the wood being used.

Choice of a Fastener.—The following factors should be considered when selecting a fastener for any given piece of work: (1) nature of the work to be done; (2) physical properties of the wood to be used. Some woods, because of their extreme hardness or the ease with which they are split, can be nailed only with difficulty, making the use of screws or bolts advisable.

Nails are the most widely used type of fasteners. The more commonly used kinds are common nails, box nails, flooring nails, casing nails, finishing nails, and roofing nails (Fig. 97).

Designation of Nail Sizes.—With the exception of roofing nails the size is designated by the term "penny," written "d." This designation refers to the length only, the thickness or gauge varying with the type of nail.

Length, gauge and approximate number per pound of common nails

Size, penny	Length, inches	Gauge number	Approximate number per pound
2	1	15	876
3	1–¼	14	568
4	1–½	12–½	316
5	1–¾	12–½	271
6	2	11–½	181
7	2–¼	11–½	16J
8	2–½	10–¼	106
9	2–¾	10–¼	96
10	3	9	69
12	3–¼	9	63
16	3–½	8	49
20	4	6	31
30	4–½	5	24
40	5	4	18
50	5–½	3	14
60	6	2	11

Nails of lighter gauge wire will run somewhat more to the pound.

Driving Nails.—Nails should be hit squarely on the head with the center of the hammer face when driving. This prevents bend-

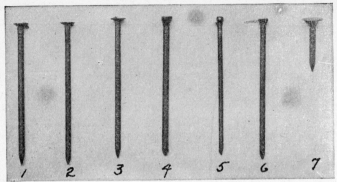

FIG. 97.—Types of nails in common use: 1, common nail; 2, box nail; 3, barbed box nail; 4, flooring nail; 5, finishing nail; 6, casing nail; 7, roofing nail.

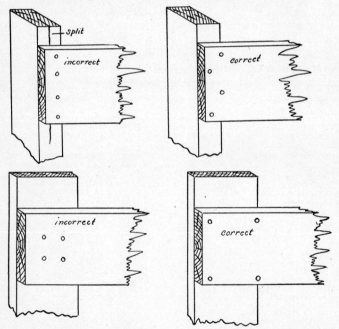

FIG. 98.—Correct and incorrect nailing. Nails in a line may split the wood.

ing the nail, lessens the chance of splitting the wood, and results in the strongest joint. Figure 98 shows good and bad methods of placing nails. Lubricating nail-points with soap or wax tends to prevent trouble with bending.

Prevention of Splitting.—When nailing hard wood prevent splitting by selecting nails of a size suited to the work. Start the nail with the edge of the point across the grain (Fig. 99).

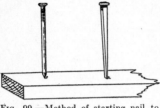

This cuts the grain and does not wedge the wood fibers apart so badly.

Setting Nails.—Casing or finishing nails are used where it is desirable to set the nails, to permit the finishing of the surface. After they have been driven nearly flush a cup-pointed set of the proper

FIG. 99.—Method of starting nail to prevent splitting.

size is used to sink them below the surface (Fig. 100).

Toe-nailing.—Where it is desired to fasten a piece that butts up against another by nailing, it can be done as shown in figure 101.

100   101   102

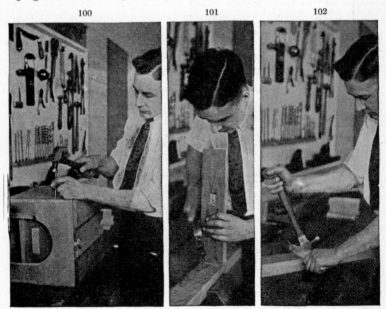

Fig. 100.—Setting a nail.
FIG. 101.—Toe-nailing.
FIG. 102.—Drawing nail. Note block beneath hammer.

This is termed toe-nailing. The nails should be driven as straight down as possible to secure a good penetration in the lower piece. To prevent displacement of the parts being nailed, drive a nail through the stationary piece first (Fig. 103). Figure 102 shows how to use a block for a fulcrum when pulling a nail.

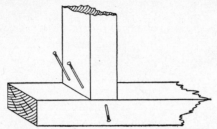

FIG. 103.—Toe-nailing. Note small nail driven from below to hold parts in alignment.

Types of nails and suggested uses

Common—most repair work on farm buildings.
Box (smooth or barbed)—boxes and crates.
Cement-coated—beehives, boxes, etc.
Finishing—interior finish and cabinet work.
Casing—heavier work than finishing nails.
Flooring—blind nailing of floors.
Cut—open and blind nailing of floors.
Roofing (barbed, smooth, galvanized)—prepared roofing.

Wood Screws.—Where a more secure fastening is desired than can be provided with nails, or where it may be necessary to take the joint apart occasionally, screws are used as a means of fastening. They are made from a number of materials, as iron, brass, and

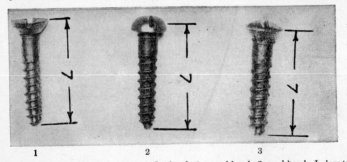

FIG. 104.—Common types of screws: 1, flat head; 2, round head; 3, oval head; L, length.

bronze, to meet various conditions. Iron screws are also finished in a variety of finishes, as bright, blued, brassed, nickeled, and japanned. All of the screws named are obtainable with flat heads, round heads, or oval heads as shown in figure 104. The flat head,

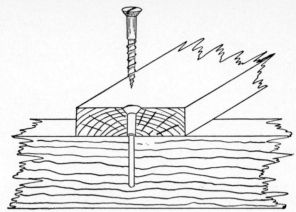

Fig. 105.—Method of drilling and countersinking for wood-screw. Hole countersunk for screw-head and hole drilled for screw-shank in top piece. Smaller hole drilled in second piece to engage screw-threads.

Fig. 106.—Screw-drivers should be filed to fit the work.

Fig. 107A.—Coach or lag screw with method of measuring length.

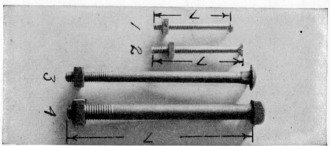

Fig. 107B.—Types of bolts: 1, round-head stove bolt; 2, flat-head stove bolt; 3, carriage bolt; 4, machine bolt. Carriage bolts are obtainable with conical and fancy shaped heads and machine bolts can be obtained with hexagon and finished heads. Length measurement is indicated by "*L.*"

bright (written F.H.B.), is the one most commonly used. The size of wood screws is designated by the length in inches and the diameter, expressed in numbers of the American Screw Gauge.

Driving Screws.—When driving screws a hole (Fig. 105) should be bored to the depth of the shank of the screw large enough to permit the screw to be pushed through it. Determine size with a caliper. The portion of the hole occupied by the threaded part of the screw should be made with a smaller drill to cause the thread to engage the wood. If the screws to be used are of the flat-head type the holes should also be countersunk. Use as large a screw-driver as the head of the screw will allow, and one filed to fit the slot in the screw (Fig. 106). Apply a lubricant, as soap, to the thread of the screw, and where possible clamp the work in a vise before drawing it up to secure a tighter fit.

Coach screws, or lag screws, are heavy wood screws fitted with a square head to permit turning with a wrench. Their size is designated by the diameter and length, both expressed in inches. The length is measured as shown in figure 107A. They are often used to hold machinery in place.

Bolts are used where greater strength is desired than can be obtained with nails or screws or where it may be desired to construct an object that can be quickly taken down or set up, as a take-down shipping crate. The ones commonly used on the farm are made in three styles, carriage bolts, machine bolts, and stove bolts (Fig. 107B).

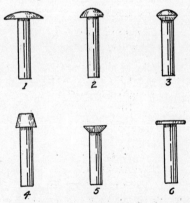

Rivets.—Although principally used as fasteners for metal, rivets are sometimes used in woodwork, as in the case of wagon-box work. They are made of annealed iron, which is soft and heads easily. Types of heads are seen in figure 108.

FIG. 108.—Rivets, ¼ x 1¼, showing common types of heads. Lower ends are placed even, showing point on head from which length measurements are taken. 1. Wagon box head. 2. Round head. 3. Countersunk oval head. 4. Cone head. 5. Countersunk head. 6. Flat head.

Corrugated Fasteners.—Glued work can often be strengthened by the use of corrugated steel fasteners shown in figure 109.

5

They are driven into the back of the work and hold the parts in position.

Glue is used where the pieces to be joined are too small to permit the use of any other fastener, or where an invisible joint is desired.

It is prepared from a number of substances, the best for wood joining being made from ox-hides. While a good hot glue is the strongest, a liquid glue of some standard brand is recommended for

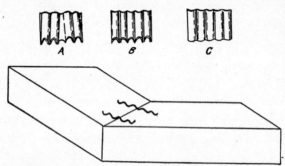

Fig. 109.—Corrugated fasteners and an example of their use: *A*, divergent type, saw-tooth edge, used for drawing joints together; *B*, parallel corrugations, saw-tooth edge; *C*, parallel corrugations, plain edge. Parallel corrugation type best to use for ordinary close work.

the farm shop because of its convenience, and because of the experience and skill required to prepare and use hot glue successfully.

For woodwork not lower than a No. 1½ grade should be used. Dependence should not be placed on the color when making a selection, as frequently a dark-colored hide glue will show more strength than a light-colored one that may have been through a bleaching process. Sheet glue is not always better than a pulverized one, as many suppose. It is possible to prepare any grade of glue in any form.

Preparing and Using Glue.—A pound of No. 1½ glue will take up from 1½ to 2 pounds of water. This should be applied cold and allowed to stand until the glue softens. After soaking, the glue should be dissolved by heating at a temperature not to exceed 150 degrees F. The work to be glued should be dry, clean, perfectly fitted, and warm, the hot glue being quickly applied and the work clamped up to dry. Coat all meeting surfaces thoroughly, but do not apply glue in excess. It should stand for at least 24 hours before being worked upon, the time depending somewhat upon the weather.

Storage of Fasteners.—Every care should be taken to avoid mixing the various sizes of nails, screws, and other small fasteners. The use of a convenient, marked container for each size, as suggested on page 6, is the best method of doing this.

Use of Screws.—The following table, adapted from the catalog of the American Screw Company, gives the nearest size of wood twist drill and auger bit to use for boring the hole for the shank, the pilot hole for the threaded portion of the screw, and the hole for counter-sinking the head (Fig. 105).

Sizes of Drills and Auger Bits for Setting Screws Commonly Used

Number of screw.	4	6	7	8	10	12	14	16	18
Diameter of screw shank.	$\frac{7}{64}''$	$\frac{9}{64}''$	$\frac{5}{32}''-$	$\frac{5}{32}''+$	$\frac{3}{16}''$	$\frac{7}{32}''$	$\frac{15}{64}''$	$\frac{17}{64}''$	$\frac{19}{64}''$
Number of twist drill for shank.	4	5	5	6	6	7	8	9	10
Number of twist drill for threaded portion.	2	3	4	4	4	5	6	7	8
Size of auger bit to counter-sink head.	$\frac{4}{16}''$	$\frac{5}{16}''$	$\frac{5}{16}''$	$\frac{6}{16}''$	$\frac{6}{16}''$	$\frac{7}{16}''$	$\frac{8}{16}''$	$\frac{9}{16}''$	$\frac{10}{16}''$

QUESTIONS AND EXERCISES

1. Name some of the fasteners that you have seen used in repair and construction work, and give the purpose for which each was used.
2. What are some of the conditions under which the use of screws for joining pieces of wood would be advisable?
3. List the number, sizes, and types of screws, bolts, and nails that it would be advisable to have in the farm shop.
4. Suggest a convenient method of storing these supplies.
5. What objection is there to driving nails close together when fastening two pieces of wood together by nailing?
6. What can be done to prevent trouble from bending when driving nails into hard wood?
7. How can splitting be lessened when nailing and how can nails be drawn easily?
8. Explain how toe-nailing is done. When would this method of nailing be used?
9. How is glue prepared for use?
10. How would you prepare glue for use on maple or birch?

CHAPTER VIII

DEVICES FOR THE FARM SHOP

Job 1. **The miter box** is useful for sawing moulding or small material to which it is difficult to fit a square. It may also be used for cutting a number of small pieces to a uniform length, as when cutting the slats for a potato crate (Fig. 110).

Stock List

No. Pieces	Material	Dimensions	Where used
1	Pine	$^{13}/_{16}''$ by 4'' by 20''	Front.
1	Pine	$^{13}/_{16}''$ by 5-5/8'' by 20''	Bottom.
1	Pine	$^{13}/_{16}''$ by 3-1/2'' by 20''	Back.
8 flat-head bright wood screws 1-3/4'', No. 10.			

Construction.—1. Reduce the pieces to the finished dimensions by jointing the edges and squaring the ends.

2. Drill and countersink back for four No. 10 F. H. B. screws. Arrange screws in staggered position as shown for the front to secure greater strength and to prevent splitting.

3. Set the marking gauge at 1/2'' and gauge a line on the inside of front, 1/2'' up from lower edge. This indicates the amount that the front projects below the bottom. With this line as a guide, drill and countersink screw holes as for the back.

4. Apply glue thinly to meeting surfaces, tack in position or clamp in the vise and assemble with screws. Clamp in vise near the screw that is being turned in to permit drawing up tight.

5. At a point 3'' from the right-hand end of the miter box, square across the top, being sure that the blade of the square bears firmly against the box. Also square down to the bottom on both sides from the point where this line intersects the upper edges. Saw carefully down to the bottom on these lines.

6. Lay off 3'' from the left-hand end and locate the point A. Place the square across the top of the miter box so that the figure 12 on the blade coincides with the point A and swing it until the figure 12 on the tongue coincides with the same edge. With the square held in this position mark along the blade marking the cuts at A and B.

7. Carefully square across from A and locate the point C.

8. Hold the square at C as it was held at A and mark the points C and D.

9. Square down the sides at A, B, C and D and saw down carefully on these lines to the bottom board.

10. Bore a 1/2'' hole in the end for hanging as indicated in drawing.

68

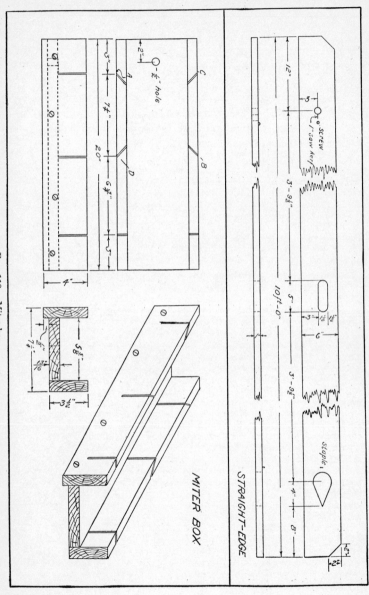

Fig. 110.—Miter box.

Job 2. **The straight edge** is used for a guide when drawing lines for straightening the irregular edges of boards, and to provide a level seat against rough timbers which do not present a good bearing surface for the comparatively short length of the level. Level or perpendicular lines can also be projected from point to point by means of the straight edge and level (Fig. 110).

Stock List

1 piece of straight grained pine, 1″ by 6-½″ by 10′ long surfaced on 4 sides (S4S).
1 round head blued wood screw, ⅞″, No. 10.
1 staple tack.

Construction.—1. Select a straight-grained pine board of sufficient size, and smooth plane both sides lightly to remove planer marks.

2. Select a second straight-grained board of equal length. To secure a straight edge two edges must be jointed at one time.

3. Clamp the boards together and place in the vise with the grain running to the left as the workman stands facing the bench.

4. See that the jointer is keen and is set to take a light uniform shaving across the full width of the bit. Joint both boards carefully at one time.

5. Keep the edges square by making frequent tests with the try square.

6. Test roughly for straightness by sighting along the edge.

7. When edge is apparently straight by sighting test, separate the boards and place the test board upon the straight edge with the two jointed edges together. Mark the points which touch for further planing.

8. If the above test does not show a perfect edge replace the boards together and continue jointing and testing as above until no light can be seen between the edges when placed together.

9. When the working edge has been jointed straight, joint the other edge parallel to it, making the straight edge 6″ wide.

10. Measure the length and square and cut the ends.

11. Set the sliding tee bevel at 45 degrees and mark and cut the corners as indicated in the drawing.

12. Set the gauge at 3″ and using the working edge as a guide gauge a line the whole length of the straight edge 3″ from the edge.

13. Directly in this line and 12″ from the end bore a 1″ hole.

14. Extending from this hole toward the center of the straight edge make a saw kerf about 1″ long in this gauge line. At the base of the saw kerf turn in a ⅞″, No. 10 round head wood screw. Turn the slot parallel with the gauge line and dress it out with a slim taper file. The saw kerf forms a means for attaching the line supporting the plumb-bob while the screw head supports it so that it swings free from the board.

15. With a point in the gauge line 12″ from the other end as a center bore a 2″ hole with the expansive bit and lay out and cut to the shape shown with the compass saw. This forms an opening for the plumb-bob to swing in. The line is prevented from swinging too far and becoming tangled when carrying by the staple placed over it as shown.

16. Locate and square a line across the center of the straight edge.

17. Set the gauge at 3-¾″ and using it against the working edge, gauge a short line across the one just made with the square to serve as a center line for the handle.

18. Set the expansive bit at 1-½″ and with points in the gauge line just made 1-¾″ on either side of the center line, bore two holes forming the ends of the handle.

19. Set the gauge at 1-½″ and gauge a line forming the upper edge of the handle. The lower edge coincides with the line first gauged 3″ from the working edge.

20. Remove the waste wood in the handle by making two parallel cuts with the compass saw along these gauge lines.

21. Smooth up the inside of the handle and plumb-bob opening with the wood rasp, removing sharp corners.

22. Give at least two coats of good out-door paint to lessen absorption of moisture and possible change of shape.

23. Arrange supports on interior wall surface so that it may be stored without warping. Edge may be made of different lengths to fit work at hand but if made longer, the width should be increased to prevent springing when in use.

Job 3. **A saw-filing clamp** is necessary to hold saws while being fitted. For emergency use it can be quickly made by using a wedge to tighten the swinging jaw instead of the cam lever shown (Fig. 111).

Stock List

No. Pieces	Material	Dimensions	Where used
1	Maple	¹³/₁₆″ x 8″ x 2′	Stationary jaw.
1	Maple	¹³/₁₆″ x 8″ x 1′ 2″	Swinging jaw.
1	Maple	¹³/₁₆″ x 1-¾″ x 6″	Cam lever.
1	Maple	½″ x 1″ x 8″	Hinge strip.

Hardware

3	Rivet burrs	³/₁₆″ ⎫	
3	Common wire nails	10d ⎬	Hinge.
1	Round head screw	1″, No. 12″	Adjusting screw for cam lever.
1	Carriage bolt	¼″ x 4″	Fulcrum for cam lever.
1	Band iron	⅛″ x 1″ x 2″	Wearing plate for cam lever.
36	Brads		Fastening for rubber jaws.
6	Common nails	3d	Hinge strip.
2	Rubber packing	1″ x 8″	Clamping jaws.

Construction.—1. Select a piece of maple ¹³/₁₆″ x 8″ x 3′ 5″ long. Joint lightly to secure a working edge and smooth plane to secure a working face.

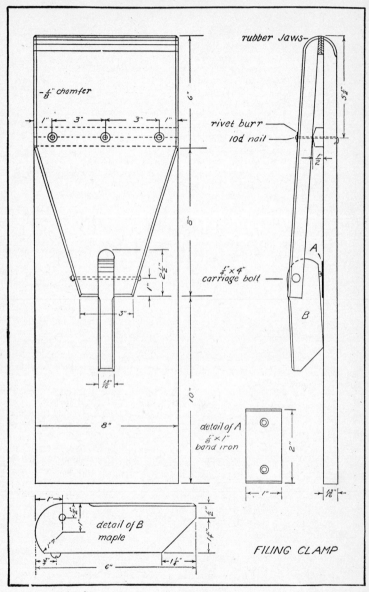

FIG. 111.—Filing clamp.

2. Square and cut stationary jaw to length. Round off top edge roughly with saw and plane.

3. Square and cut swinging jaw to length shown. Set gauge to ½ width of board and using it against working edge gauge center line down length of board.

4. Square a line across 1″ from the bottom to locate position of ¼″ bolt used as fulcrum for clamping lever.

5. Gauge lines $7/_{16}$″ on each side of center line locating edges of slot for clamping lever.

6. At the lower end of the swinging jaw locate points 1-½″ on either side of the center line and lay out and make diagonal cuts along the sides of swinging jaw with the rip saw. Round off top edge as indicated and run a ⅛″ chamfer all around.

7. Bore a ⅞″ hole in the center line forming the top of slot for clamping lever and remove wood below by rip sawing along gauge lines representing sides of slot.

8. Make hinge strip of maple ½″ thick and 1″ wide and bevel top as indicated in the side view.

9. Fasten in position across stationary jaw with 3d nails. Use steel square to insure placing it at right angles with edge.

10. With $5/_{32}$″ twist drill make 3 holes, spaced as shown along the top edge of this hinge strip. Holes may be started with nail or awl to make the drill hold its position.

11. Place swinging jaw in position and by means of nail or awl inserted from the back, mark position for $5/_{32}$″ holes in the swinging jaw. Drill holes.

12. Cut strips for jaws from sheet rubber packing using wet knife against steel square as a guide, the material to be placed on flat surface for cutting. Nail strips in position on jaws with ½″ brads.

13. Lay out and make cam lever as shown in detail of "B". Curved end may be pared to shape with sharp chisel. Drill hole for 1″ No. 12 round head screw to be used as adjusting screw to regulate tension and take up wear.

14. Cut a 2″ length of ⅛″ by 1″ band iron. Bevel ends with file and drill and countersink holes for ½″, No. 7 F. H. B. screws.

15. Assemble clamping lever and swinging jaw and place in position on stationary jaw. Mark position of holes for screws holding wearing plate "A".

16. Drill holes and screw wearing plate in position.

17. Assemble swinging jaw and stationary jaw, using 3 10d nails. Place nail heads on the anvil and clinch the points securely bending each over in the form of a hook.

18. Turn the adjusting screw in or out as the case requires until the jaws clamp with a firm pressure.

19. Clamp the jaws together and shape up the top ends with a sharp smoothing or block plane.

20. Give the wood a thorough coating of floor or machine oil being careful to protect the rubber jaws while so doing. Clamp as shown is made for use in bench vise. If so desired the stationary part can be made longer and fitted with a base at the bottom upon which the workman stands. When so made the height should be about 4 feet for the average man.

Job 4. **Saw-horse.**—Horses or trestles are necessary to support work under construction in the shop. They are also used about the farm when making repairs or alterations for the same purpose. A good horse should be light, strong, and rigid. The trussed construction of the one shown gives it these qualifications (Fig. 112).

Stock List

No. Pieces	Materials	Dimensions	Where used
1	N. C. Pine	1–¾″ x 3–¾″ x 3′	Top
1	N. C. Pine	¹³/₁₆″ x 5″ x 3′	Truss
4	N. C. Pine	¹³/₁₆″ x 4–½″ x 2′	Legs
2	N. C. Pine	¹³/₁₆″ x 5″ x 8–⅝″	End braces

Hardware

1 dozen F. H. B. screws	1–¾″, No. 9	Legs
1 dozen F. H. B. screws	1–¾″, No. 9	End braces
½ dozen finishing nails	10d	Top

Construction.—1. Rip saw and joint material to widths required.

2. Square and cut top to length. Lay out gains for legs by gauging lines 1″ from edge on each side of top. See isometric detail.

3. Apply sliding tee bevel to steel square and set at 5–⅝″ on blade and 2–¹/₃₂″ on tongue to secure angles for leg. Or, on wall board, make full size drawing of one half of end view by making vertical center line and laying off ½ width of top and bottom at right angles to this at a distance of 1 foot 10–½″ apart. An oblique line connecting these points will then give the length of the leg and the angle at which it should be cut.

4. With bevel set as above, project lines across the end of top connecting the under side with the gauge lines just made. Set the gauge to the point where the oblique lines across the end of top meet the under surface and gauge lines at this distance from the edge back the width of the leg, 4–½″. Square the top 4–½″ from the end, cut to gauge lines with saw, forming shoulders, and with rip saw cut along gauge lines, removing waste wood. Make all saw cuts in waste wood.

5. With sliding tee bevel set at same angle lay out and cut 4 legs, 2 feet long.

6. Using same angle, layout and cut end braces. As thicknesses of boards vary slightly, secure tight fit in halved joint by placing board to be used as truss in position over end brace and marking on each side with a sharp knife joint. A tight joint is essential. Should too snug a fit be secured it can be relieved by smooth-planing lightly.

7. Lay out and make truss which goes under top. Cut curves at ends with compass saw or jig saw. The same precautions should be observed in making the halved joints that were taken when making the end braces.

8. Drill and countersink legs and end braces to take the screws listed.

9. Assemble legs and top, applying glue to meeting surfaces and testing with steel square to see that leg stands perpendicular to top. If screw points are dipped in oil they should turn into soft wood without drilling. If drilling is necessary because of dense, pitchy wood, use drill smaller than was used for body of screw to enable screw threads to hold.

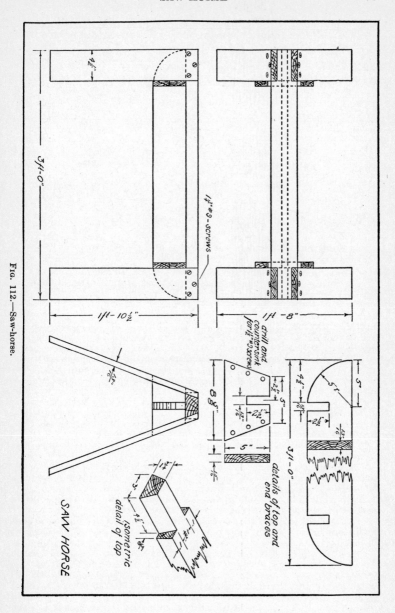

Fig. 112.—Saw-horse.

10. Assemble truss and end braces. Place in position beneath top and screw on legs, applying glue lightly to meeting surfaces.

11. Nail truss to under side of top at each end with 10d finishing nail. Drive four 10d finishing nails through top into truss. Set all nails below surface of wood.

12. If saw-horse does not set securely on level surface block up the short leg, set dividers at a distance slightly greater than the opening between short leg and the floor and with saw-horse remaining in this position, scribe around each leg and cut off at the scribed mark.

13. Smooth down all projecting edges with plane and apply several coats of machine oil or floor oil or give two coats of outside paint to make it weather resistant.

Job 5.—**A mallet** is a necessity when beating out mortises with a chisel, as the use of a hammer on a chisel handle destroys the handle. It is also useful in making repairs to farm machinery, driving in bushings and marking gaskets, where the use of a hammer might cause injury to the surface struck. The mallet shown can be made either with or without the sole leather face (Fig. 113).

Stock List

No. Pieces	Material	Dimensions	Where used
1	Birch, or other dense, tough wood	2-¾″ x 3-¾″ x 6″	Head
1	Hickory or white ash	1″ x 1-¾″ x 12″	Handle
2	Sole leather	2-¼″ diameter	Head
2 doz. 1½″ brads			Head

Construction.—1. With gauge run center line lightly lengthwise around head. Locate the mid-point of length and square a line around head at right angles to center line.

2. With these center lines as guides lay out mortises for handle 1″ by 1-¹¹/₁₆″ at the top and 1″ x 1-⅜″ at the bottom.

3. With a ⅞″ bit bore a hole through the center of the mortise, boring half way in from each side.

4. Beat out the mortise with a ¾″ chisel, beginning at the center and working toward the ends of the mortise. When mortise is cleaned up smooth up sides to line, paring the inside surfaces smooth and true. Read directions for use of chisel and be careful to avoid getting mortise too large.

5. Lay out mallet head to shape shown in side view and cut to shape. The use of miter box is advised.

6. Remove construction marks by planing and run a ¹/₁₆″ chamfer all around. If desired sole leather face can be inserted by locating center by means of diagonals, setting the expansive bit at 2-¼″ and boring to a depth equal to the thickness of the sole leather. Soak leather and cut circle with washer cutter if available, otherwise use thin sharp knife. Apply glue to mallet face and pound leather into position. Fasten with ½″ brads.

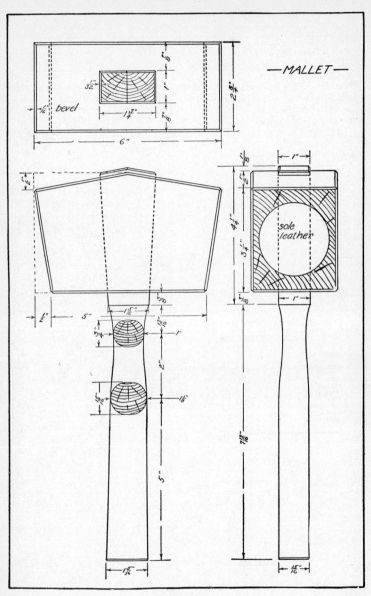

Fig. 113.—Mallet.

7. Gauge center lines on handle and at proper points lay off widths as indicated on the drawing. Square around the handle at a point $7\text{-}^{13}/_{16}''$ from lower end and use care to preserve sharp, square shoulder here while shaping the lower portion of the handle. Work lower portion of handle to shape shown with draw knife and wood rasp. Finish by scraping with glass.

8. When finished, lower part of handle should slide freely through mortise in mallet head and upper portion should be tapered to fit mortise. Test frequently and secure perfect fit. When fitted, place in position and laying rule flat against top of mallet head mark top end of handle at same angle as mallet head, giving $\frac{1}{8}''$ projection. Cut to this angle and finish with light chamfer at top and bottom of handle.

9. Clean and smooth all surfaces and apply several coats of machine oil or floor oil.

Job 6.—Bolt, Nail, and Screw Cabinet.—There is a continual need on the farm for nails, screws, staples, and bolts of various sizes; making it necessary to carry a supply of these articles in assorted sizes. The cabinet shown keeps them separate and in a convenient manner for use, as the till containing the size needed can be removed from the cabinet and carried to the bench. The contents of the drawers can best be indicated by wiring a bolt or nail of the size contained on the front of the drawer (Fig. 114).

Stock List

No. Pieces	Material	Dimensions	Where used
1	Pine or basswood	$^{13}/_{16}''$ x 13-½″ x 3′ 5-⁷/₁₆″	Top.
1	Pine or basswood	$^{13}/_{16}''$ x 1-⁹/₁₆″ x 3′ 3-⁷/₁₆″	Top casing.
2	Pine or basswood	$^{13}/_{16}''$ x 12-½″ x 5′ 5-¹/₁₆″	Ends.
8	Pine or basswood	$^{13}/_{16}''$ x 12″ x 3′ 2-³/₁₆″	Shelves.
2	Pine or basswood	½″ x 3″ x 4′ 9-½″	Braces.
5	Pine or basswood	$^{13}/_{16}''$ x 7-³/₁₆″ x 12″	Top shelf partitions.
35	Pine or basswood	$^{13}/_{16}''$ x 5-⅝″ x 12″	Shelf partitions.
48	Pine or basswood	$^{13}/_{16}''$ x 6″ x 6″	Drawer fronts.
48	Pine or basswood	$^{13}/_{16}''$ x 5-½″ x 5-½″	Drawer backs.
2	Pine or basswood	¾″ moulding 13-¼″ long	Beneath top at ends.
1	Pine or basswood	¾″ moulding 3′ 3-¹⁵/₁₆″ long	Beneath top in front.

Hardware

48	Light galvanized iron 16-½″ x 11-½″		Drawer sides and bottoms.
1-½ lbs.	10d casing nails		Ends, shelves and top.
¼ lb.	6d common nails		Braces.
2 lbs.	3d common nails		Drawers.
1 doz.	1-½″ brads		Mouldings.
4 doz.	drawer pulls		Drawers.

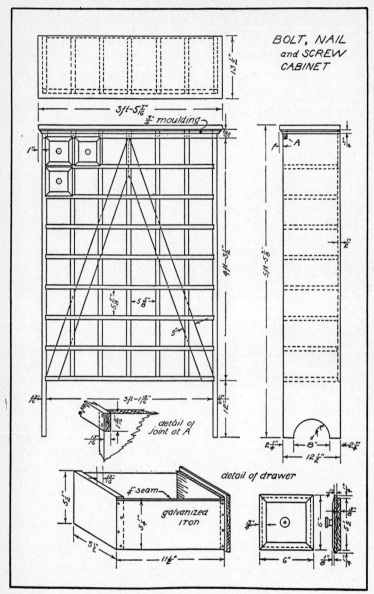

FIG. 114.—Bolt, nail, and screw cabinet.

Construction.—1. Joint sides to size desired, square and cut to length. Where material cannot be secured in sufficient width to make sides of cabinet, sides can be built up of narrower stock and secured by cleats placed beneath top of cabinet and directly below bottom shelf.

2. Lay out and cut grooves $^3/_{16}''$ deep for housing ends of shelves. Lay out and cut semi-circular piece from bottom with compass saw or jig saw and make joint for front at top as shown in detail of joint at " A ". Grooves can be cut on circular saw, if available. If not, gauge line along each edge $^3/_{16}''$ from inside surface, clamp or nail lightly a short piece of board across the stock where cut is to be made and using this as a guide saw down to the gauge marks being careful to keep the saw cuts in the waste wood. Remove the waste wood by paring with a chisel.

3. Joint shelf edges. Square and cut to proper length. Shelves can be built up of narrower stock if necessary.

4. Place bottom and top shelves in position and nail in place. If available apply glue to meeting edges. Rip out and joint a piece $^{13}/_{16}''$ material $1-^9/_{16}''$ wide to go across front. Square, cut to length and nail in place.

5. Lay out and cut top to size and nail in place.

6. Make middle top shelf partition and fit it carefully in place making sure that it is exactly in the center.

7. By use of steel square beneath top shelf adjust the cabinet frame to square position and hold it so by means of temporary diagonal brace nailed across the front from corner to corner.

8. Measure carefully the length of the diagonal braces for the cabinet and obtain the angles of cut at the top and bottom. This is most easily done by turning the cabinet on its face and applying the braces directly to the back in position for measuring and laying out angles. Cut to size and nail firmly in place with 6d common nails. See that cabinet is square while doing this. Temporary brace can now be removed.

9. Cut remainder of top shelf partitions and nail in place. Fasten bottoms by nailing up through from shelf beneath.

10. Insert second shelf and after nailing cut and nail partitions as before. Insert each shelf in turn, putting in and nailing partitions before next shelf is inserted. Tops of partitions are fastened by driving a nail at front and back obliquely through the shelf above into the top of the partition.

11. Lay out and construct drawer fronts as shown in detail using circular saw, if available. If not, construct rabbet around edges by sawing down to proper depth in miter box and after gauging around edge remove waste wood with chisel. Make chamfer on front of till with plane.

12. Cut back for drawers $5-\frac{1}{2}''$ x $5-\frac{1}{2}''$ as shown in detail.

13. From light weight galvanized iron or roofing tin, cut sheets $16-\frac{1}{2}''$ x $11-\frac{1}{2}''$. Fold over a $\frac{1}{4}''$ seam on each $11-\frac{1}{2}''$ edge leaving a sheet $16''$ x $11-\frac{1}{2}''$. Bend this sheet at right angles $5-\frac{1}{4}''$ from each $12''$ edge, forming sides and bottom of drawer. Square corners can be bent by first marking location and then clamping metal between boards. After bending bottom, put back and front in position and nail in place with 3d common nails.

14. Fasten drawer pulls to drawer fronts. Spools cut in two may be used for drawer pulls or cheap japanned pulls obtained at the hardware store.

15. Place ¾″ cove moulding around cabinet beneath top as a finish, mitering the corners and nailing with 1–½″ brads.

16. Give coat of paint, if desired, and fasten against wall in convenient position near bench.

Job. 7.—**Tool Board.**—Where tools are in constant use a means of storing should be adopted that will be convenient, protect, their edges and indicate the exact place that a tool should go when returned to the shop. Order and neatness in the shop increase the service that may be obtained from it and the tool equipment. The tool board is preferably made open as shown (Fig. 115) but, where necessary, can be built with deeper sides and fitted with doors of ¼-inch mesh galvanized wire screening which permits locking up the tool equipment.

Stock List

No. Pieces	Material	Dimensions	Where used
6	Pine or basswood	$^{13}/_{16}″$ x 7–¼″ x 7′ 11″	Back
1	Pine or basswood	1″ x 2″ x 8′	Top of frame
2	Pine or basswood	1″ x 2″ x 3′ 6″	Ends of frame
1	Pine or basswood	1″ x 2″ x 8′	Tool supporting strip at C
1	Pine or basswood	1″ x 4″ x 8′	Shelf at bottom
3	Pine or basswood	$^{13}/_{16}″$ x 3″ x 3′ 5″	Cleats for back

Hardware

5 dozen F. H. B. screws	1–½″ No. 9	For fastening cleats to back
½ pound 8d casing nails		For fastening frame to back

Small quantity light and dark paint.

Construction.—1. Joint boards from which back is to be made, numbering them as fitted so that they may be reassembled in the same order.

2. Make three cleats of $^{13}/_{16}″$ material 3′ 5″ in length, running a ¼″ chamfer all around.

3. Assemble boards to be used for back face downward on the sawhorses putting best face out. If available apply glue lightly to meeting edges and pull snugly together with clamps.

4. Lay out the position of back cleats and with small nails tack back cleats in position.

5. Drill holes in cleats for No. 9 screws and countersink, putting three screws into each board at each cleat. Be careful to drill only through cleat letting screw make its own hole in back board. Nails can be used in assembling the back if desired. In this case mark position of cleats on the face of the boards and drive nails through from the front, using

6

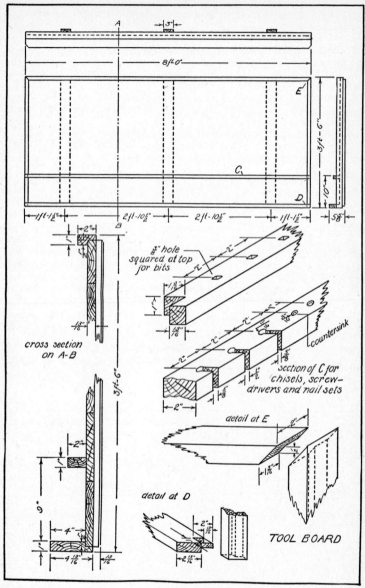

FIG. 115.—Tool board.

5d box nails, clinching them on the back. Smooth plane face of board if necessary first setting nails lightly if nails were used in assembling.

6. Square ends of assembled back board and cut to length.

7. From 1″ material, rip sufficient material 2″ wide for top and ends of frame and tool support at C. Joint edges.

8. Cut ½″ x ¹³/₁₆″ rabbet in one edge of this material to be used for frame.

9. Set sliding tee bevel at 45-degree angle and cut joints for upper corners of frame as shown in detail at E. Cut lower end of end piece square off as shown in detail of D.

10. Nail top and ends of frame in place using 8d casing nails.

11. From 1″ material rip a piece for bottom shelf and joint to 4 inches wide. Cut to length, making joint as shown in detail at D.

12. Cut 2″ strip "C" to length and after determining what tools it shall support, prepare the openings for them as suggested in detail of C. Positions for these openings can best be determined by laying the tool board flat upon the horses and placing upon it the tools it is to support, arranging them in the most convenient manner.

13. Nail C in position, joining to frame as shown in detail of C.

14. Give at least two coats of light colored paint, light gray preferred.

15. When dry put in position over or near bench and place hooks for supporting tools. Arrange planes on bottom shelf with strip under noses to keep cutting edge from contact with shelf.

16. With tools in position, outline around each with pencil. Remove tools and paint in silhouette with dark contrasting paint.

Job 8.—**Shoulder Tool Box.**—Repairs and alterations about the farm are often remote from the buildings. A convenient method of carrying such tools as will be needed in making the repair, serves as a help and tends to prevent the loss and damage of tools (Fig. 116).

Stock List

No. Pieces	Material	Dimensions	Where used
1	Pine or basswood	¹³/₁₆″ x 2″ x 2′ 7–⅞″	Handle
2	Pine or basswood	¹³/₁₆″ x 8″ x 11–½″	Ends
2	Pine or basswood	⅜″ x 4–⅜″ x 2′ 7–½″	Sides
1	Pine or basswood	½″ x 7″ x 2′ 8″	Bottom
		Hardware	
20	F. H. B. screws	1″ No. 7	Sides and bottom
2	F. H. B. screws	1-¾″ No. 9	Handle
12	Box nails	5d	Bottom
	Small quantity paint and glue.		

Construction.—1. From straight grained material rip a piece 2-⅛″ wide and joint to 2″ wide.

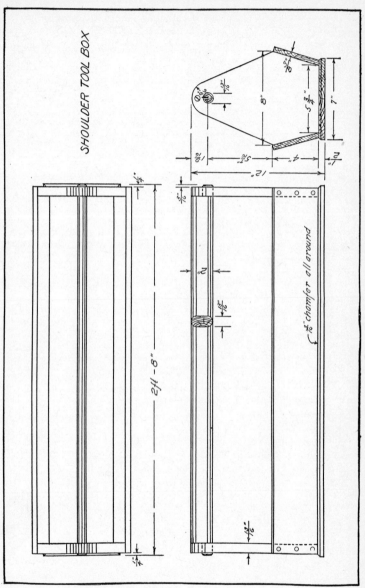

Fig. 116.—Shoulder tool box.

2. At points 2 feet 5-⅞″ distant from each other, square around the stick so formed and cut shoulders for ends of handle. Cut projections so formed 1-⅛″ long and dress to press fit for ¹³/₁₆″ hole.

3. With jointer remove corners of handle and work to shape shown in turned section.

4. Joint piece of ¹³/₁₆″ material to 8″ wide to form ends and with gauge draw center line lengthwise.

5. Square and cut across the end of board forming bottom of end piece.

6. At a point 4″ above this, square a second line across the board representing the widest portion of the end.

7. Measure 5-⁷/₁₆″ above this, and again square across the board.

8. Using a radius of 1-⁹/₁₆″ and the intersection of the line last squared with the center line as a center describe a circle with the compasses. A portion of this circumference represents the top of the end.

9. Draw lines from the end of the line squared across the widest part of the end tangent to this circle.

10. On the bottom edge measure in from each side 1-⅛″ and draw lines from points so located to ends of line across widest part of end.

11. Cut out end on lines so laid out, using compass saw for curve at top or paring it to shape with sharp chisel.

12. Bore ¹³/₁₆″ hole at point used as center in laying out curve at top and drill hole for No. 9 screw above it. Two ends are to be made from these directions. If carefully made the first may be used as pattern for second.

13. From ⅜″ material, 4-½″ wide. make two sides of the size indicated. Secure bevel for bottom edge by setting tee bevel on lower corner of end just made.

14. From ½″ material cut bottom to size shown.

15. Assemble ends and handle and fasten sides to ends, using glue in joints, if available. Sixpenny nails may be used for fastening sides instead of screws, if desired.

16. Put bottom in position and mark for projection. Run ⁸/₁₆″ chamfer around edges. Replace and fasten with nails and screws as indicated in stock list, using screws at ends and nails in sides. Use care to see that nails do not come out on sides when nailing bottom to sides.

17. Smooth up with sandpaper and apply 2 coats of paint.

Job 9.—Farm Bench.—Construction and repair work can best be done on a solid, plane surface such as is provided by the top of a good bench. Farm shop work is of a varied nature, involving both wood and metal work, and the bench should provide for both.

The bench shown has a strong vise with iron plates set in the meeting surfaces of the jaws permitting its use, to a certain extent, in metal work. The use of a 2″ x 2″ angle iron for this purpose, extending it along the front edge of the bench, is a desirable construction for a bench to be used much in repair work, as it provides a surface upon which bolts and nails may be straightened and a cold chisel used for cutting. The addition of a steel vise is advisable where it can be obtained (Figs. 117 and 118).

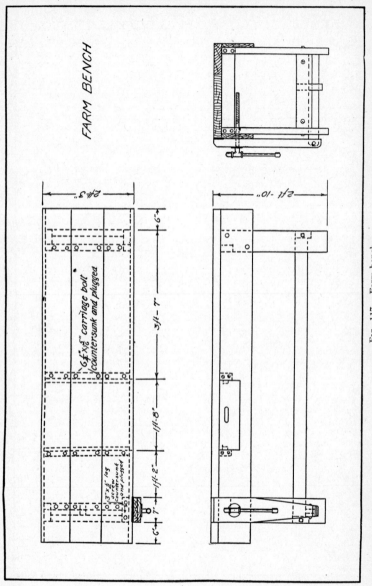

FIG. 117.—Farm bench.

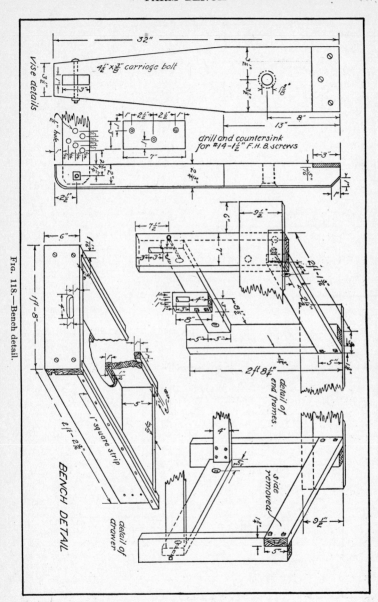

Fig. 118.—Bench detail.

Stock List

No. Pieces	Material	Dimensions	Where used
1	Maple	$1''$ x $9-\frac{1}{2}''$ x $8'$	Front apron.
1	Pine	$^{13}/_{16}''$ x $9-\frac{1}{2}''$ x $8'$	Rear apron.
3	Maple	$1-\frac{3}{4}''$ x $5''$ x $2'$ $1-^{3}/_{16}''$	Intermediate and right hand cross sills.
1	Maple	$1-\frac{3}{4}''$ x $5''$ x $1'$ $11-^{7}/_{16}''$	Left cross sill.
3	Maple	$1-\frac{3}{4}''$ x $5''$ x $2'$ $8-\frac{1}{4}''$	Legs.
1	Maple	$1-\frac{3}{4}''$ x $7''$ x $2'$ $8-\frac{1}{4}''$	Left front leg.
2	Maple	$1-\frac{3}{4}''$ x $5''$ x $1'$ $9-^{7}/_{16}''$	Lower cross members.
2	Pine	$^{13}/_{16}''$ x $4''$ x $6'$ $8-\frac{1}{2}''$	Lower lengthwise leg braces.
1	Maple	$1-\frac{3}{4}''$ x $3''$ x $8''$	Guide for vise adjustment.
1	Maple	$2-\frac{3}{4}''$ x $7''$ x $2'$ $8''$	Swinging jaw of vise.
1	Maple	$1''$ x $3''$ x $2'$ $2-^{3}/_{16}''$	Lower adjustment of vise.
2	Pine	$^{13}/_{16}''$ x $1-\frac{1}{2}''$ x $2'$ $1-^{3}/_{16}''$	Drawer guides.
1	Pine	$^{13}/_{16}''$ x $6''$ x $1'$ $8''$	Drawer front.
2	Pine	$^{13}/_{16}''$ x $6''$ x $2'$ $1-^{9}/_{16}''$	Drawer sides.
1	Pine	$^{13}/_{16}''$ x $5''$ x $1'$ $5''$	Drawer back.
3	Pine	$\frac{1}{2}''$ x $8-\frac{1}{2}''$ x $1'$ $5''$	Drawer bottom.
2	Pine	$1''$ x $1''$ x $2'$ $1\frac{3}{8}''$	Sliding shoes for drawer.
3	Maple	$1-\frac{3}{4}''$ x $9''$ x $8'$	Top.

Hardware

No. Pieces	Material	Dimensions	Where used
2	Iron	$^{5}/_{16}''$ x $3''$ x $7''$	Vise jaws.
6	F. H. B. screws	$1-\frac{1}{2}''$, No. 14	Vise jaws.
1	Steel bench screw	$1-\frac{1}{4}''$ x $17''$	Vise.
1	Carriage bolt (with washer)	$\frac{3}{8}''$ x $4-\frac{1}{2}''$	Vise.
1	Iron pin	$\frac{1}{2}''$ x $4''$	Vise.
6	Carriage bolts (with washers)	$\frac{3}{8}''$ x $5-\frac{1}{2}''$	For bolting cross sills to top of legs
1	Machine bolt (with washer)	$\frac{3}{8}''$ x $6-\frac{3}{4}''$	Cross sill to top of left front leg.
4	Machine bolts (with washers)	$\frac{3}{8}''$ x $6-\frac{3}{4}''$	Lower cross members to legs.
2	Carriage bolts (with washers)	$\frac{3}{8}''$ x $6-\frac{3}{4}''$	Vise adjustment guide to left cross member.
8	Carriage bolts (with washers)	$\frac{3}{8}''$ x $3-\frac{1}{4}''$	Aprons to legs.
16	F. H. B. screws	$2''$, No. 12	Lengthwise leg braces to legs.

No. Pieces	Material	Dimensions	Where used
8	F. H. B. screws	2-½", No. 14	Intermediate cross sills to aprons.
4	F. H. B. screws	2", No. 10	Drawer front to sides.
8	Casing nails	8d	Drawer back to sides.
12	Box nails	5d	Sliding shoe to drawer side.
12	Box nails	5d	Drawer guides to intermediate sills
2	Coach screws	½" x 3"	Top back of vise.
24	Carriage bolts (with washers)	⁵/₁₆" x 6-¼"	Top to cross sills.

1 quart of floor oil or light machine oil for finishing.

Construction.—1. Using 1-¾" maple or birch rip out and joint to 5" wide, material for three legs. Square and cut to 2 feet 8-¼" long.

2. Select best faces for outside and when in this position lay out gains 5" x 1-¾" at top for joint with cross sills, as shown in detail of end frames.

3. At a point 7-½" from the bottom, square a line across the inside of legs and ⅞" from outer edge bore a ⅜" hole in this line. Lay out work on both sides and bore from both sides to center.

4. Cut gain at upper end with saws and, with marking gauge, make center line along the face of the gain. Bore a ³/₈" hole 1" from top and 1" from bottom on this line. Lay out and bore from both sides as before.

5. Joint a piece of 1-¾" material to 7" wide and square and cut to 2' 8-¼" long for leg back of vise.

6. Square a line across the top end of this leg on the inside, 2-½" down from the top. With the gauge set at 2-⅞", gauge a short line along the right hand edge of the leg intersecting the line just squared across it. Locate this intersection on both inside and outside faces. With a 1" bit countersink from the front ½" deep at this intersection.

7. With ⅜" bit continue boring from the front half way through. Reverse and finish hole from the back as in the case of the other three legs.

8. Seven and one-half inches up from the bottom and ⅞" in from left-hand edge locate center of bolt hole joining leg to lower cross member. Lay out on both sides and using ⅜" bit bore the hole, working from both sides and meeting in the center.

9. On center line of leg and 3" up from bottom lay out a 1" x 2" mortise. Lay out mortise on both sides of leg and work from both sides to center. Bore 3 ⅞" holes on center line to remove waste wood.

10. Square and cut to a length of 2' 1-³/₁₆", 3 pieces of 1-¾" maple or birch for cross sills. Joint to 5" wide.

11. Square and cut to length of 1 foot 11-⁷/₁₆", 1 piece of maple or birch 1-¾" in thickness for cross sill at vise end of bench. Joint to 5" wide.

12. Square a line across each end of the cross sill to be used at the right hand end of the bench ⅞" from the end. Set the gauge at 1" and

gauge short lines on each side of the cross sill intersecting the line just squared across. Bore ⅜″ holes at these intersections, corresponding to holes in upper ends of legs. In boring holes in separate pieces that are to be joined it is essential that the work be laid out and bored from the meeting surfaces. To secure a good appearance as well, all work should be laid out on both sides and worked from both sides to the center.

13. Lay out and bore rear end of cross sill for vise end of bench in same manner as for one just made. For end next to vise bore 1″ hole through center of cross sill, 6–½″ from end. Obtain the center of the end by means of intersecting diagonals and bore a ⅜″ hole into the end of the cross sill until it meets the 1″ hole just bored.

14. From 1–¾″ maple or birch square and cut 2 lower cross members 1′ 9–⁷/₁₆″ long. Joint to 5″ wide and lay out and bore ends as described for end of cross sill next to vise in 13.

15. Assemble legs, cross sills and lower cross members using bolts listed for the purpose. When assembling cross members with legs put nut in 1″ hole, insert machine bolt with washer beneath head through leg and turn bolt into nut by means of wrench on head. Machine bolts are used here because of square head which permits turning them in as outlined.

16. Select a straight grained maple board 1″ in thickness that will joint to 9–½″ wide. Joint to width, square and cut to 8′ long.

17. Square across the inside face 6″ from each end to mark location of outer edge of legs.

18. Lay out and cut drawer opening 6″ deep by 20″ wide in upper edge of board, 2′ 3″ from vise end of bench. Bore ½″ hole at lower corner of drawer opening in waste wood. Cut down to hole on squared marks with cutting-off saw and start lengthwise cut with compass saw. Finish with rip saw.

19. Lay out and make the back apron from ¹³/₁₆″ pine or basswood, the same as 18 omitting the drawer opening.

20. Assemble the front and rear aprons and right and left leg assembles. Fasten aprons in place temporarily with 6d nails, adjusting legs carefully to place with square before nailing. Bore ⅜″ holes and insert two 3″ x 3–¼″ carriage bolts at each end, using washers beneath nuts. Bolts at vise end on front apron must be countersunk flush with surface of apron.

21. Place two remaining cross sills in position at either side of drawer opening and fasten in position with F. H. B. screws as listed in stock list. Drill and countersink apron to take body of screws easily. Drill end of sills with drill corresponding to size of screw at base of thread.

22. Dress two pieces of ¹³/₁₆″ pine to 1–½″ wide. Square and cut to 2′ 1–³/₁₆″ long and nail in place 1″ down from top of intermediate sills to serve as drawer guides.

23. Construct drawer to fit opening as shown in detail. All joints should be rabbeted and meeting surfaces except edges of bottom covered with glue before assembling. Sides are laid out and made in right and left patterns. Bottom of ½″ material slides in groove which permits expansion and contraction. Grooves and rabbets can be cut on circular saw, if available, otherwise use rabbet plane or saw and chisel. Bottom can be made of galvanized iron nailed directly to lower edges of front, sides and back of drawer. In this case omit lengthwise grooves in side pieces.

Thin lumber can be used in same way but it is likely to open joints of drawer through swelling.

24. Square and cut out two pieces of $^{13}/_{16}''$ material 6' 8-½'' long for lower lengthwise leg braces. Fasten in place using F. H. B. screws as listed in stock list.

25. Select the planks for the top and fit edges by jointing until they meet perfectly. Planks must be dry to avoid shrinkage.

26. By means of clamps squeeze planks in position and with the steel square draw a center line over each cross sill, locating position of bolt holes. Bolt holes at outer ends of intermediate cross sills must be offset to avoid striking screws securing cross sills to aprons.

27. Countersink bolt holes in top of bench 1'' to permit plugging. Bore holes in top, boring two ½'' holes back of vise as shown for ½'' x 3'' coach screws. These are also countersunk to permit plugging.

28. Place first plank in position and bore holes through cross sills. Insert bolts and fasten in place, using washers under all nuts. Use lag screws back of vise as shown.

29. Place second plank in position and by means of clamps pull tightly against first. Mark position of holes in cross sills by inserting bit through holes in plank. Remove plank and bore holes in sills, drawboring slightly by setting point of bit $^1/_{16}''$ nearer plank fastened in position than marks made on cross sills.

30. Replace plank in position and draw up with clamps. Insert bolts, drive them home and draw up tightly with nuts. The drawboring helps to secure a tighter joint.

31. Repeat this process with the third plank.

32. Square across each end of the bench at the ends of the aprons and cut off.

33. Cut plugs and plug all bolt holes in bench top, setting them in glue.

34. Cut plugs flush with saw and plane top to an even surface.

35. Prepare plates for vise jaws. For directions see forge work, job 5.

36. From 2-¾'' maple or birch, make swinging jaw for vise as shown in detail and fit iron plate to top fastening with screws as listed in stock list. Mark and drill for screws before attempting to turn them in.

37. From a piece of maple 1'' x 3'' and 2' 4-³/₁₆'' long, make the lower adjustment for vise. Bore as shown in detail and bolt to lower end of vise jaw.

38. Cut a block of maple 1-¾'' x 3'' x 8'', mortising it and bolting it to lower cross member of end frame as shown in detail.

39. Push lower vise adjustment through mortise in leg and holding swinging jaw in its proper place, mark the position of hole for bench screw in leg.

40. Bore hole, fit nut to inside of leg, put bench screw in place and draw vise up.

41. With vise drawn up mark position of iron plate on bench.

42. Remove vise and fit iron plate to bench letting it project about ⅛''.

43. Reassemble vise and after smoothing up rough spots on bench with plane and sandpaper, apply several coats of floor oil or light machine oil.

Job 10.—**Stitching Horse.**—The repair of harness is a duty common to every farm. The stitching horse described is designed to hold the straps securely in a convenient position for stitching, making good work possible (Fig. 119).

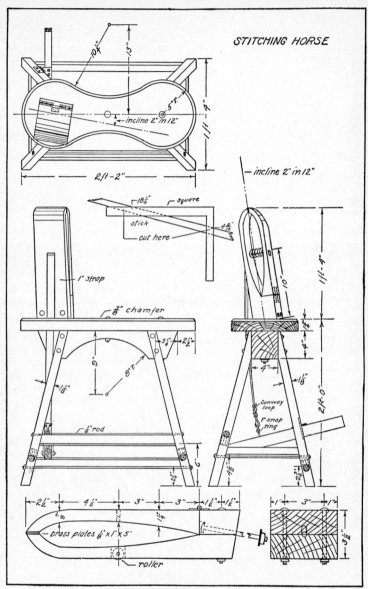

FIG. 119.—Stitching horse.

Stock List

No. Pieces	Material	Dimensions	Where used
1	Pine S2S	1–¾″ x 10″ x 2′ 2″	Seat.
1	Pine S4S	4″ x 4″ x 1′ 9″	Block beneath seat.
4	White ash	1–⅛″ x 1–⅛″ x 2′	Legs.
2	White ash	1–⅛″ x 1–⅛″ x 1′	End braces.
1	White ash	1–⅛″ x 1–⅛″ x 1′ 10–¾″	Right side brace.
1	White ash	1–⅛″ x 1–⅛″ x 1′ 9–¼″	Left side brace.
1	White ash	1″ x 1–½″ x 1′ 7″	Treadle.
2	Maple S4S	1–¾″ x 5″ x 1′ 4″	Clamp.

Hardware

2	Iron rods, threaded and supplied with nuts and washers	¼″ x 1′ 2–¼″	Tension rod beneath braces.
1	Iron rod, threaded and supplied with nuts and washers	¼″ x 2′ 1–¼″	Tension rod beneath right side brace.
1	Iron rod, threaded and supplied with nuts and washers	¼″ x 1′ 11″	Tension rod above left side brace.
1	Band iron	⅛″ x 1″ x 5″	Stirrup for treadle.
1	Band iron	⅛″ x 1–½″ x 5″	Latch for treadle.
1	Band iron	⅛″ x 1–½″ x 3″	Latch for treadle.
1	Iron harness ring	1″ diameter	Treadle.
1	Snap	1″	Treadle.
1	Bent eye bolt	¼″ x 2–¼″	Treadle.
1	Conway loop	1″	Treadle.
1	Strap	1″ x 3′	Treadle.
1	Common nail	30d	Pin for roller in fixed jaw.
1	Spool	medium size	Roller.
1	Compression coil spring	1–½″ x 3″	Between jaws.
2	Steel butts	2″ x 2–½″	Movable jaw.
4	Common nails	3d	Fasteners for attaching strap to movable jaw.
4	F. H. B. screws	1″ No. 7	Treadle latch.
2	Carriage bolts	¼″ x 1–¾″	Treadle stirrup.
2	Carriage bolts	¼″ x 6–½″	Legs.
2	Carriage bolts	¼″ x 5–½″	Legs.

No.	Pieces Material	Dimensions	Where used
1	Carriage bolt	$5/16''$ x 6' $1/4''$	Rear end of seat.
1	Carriage bolt	$3/8''$ x 8–$1/4''$	Front end of seat.
1	Washer	$3/8''$	
3	Washers	$1/4''$	
1	Washer	$5/16''$	
2	Brass	$1/8''$ x 1'' x 5''	Top of clamp.
12	F. H. B. screws	$1/2''$ No. 5	Top of clamp.
	Small quantity of shellac for finishing.		

Construction.—1. Select a piece of straight grained pine plank, S2S and joint to 10'' wide.

2. Select the working edge and square two lines across the plank 2' 2'' apart locating ends at seat.

3. Set gauge at 5'' and gauge center line the full length of seat.

4. Using radii and centers given lay out curves for sides and ends of seat. Curves for sides may be laid out with a strip of cardboard as a radius, driving a nail through one end to serve as a center and punching a hole in the other through which the pencil point is inserted.

5. Cut seat to shape with compass saw or jig saw. Finish with spoke shave.

6. Run a $1/4''$ chamfer around the top with spoke shave.

7. Select a straight grained piece of white ash or hickory for legs and by ripping and jointing reduce to 1–$1/8''$ x 1–$1/8''$ in cross section.

8. Obtain length of leg and angle for top and bottom cut by applying steel square as shown in the drawing. Mark along outside of tongue and blade for cut.

9. With square in this position mark at the 22–$1/2''$ division for the top of the leg.

10. Above directions give angle of leg as seen in end view. Angle for side may be obtained in the same way or sliding tee bevel may be set at 1–$1/2''$ on the tongue and 6'' on the blade of the square to give the same cut, holding the beam of the tee bevel against the tongue of the square while setting it. Legs must be laid out in pairs, right and left.

11. Cut angles at top and bottom of legs.

12. Place legs in the position they are to occupy and mark locations of mortises to receive stub tenons of side end braces.

13. With the try square and gauge lay out a mortise $3/8''$ x 1–$1/8''$, 4–$1/2''$ from the floor line on the inside of each leg to receive stub tenons on end braces. Work the mortises $1/2''$ deep.

14. Obtain exact length of end braces by drawing a center line on wall board or smooth bench top and laying out end view full size on this center line. Length of side braces can be found in the same way. Measurements can be taken from the drawing direct.

15. Using same stock as for legs cut end braces to length, allowing for $3/8''$ tenon at each end. Angle of cut is the same as for bottom of leg and may be obtained as in (14) or by using the figures 1–$1/2''$ and 6'' on the tongue and blade of the square respectively, holding the beam of the sliding tee bevel against the tongue of the square when setting. Lay out sides of tenon with gauge and fit it carefully to the mortise.

16. Bore holes in center line of leg directly beneath end braces for ¼" tension rod as shown.

17. In the same way make mortises for right side braces 2¾" above floor line and bore holes for ¼" tension rod directly beneath them.

18. Make and fit right side brace using same angles as for end braces. Obtain length from drawing (14).

19. Six inches from floor line lay out mortises in left legs ⅜" x 1⅛" and work to ½" deep for left side brace.

20. Make left side brace from 1–⅛" x 1–⅛" material. Obtain length from drawing (14) and cut angles the same as for leg ends. Bore holes for tension rod above this brace to be out of the way of the treadle stirrup which is bolted beneath this brace.

21. Cut rods from ¼" round, mild steel and thread as directed in Chapter XV. Lengths may be obtained from drawing.

22. Select a piece of straight grained pine S4S, 4" x 4" x 1' 9" for block beneath seat and mark and cut ends to same angle as legs.

23. With an 8" radius and a center located 9" from the top edge of the piece and in a line drawn at right angles to its mid-point, draw an arc as shown, laying out the curve for the under part.

24. With compass saw, jig saw or turning saw cut along this line and smooth up the work with the spoke shave.

25. With sliding tee bevel set at same angle as for legs, lay out position of legs upon this block as shown in drawing.

26. Bore holes and bolt legs to block with bolts listed. Leave bolts untightened until braces are put in place.

27. Bore hole for bolt holding treadle stirrup in forward end of left side brace and insert bolt.

28. Place braces in position, insert rods and tighten up bolts and rods.

29. Adjust seat in position on foundation block, with center lines coinciding and bore ⁵/₁₆" hole at center and rear of seat. Bolt seat to foundation block with bolts listed.

30. Make irons for stitching horse as directed in Chapter V.

31. Using 1–¾" x 5" maple S4S make clamping jaws as shown in drawing. Lay out curves for outside and inside cuts by clamping pieces together and squaring across at the intervals noted. Waste wood on the inside can be removed by making saw kerfs down to the line at short intervals and removing the waste wood with a chisel, smoothing up the surface with the spoke shave. Clamping jaws are most easily made by first laying them out as directed and then having them cut on a band saw.

32. Bore and bolt jaws together, using 2–⅜" carriage bolts as listed.

33. Set the bevel at 1" and 6" on the tongue and blade of steel square and mark angle for base cut of clamping jaws. Cut at this angle.

34. Square across clamping jaws 3" up from bottom and cut through 1 section forming movable jaw. Make movable jaw on side indicated in the drawing.

35. Bore ⅜" hole in center of bottom end of jaws for bolt, securing clamp to seat and foundation block. Countersink 1" deep as indicated.

36. Cut mortise at point indicated in stationary jaw and bore hole for pin supporting roller at such a point that the circumference of the roller projects about ⅛" beyond outside surface of fixed jaw. Put roller in position and drive in pin which may be made from a piece of 30d spike.

37. Make opening for strap through movable jaw at a point opposite top edge of roller. Round outer edge of opening where strap must bend over it.

38. Cut, drill and countersink brass plates used for lining meeting surfaces of jaws. Place in jaws and with file dress upper edges of brass plates to fit smoothly when jaws are closed.

39. Place clamp in position and bolt to seat. Bore $\frac{3}{8}''$ hole for this purpose in the seat 5'' from the end and in the center line of the seat.

40. Using 1'' x 1-$\frac{1}{2}$'' ash S4S make treadle 19'' long and $\frac{3}{4}$'' from one end, bore a $\frac{1}{4}$'' hole in the center of 1-$\frac{1}{2}$'' side for stirrup bolt. Six inches from this hole bore a $\frac{1}{4}$'' hole in the center of 1'' side for eye bolt holding ring for snap. Place treadle in position and mark location of latch iron. Fasten latch iron in place and bolt treadle to stirrup.

41. Locate position of latch on right front leg and with chisel cut a gain setting face of latch flush with surface. Drill leg, and screw latch in position.

42. Locate point in seat where strap will pass through from roller to eye bolt in treadle and make opening for it with $\frac{3}{8}$'' bit and chisel. Strap should work freely through this opening.

43. Place coil spring between jaws and insert strap. Bevel end of strap and bend down about 1-$\frac{1}{2}$'', fastening it to the outside of the movable jaw with 4 threepenny nails.

44. Pass strap through slot cut in seat and fasten to ring in treadle with snap and Conway loop.

45. Smooth up work with No. 1-$\frac{1}{2}$ sand paper and apply shellac with oiled pad.

Supplementary Devices for the Farm Shop

1. Bench hook.
2. File, soldering copper, hammer, hand-axe, and other tool handles.
3. Adjustable painting trestles.
4. Revolving painting and finishing stand.
5. Filing clamp for timber saw.
6. Filing clamp for small circular saw.
7. Combination rip and cross-cut circular saw table.
8. Stand for tool grinder.
9. Tool rests for grinder.
10. Tool chest.
11. Drawing board or drafting table.
12. Wall case for shop reference books, catalogs, and blue prints.
13. Jig saw.
14. Speed lathe, using belt-driven grinder as head.

CHAPTER IX

DEVICES FOR THE BARN AND DAIRY

Job 1.—**Milking Stool.**—A light, strong milking stool that is easily kept clean is a necessity on the dairy farm. The stool illustrated meets these requirements (Fig. 120).

Stock List for Stool

No. Pieces	Material	Dimensions	Where used
2	Pine or Basswood S2S	$^{13}/_{16}''$ x 9'' diameter	Top.
3	White Ash or Hickory	$\frac{7}{8}''$ x $\frac{7}{8}''$ x 12''	Legs.
6	F. H. B. screws	1–$\frac{1}{2}''$, No. 9	Top.

Stock List for Boring Jig

1	Maple or other hardwood	2'' x 2'' x 5–$\frac{3}{4}''$	Guide.
1	Maple or other hardwood	$\frac{1}{2}''$ x 2'' x 7–$\frac{3}{4}''$	Base.
1	F. H. B. wood screws	1'', No. 7	Center.
2	F. H. B. wood screws	1–$\frac{1}{2}''$, No. 9	Fastening base to guide.

Construction.—1. Set the dividers at a radius of 4–$\frac{1}{2}''$ and lay out two 9'' circles on straight grained pine or basswood stock, S2S.

2. With the compass saw or jig saw, cut out these circles being careful to follow the line and to keep the edge square with the stock.

3. Set the dividers at 3–$\frac{3}{4}''$ radius and with the same center describe a second circle on one of the pieces just cut out.

4. With the same radius step around this circumference, dividing it into 6 equal parts, locating the positions of the screws holding the two parts of the top together.

5. Drill and countersink at these points for 1–$\frac{1}{2}''$, No. 9 F. H. B. wood screws.

6. Apply glue to meeting surfaces, place the pieces comprising the top together with the grain of the wood crossing at right angles and fasten with screws. Set aside to dry. When driving screws clamp the piece in the vise near the screw being turned in. This permits the work to be drawn up much tighter.

7. From straight grained ash or hickory, split 3 legs 1'' x 1'' x 12'' long. Wood can be split straighter by splitting each time through the center until the size desired is obtained rather than by attempting to split a small piece from the side of a large block.

8. With plane reduce pieces to $\frac{7}{8}''$ x $\frac{7}{8}''$.

9. Plane off corners making piece octagonal.

10. Again remove corners making piece 16 sided and finish round with light strokes of the plane.

11. Bore a $\frac{7}{8}''$ hole in a hard wood block and fit legs to it.

7

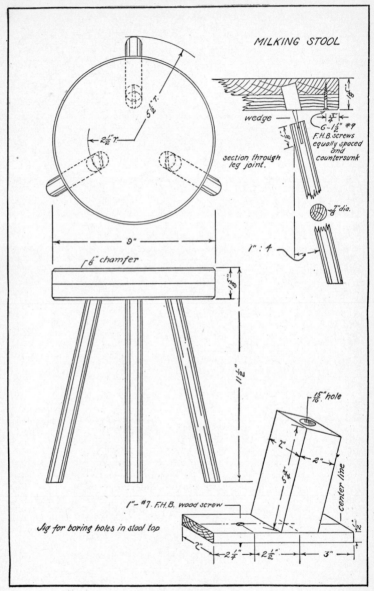

FIG. 120.—Milking stool.

12. Make a 1-⅛" saw kerf with compass saw in top of each leg as shown in "section through leg joint."

13. Prepare wedges for these saw kerfs as indicated.

14. When top is dry finish edge by means of sharp spoke shave set to take a light shaving. Finish to true circle. Keep edge at right angles to face by frequent tests with try square.

15. Run a ⅛" chamfer clear around top and bottom edges as shown.

16. Set dividers at the same radius used in laying out the circle for the screws and starting at a point in this circumference midway between two of the screws, again step around this circle.

17. Selecting every alternate one of these points, draw lines through them to the center of the circle forming the center lines in which the legs are located. Mark these lines on the edge of the stool so that their position may be determined when they are covered by the boring jig.

18. Place the boring jig in position with center screw turned into center of stool top from beneath. Turn about this point until its center line coincides with one of the marks made on the edge of the stool top.

19. Clamp the top and boring jig in the vise and with a ⅞" bit inserted in the guide, bore a hole for the leg. Repeat for the remaining 2 legs. Guide of boring jig should be made of such length that the bit will not bore through stool top when turned in full length.

20. Coat wedges, ends of stool legs and hole in stool top with glue and, placing top on smooth, hard surface, drive legs into place. Start legs with wedges placed diagonally across grain to avoid splitting either upper or under part of top. If desired, legs may be secured by inserting a 1-½", No. 9 F. H. B. screw into end from the top. In this case do not place saw kerf in top of leg.

21. Set stool on level surface and, if necessary, block under short leg until stool top stands parallel with surface upon which legs rest.

22. Measure from upper surface of top to surface upon which stool stands.

23. Subtract 11½" (stool height) from this measurement and set dividers at the difference obtained.

24. With dividers set at this difference, scribe around the bottom of each leg as the stool stands in this position.

25. Cut legs off on these scribed marks.

26. Smooth up work by sand papering and apply a priming coat of paint.

27. When dry, putty defects, if any, and apply a coat of light gray auto enamel or other durable high gloss paint.

BORING JIG

1. Select a short section of 2" x 2" maple or other hardwood. Locate center of each end by bisecting diagonals and with a ¹⁵/₁₆" bit bore from each end to the center.

2. Cut angle where guide joins base by applying the square at 2" on the tongue and 8" on the blade.

3. Square other end and cut to required length to permit bit used to bore hole of proper depth.

4. Using maple or other hardwood, make base to size shown. Gauge center line full length and join guide to it by means of 2 screws inserted from beneath.

5. Insert center screw at point indicated and by placing ¹⁵/₁₆" bit in guide, bore hole through base.

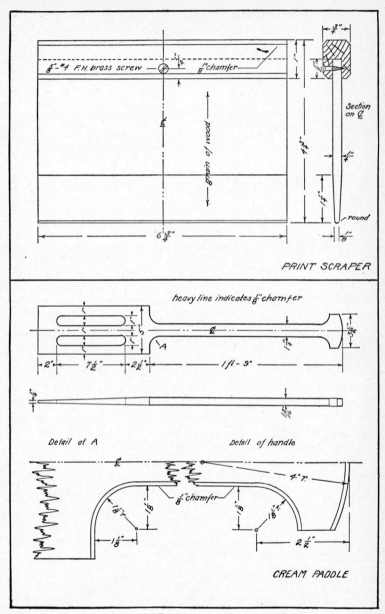

FIG. 121.—Print scraper and cream paddle.

Job 2.—**Print Scraper.**—To secure butter prints of uniform weight, it is necessary to strike the bottom even with the under edge of the print used. The scraper used must not adhere to the butter, must resist wear and warping, and must be easily kept clean. The scraper shown possesses these qualities and is easily made in the farm shop (Fig. 121).

Stock List

No. Pieces	Material	Dimensions	Where used
1	Maple	¾″ x 1″ x 6–¾″	Back.
1	Maple	¼″ x 6–¾″ x 4–¾″	Blade.
1	Flat head brass screw	⅝″, No. 4	Back.

Construction.—1. Joint the edge of a $^{13}/_{16}$″ maple board.

2. If circular saw is available, set it to cut ½″ deep and cut ¼″ x ½″ groove in center of jointed edge. If saw outfit is not available, work groove with combination plane or layout groove with gauge and work out with chisel.

3. When groove is completed rip and joint to size indicated and run a ⅛″ chamfer on all edges.

4. Square ends and cut to length.

5. Square and cut from ¼″ maple a piece 4–¾″ x 6–¾″ with the grain running parallel with the short dimension.

6. Square a line across each side 1–¼″ from the end and by planing reduce to a ⅛″ edge as indicated in the "Section on Center Line."

7. Fit to groove in back and drill and countersink hole for F. H. Brass screw ⅝″, No. 4. A $^{13}/_{16}$″ hole may be drilled through and wood pin used for fastening, if desired.

8. Smooth up work with No. 1 sand paper, used lengthwise of grain.

Job 3.—**Cream Paddle.**—Cream must be stirred during the cooling process to bring all parts of the mass into contact with the cooling agent. It is also desirable to stir cream when ripening to be sure that the starter used is thoroughly mixed with the cream. The stirring paddle shown is easily cleaned because of rounded corners and smooth construction, and at the same time, is rapid in its action because of the slotted blade (Fig. 121).

Stock List

1 piece	Straight grained maple	$^{13}/_{16}$″ x 5″ x 2′ 9″	For handle and blade.

Construction.—1. Select a straight grained maple board, S2S, and smooth plane lightly to remove planer marks.

2. Joint edges, establish working edge and reduce to 5″ wide.

3. Square and cut to 2′ 9″ long.

4. Set gauge at 2–½″ and gauge center line full length.

5. Set dividers at 4″ and selecting a point in the center line 4″ from

one end as center, describe an arc laying out the curved end of handle as shown in "Detail of Handle."

6. Establish points 1–¾" on either side of the center line and gauge lines through these points laying out the sides of the handle.

7. Square a line across the work 2–½" from the handle end.

8. Using the intersections of this line with the lines just gauged as centers and a radius of 1–⅛" describe arcs outlining the under curve of the handle.

9. Gauge lines tangent to the curve and parallel to the center line outlining the shaft of the handle.

10. At a point 1′ 7–⅞" from the handle end, square a line across. The intersection of this line with the lines gauged 1–¾" from the center line locates the centers used in laying out the curve at the upper end of the blade.

11. With a radius of 1–⅛" and the above intersections as centers, lay out these curves.

12. At a point 1′ 9" from the handle end, square a line across tangent to the arcs just made, locating the shoulders of the blade.

13. On the blade locate points 1" on each side of the center line and with the gauge run lines through these points locating the center lines of the slots in the blade.

14. At a point 2′ from the handle end, square a line across the blade intersecting these lines, locating centers of 1" holes forming upper ends of slots.

15. With 1" bit, bore these holes.

16. In similar manner locate and bore holes forming lower ends of slots 2–½" from lower end of blade.

17. Set gauge and run lines locating sides of slots.

18. With compass saw rip along these lines, making saw cut in waste wood.

19. With compass saw make curved cuts at upper and lower end of handle. When straight cut has been started sufficiently to admit rip saw, insert rip saw and finish with this tool.

20. Pare curved portion at top of handle to shape with chisel.

21. With smoothing plane taper blade to ¼" thickness at lower edge as shown, working equally from both sides.

22. Smooth up edges with spoke shave and wood rasp and run a ⅛" chamfer as indicated.

23. Remove roughness by scraping and sanding lengthwise of grain with No. 1 sand paper.

Job 4.—Print Tray.—Butter when printed is frequently too soft to wrap without damage. A wood tray, made from a non-odorous wood, serves as a means of temporary storage in a cooling room until it has hardened sufficiently to permit wrapping and packing (Fig. 122).

Stock List

No. Pieces	Material	Dimensions	Where used
2	Maple S2S	½" x 8–¼" x 2′ 8"	Top.
2	Maple S2S	¹³⁄₁₆" x 2" x 1′ 4–½"	Cleats.
12	F. H. Brass screws	1" No 7	Top.

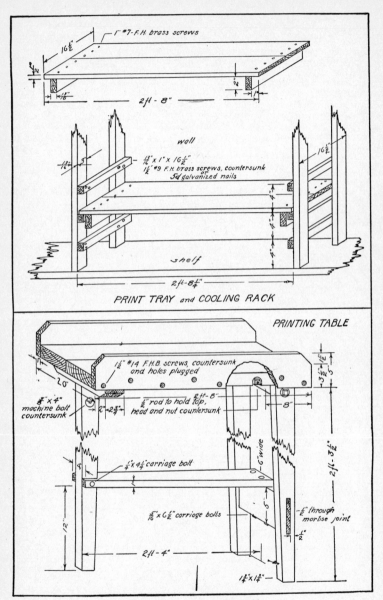

FIG. 122.—Print tray and printing table.

Construction.—1. Joint edges of material for top, establishing working edge. Top may be made from several narrow strips aggregating the width, if desired.

2. Square material and cut to length.

3. One and three-eighths inches from each end, square a line across locating screw holes.

4. Bore and countersink screw holes for 1″ No. 7 F. H. Brass screws.

5. By ripping and jointing, prepare stock $^{13}/_{16}$″ x 2″ wide.

6. Square and cut from this 2 pieces each 16–½″ long.

7. Turn pieces comprising top, bottom upward, and square a line across 1″ from each end, locating the outside edge of the cleat.

8. Place cleats in position and fasten top with 1″, No. 7 F. H. Brass screws.

9. Smooth plane top lightly to remove planer marks and finish with No. 1 sand paper. Screws should be countersunk slightly below surface.

Job 5.—**Cooling Rack for Print Trays.**—A rack is convenient for storing prints previous to wrapping, the trays act as removable shelves, and permit the circulation of cool air about the butter, causing rapid cooling (Fig. 122).

Stock List

No. Pieces	Material	Dimensions	Where used
4	Spruce	$^{13}/_{16}$″ x 3″ x 3′ 0″	Corners.
16	Spruce	$^{13}/_{16}$″ x 1″ x 1′ 4–½″	Tray rests.

Hardware

64	F. H. Brass screws	1–½″, No. 9	Tray rests.
	or ½ lb. galvanized	5d	Tray rests.
	nails		

Construction.—1. Joint edge of board at least 3′ in length.

2. Set gauge at 3″ and using it against working edge, just established, gauge a line the length of the board.

3. Rip along this line and joint piece to width, 3″.

4. Square and cut to length, 3′. Cooling rack is most easily secured in place when corners are made long enough to reach from shelf to ceiling.

5. In same way, prepare the 3 remaining corners.

6. Joint the edge of a board and setting the gauge at 1″ gauge a line at this distance from the edge.

7. Rip along this line and joint edges to size.

8. From material so prepared, square and cut 16 pieces 16–½″ long for tray rests. This can best be done by nailing a stop in the miter box 16–½″ from the square cut and using this as a gauge in cutting.

9. Lay the 4 pieces comprising the corners, side by side with the bottoms even and at intervals of 4″ square lines across them.

10. Drill and countersink tray rests for 1–½″, No. 9. F. H. Brass screws and fasten in place or nail tray rests in place with 5d galvanized nails.

11. Set assembled end frames on shelf, 2′ 8–¼″ apart and fasten by toe nailing to wall, ceiling and shelf. Ends should be placed so that trays slide in and out freely.

Job 6.—**Butter Printing Table.**—A solid support upon which butter may be placed for handling is necessary when making it into prints. The table shown is desirable for this purpose. The side rails prevent the butter from being crowded off the table, and the three-legged construction causes it to stand firmly on the floor (Fig. 122).

Stock List

No. Pieces	Material	Dimensions	Where used
2	Maple S2S	1-¾ʺ x 9ʺ x 2′ 8ʺ	Top.
2	Maple S2S	1ʺ x 5ʺ x 2′ 8ʺ	Sides.
2	Maple S2S	1-¾ʺ x 2-¾ʺ x 2′ 3-½ʺ	Front legs.
1	Maple S4S	1-¾ʺ x 2-¾ʺ x 2′ 1-¾ʺ	Rear leg.
1	Maple S4S	1-¾ʺ x 2-¾ʺ x 1′ 6ʺ	Cross piece at top of rear leg.
1	Maple S4S	1-¾ʺ x 2-¾ʺ x 1′ 2-½ʺ	Cross piece at top of front legs.
1	Maple S4S	1ʺ x 5ʺ x 1′ 6ʺ	Cross piece at lower end of front leg.
1	Maple S4S	1ʺ x 6ʺ x 2′ 4ʺ	Brace between rear and front legs.

Hardware

2	Rods, threaded with nut and washer at each end	½ʺ x 18ʺ	Bottom.
1-½	doz. F. H. B. screws	1-½ʺ, No. 14	Sides.
3	Machine bolts with washers	⅜ʺ x 4ʺ	Fastening legs to cross pieces
1	Carriage bolt with washer	¼ʺ x 4-¼ʺ	Rear leg.
7	Lag screws with washers	⅜ʺ x 2-¾ʺ	Fastening legs to top.
2	Carriage bolts with washers	⁵/₁₆ʺ x 6-½ʺ	Fastening center brace.

Construction.—1. Select 2 pieces of clear maple plank, S2S sufficiently long to make the top of printing table and joint edges until they meet perfectly.

2. Place together and square across, marking the ends 2′ 8ʺ apart.

3. 8ʺ in from each of these marks, again square across the face of both planks and with the try square carry the line across the edges.

4. Set the gauge at ⅞ʺ and using it against the top face of the planks gauge short lines intersecting the lines squared across the edges.

5. With these intersections as centers bore in from each side of each plank with a ½ʺ bit until the holes meet in the center, making holes for the half-inch rods to hold the bottom together. If hole is not clear heat a piece of ⅜ʺ rod red hot and burn it out.

6. With a chisel countersink at each side of top so that nut on end of rod will be flush with edge of top or below it. Cut wood away beneath nut as indicated in the figure, to permit tightening nut with punch after printing table is assembled.

7. Prepare two $\frac{1}{2}''$ rods 18'' long and threaded at both ends. Assemble top and draw up as tightly as possible.

8. Cut off ends of top along lines previously squared.

9. Smooth plane top and dress to even surface.

10. Joint 1'' maple S2S to 5'' wide and square and cut to 2' 8'' long.

11. Set sliding tee bevel at 45 degree angle and lay out and cut off corners as indicated.

12. Gauge two lines, $\frac{5}{8}''$ and $1-\frac{1}{8}''$ respectively, from the lower edge of side piece.

13. Drill holes as indicated along these lines for $1-\frac{1}{2}''$ No. 14 F. H. B. screws. Countersink $\frac{1}{2}''$ deep so that holes may be plugged over screw heads.

14. In same manner, prepare a second side piece.

15. Fasten side pieces to top with screws and plug screw heads. Use glue on plugs.

16. Joint a piece of plank to $4-\frac{5}{16}''$ wide and square and cut to 2' $3-\frac{1}{2}''$ long. Mark both edges for working edges.

17. Measure in from one side at one end $1-\frac{3}{4}''$ and from the other side and at the other end, the same. With a straight edge draw a diagonal line from point to point.

18. Rip along this line, forming front legs, joint sawed edges until legs are smooth and of size indicated.

19. Using the square against the working edge, square a line across $\frac{7}{8}''$ down from the top end.

20. $1-\frac{3}{8}''$ from working edge, bore a $\frac{3}{8}''$ hole in this line. Hole should be located on both sides of legs and bored from both ways to the center.

21. 12'' from bottom end of leg lay out a $\frac{1}{2}''$ x 5'' through mortise; Use gauge to lay out mortise on both sides of leg.

22. Bore from both sides with $\frac{3}{8}''$ bit, removing all the waste wood possible and beat out mortise with chisel.

23. Prepare a second leg in the same way.

24. Joint, square, and cut a block $1-\frac{3}{4}''$ x $2-\frac{3}{4}''$ x $14-\frac{1}{2}''$ to fasten top ends of front legs.

25. Set the gauge at $\frac{7}{8}''$ and using it against the face of the block gauge a line across each end.

26. With the gauge set at $1-\frac{3}{8}''$ gauge a short line intersecting this, locating the center of the bolt hole.

27. With the gauge set at $1-\frac{3}{8}''$ gauge a center line the whole length of the block.

28. 2'' from each end, bore a 1'' hole in this center line to take the nut of the machine bolt used as a fastening.

29. At the intersection of the lines on the end of the stick, bore a $\frac{3}{8}''$ hole until it meets the 1'' hole just bored.

30. Square and cut a piece of maple 1'' x 5'' x 1' 6'' to be used as lower cross piece between lower ends of front legs and lay out and work a $\frac{1}{2}''$ x 5'' tenon on each end.

31. Square a line across the center of this piece and 2'' on each side of the center line locate and bore a $\frac{5}{16}''$ hole through the piece edgewise.

32. Assemble front legs and top and bottom cross pieces, using glue on tenons of lower cross piece and machine bolts as fasteners at the top as indicated.

33. Lay out the rear leg 1-¾″ x 1-¾″ at the bottom and 1-¾″ x 2-¾″ at the top x 2′ 1-¾″ long. Cut to size. Mark one edge as working edge and square the ends from this edge.

34. 2-½″ from the top end and 1-⅜″ from the working edge, bore a 1″ hole in the rear leg, as shown.

35. By means of intersecting diagonals locate the center of the top of the leg and bore a ⅜″ hole until it meets the hole just bored.

36. From 1-¾″ x 2-¾″ stock, cut a block 18″ long for top end of rear leg. Lay out with sliding tee bevel and cut a 1″ chamfer on each end.

37. Locate the middle of this block and bore a ⅜″ hole to correspond to the one in the top of the leg. Countersink ⅝″ to permit bolt head to be flush with upper surface or below it.

38. Assemble leg and cross piece.

39. Joint a piece of 1″ stock to 5″ wide for brace between front and rear legs and gauge a line down the center.

40. Square and cut to 2′ 4″ long.

41. From points 2″ on each side of the center line at one end, draw diagonal lines to the opposite corners. Rip along these lines and finish by jointing.

42. Using the center as a guide, lay out and cut an opening 1¾″ wide and 2⅛″ deep to fit rear leg.

43. Place wide end in proper position over front lower cross piece and mark and bore holes.

44. Bolt in place.

45. Bore hole and bolt to rear leg in proper position.

46. Square line across under side of top 2″ from each end.

47. Place cross pieces in position, bore holes and fasten to top with ⅜″ x 2-¾″ lag screws.

48. Smooth up top and other surfaces with No. 1 sand paper, placed on a block and used lengthwise of the grain.

Job 7.—**Feed Box.**—A tight, light box with a capacity of about one bushel is convenient when feeding special rations or for use when an animal is tied in temporary quarters. If neatly lettered with the farm name it makes a good advertisement, when used at the fair for feeding cattle on exhibition. The shape shown permits nesting and storing in small space when not in use (Fig. 123).

Stock List

No. Pieces	Material	Dimensions	Where used
2	Pine S2S	½″ x 10″ x 1′ 9-¾″	Sides.
2	Pine S2S	¹³/₁₆″ x 10″ x 1′ 3-¼″	Ends.
2	Pine S2S	½″ x 6-⅛″ x 1′ 5-¾″	Bottom.

Hardware

36	F.H.B. screws	1″ No. 7	Sides and bottom.
8	Heavy galvanized iron	¹³/₁₆″ x 6-¼″	Corner binding.
70	Barbed box nails	4d	Corners and bottom.

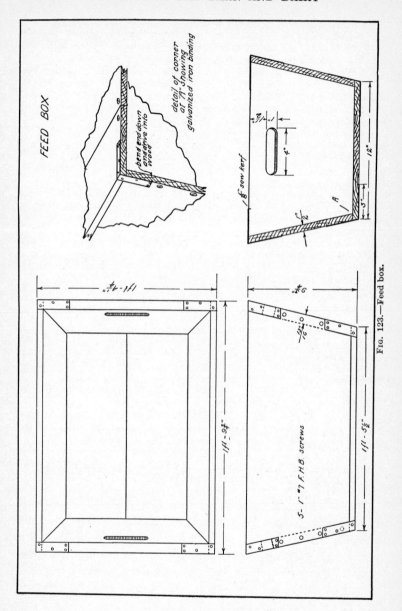

FIG. 123.—Feed box.

Construction.—1. Joint the edge of material used for sides.

2. Lay out angle of cut for ends by using the steel square with the 2-⅛″ division on the tongue and the 10″ division on the blade coinciding with the jointed edge. Mark along tongue.

3. Cut to length, making top edge 1′ 9-¾″ long.

4. Set sliding tee bevel at 1-¹/₁₆″ on tongue and 5″ on blade and bevel edges of sides to this angle.

5. Bore and countersink sides for five 1″ No. 7 F.H.B. screws in each end. Line for screws should be ⁷/₁₆″ from end.

6. In similar manner lay out and cut ends to size. Cut ends 1′ 3-¼″ long on top edge because of ½″ side material lapping over ends at corners.

7. Because of flaring construction, outside corners of ends will have to be relieved slightly by block planing. Plane until joint is tight when side and end make a right angle with each other, as shown by steel square.

8. Obtain center of end and square a line across at this point.

9. Set the gauge at 2″ and using it against the top edge, gauge a line as long as the handle across the center line. This represents the center line of the handle.

10. With a 1″ bit bore holes in the handle center line 1-½″ on each side of the line squared across the end, forming the ends of the handle opening.

11. Gauge lines locating the top and bottom edges of the handle and rip out waste wood with compass saw.

12. Smooth up interior edges with wood rasp and run a light chamfer around corners.

13. Assemble sides and ends. Square up with steel square and tack a diagonal brace from corner to corner across the top to hold in this position.

14. Fit and apply bottom, using 1″ No. 7 F.H.B. screws to attach to ends and 4d barbed box nails to attach to side. If it is desired to make the box water tight the joints should be covered with thick lead paint before assembling.

15. Bend light tin or heavy paper over corner and secure pattern for corner binding.

16. Using this pattern, cut corner binding from heavy galvanized iron. Bend down ends ⅛″ as indicated in detail, punch holes with small nail set, holding material on end of hard wood block, and nail in place.

17. Smooth up work and give priming coat.

18. Fill imperfections with putty and apply coat of auto enamel or other hard, wear-resistant paint, lettering if desired.

Job 8.—Milk Record Sheet Case.—In keeping a record of daily individual milk weighings, it is desirable to have the whole month's record visible for comparison. At the same time, it should be protected and kept clean. The case shown accomplishes these results, the record as made being kept under glass, exposing only enough of the record sheet to permit weighings to be recorded through the slot (Fig. 124).

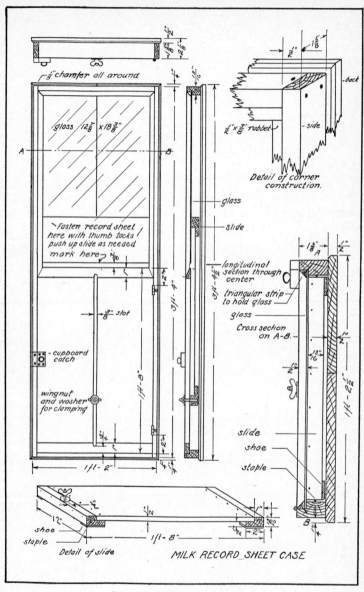

FIG. 124.—Milk record sheet case.

Stock List

No. Pieces	Material	Dimensions	Where used
2	Pine S2S	$^{13}/_{16}''$ x 1-⅝'' x 3' 4''	Sides.
2	Pine S2S	$^{13}/_{16}''$ x 1-⅝'' x 1' 1''	Ends.
2	Pine S2S	½'' x 7-¼'' x 3' 4-½''	Back.
2	Pine S2S	½'' x 6-$^{5}/_{16}''$ x 1' 6''	Door.
2	Pine S2S	½'' x 1'' x 1' 1''	Door ends.
2	Pine S2S	½'' x 6'' x 1' 6''	Slide.
2	Pine S2S	$^{13}/_{16}''$ x 2'' x 1'	Slide ends.
4	Pine S2S	$^{3}/_{16}''$ x 1'' x 2''	Shoe.
2	Pine triangular moulding	½'' x ⅜'' x 1' 8''	Sides of glass.
1	Pine triangular moulding	½'' x ⅜'' x 1' 1''	Top of glass.

Hardware

½lb.	Casing nails	6d	Side, back, door and slide.
1	Cupboard catch with screws	Small	Door.
2	Steel butts with screws	1'' x 1''	Door.
4	Chicken wire staples	¾''	Corners of slide.
2	F. H. B. screws	¾'' No. 5	In sides near hinges.
16	Brads	¾''	Shoes.
1	Glass	12-⅞'' x 18-⅜''	Front.
1	Carriage bolt with washer and wing nut	¼'' x 1-¼''	Slide.

Small quantity of glue.
Small quantity of paint.

Construction.—1. Joint the edge of a straight-grained pine board of sufficient length for the side and cut a rabbet ⅜'' wide by ½'' deep. Rabbet can be most conveniently cut on circular saw. If not available, use combination plane.

2. Gauge, rip and joint to proper width.

3. Square and cut to correct length.

4. Lay out and cut ⅜'' x $^{13}/_{16}''$ rabbet on ends to form end joint as shown in detail.

5. Prepare a second side in the same way, being careful to make them right and left.

6. From same rabbeted material, square and cut ends 1' 1'' long.

7. Using glue on meeting surfaces assemble sides and ends. Nail with 6d casing nails. Set nails below surface.

8. Square up frame and tack a light diagonal brace from corner to corner across the front to hold this in position.

9. Using ½'' pine S2S, joint, square and cut to length, the back. Allow a ¼'' projection all around and gauge a line lightly at this distance from the edge.

10. Apply glue to meeting surfaces and nail back in place with 6d casing nails. Run a ⅛″ chamfer clear around. Remove brace from front.

11. Joint 2 pieces of ½″ pine to 6–⁵/₁₆″ wide. Square and cut to 1′ 6″ long for door front.

12. Joint two pieces of ½″ pine to 1″ wide and square and cut to 1′ 1″ long for door ends.

13. With ³/₁₆″ drill countersink 6 holes ⅝″ deep in the edges of each door end.

14. Apply glue to ends of door front and to edges of door ends and assemble, leaving a ⅜″ slot in center as indicated. Use 6d casing nails, and set to bottom of countersunk holes. Set door aside to dry.

15. Joint, square, and glue up stock ½″ x 12″ x 1′ 6″ for slide. Set aside in clamps to dry.

16. Joint ¹³/₁₆″ pine to 2″ wide, cut a ½″ x 1″ rabbet down one face and square and cut to 1′ long for slide ends.

17. When dry remove slide from clamp. Coat meeting surfaces with glue and fasten ends to slide as shown in detail.

18. When dry attach shoes to corners, drive a staple in each corner **to form** an adjustable side bearing, bore the hole for the clamping bolt in the center of the lower end, smooth up the slide and adjust until it works freely in the box.

19. Prepare a sufficient quantity of triangular moulding to hold the glass in place. Miter cuts for corners can be made in miter box.

20. Cut glass to size required and grind lower edge round and smooth.

21. Chamfer top edge of door to ⅛″ thick, the chamfer extending back 1″.

22. Fit door to opening and attach butts. Drive ¾″ No. 5 F. H. B. screws beside butt as indicated to lessen chance of splitting.

23. Attach cupboard catch.

24. Smooth up interior of box and give two coats of paint before placing glass.

25. Place glass and fasten in place with triangular moulding as shown. Lower edge is supported with two ⅛″ blocks tacked beneath moulding.

26. Smooth up outside and give priming coat. When dry putty imperfections and apply auto enamel or other hard, drying gloss paint.

Supplementary Devices for the Farm and Dairy

1. Can-drying rack.
2. Test-bottle holder.
3. Bench for tester.
4. Window screens.
5. Window ventilators.
6. Door fastener.
7. Manger scraper.
8. Manure scraper.
9. Medicine case.
10. Bull staff.
11. Feed scoop.
12. Ensilage cart.
13. Support for milk scales.
14. Jig for nailing butter boxes.
15. Gravity feed bin and chute.
16. Breeding rack.
17. Stanchions.
18. Root cutter.
19. Line-shaft hanger.
20. Belt shifter.

CHAPTER X

DEVICES FOR THE POULTRY HOUSE

Job 1.—**A trap nest** is useful in selecting the high producers from a flock of birds for breeding stock. The type shown can be made singly from a dry goods box of suitable shape, or it can be made in groups of six or more where a greater capacity is desired (Fig. 125).

Stock List

No. Pieces	Material	Dimensions	Where used
2	Pine or basswood S2S	$\frac{1}{2}''$ x 11'' x 16-$\frac{1}{4}''$	Sides.
2	Pine or basswood S2S	$^{13}/_{16}''$ x 11'' x 12''	Ends.
2	Pine or basswood S2S	$\frac{1}{2}''$ x 6-$\frac{1}{2}''$ x 1' 10-$\frac{1}{4}''$	Bottom.
3	Pine or basswood S2S	$\frac{1}{2}''$ x 4'' x 16-$\frac{1}{4}''$	Top.
2	Pine or basswood S2S	$^{13}/_{16}''$ x 1-$\frac{1}{2}''$ x 11-$\frac{3}{4}''$	Top cleats.
1	Pine or basswood S2S	$^{13}/_{16}''$ x 1-$\frac{1}{2}''$ x 13''	Perch.
1	Pine or basswood S2S	$\frac{1}{2}''$ x 5'' x 11''	Door.
2	Pine or basswood S2S	$\frac{1}{2}''$ x $\frac{5}{8}''$ x 4''	Door cleats.
1	Maple	$^{5}/_{16}''$ x 1'' x 4''	Door catch.
2	Maple	$^{13}/_{16}''$ x $^{13}/_{16}''$ x 1-$\frac{1}{2}''$	Top buttons.
2	Pine	$^{13}/_{16}''$ x 2-$\frac{1}{2}''$ x 11''	Door guides.

Hardware

2	F.H.B. screws	1-$\frac{1}{2}''$, No. 9	Buttons.
1	Chicken wire staple	$\frac{3}{4}''$	Door catch.
1	Wire	No. 9, 3' 1''	Swinging bale for door.
3	Doz. box nails	6d	Sides and bottom.
4	Doz. box nails	3d	Top, guides and perch.
2	F. H. B. screws	$\frac{5}{8}''$, No. 5	Door catch.

Small quantity of carbolineum or similar disinfectant.

Construction.—1. Joint, square, and cut sides to length.

2. Joint, square, and cut ends to length.

3. Square center line across front end.

4. Set compass with radius of 3-$\frac{1}{2}''$ and with a point in the center line just squared, 4'' from the lower edge of the board as a center, describe an arc locating the top of the door.

5. 3-$\frac{1}{2}''$ on each side of the center line, square lines across the end meeting the arc just drawn and locating the sides of the door.

6. With the compass saw cut out the door opening and if necessary smooth up edges with wood rasp.

7. Assemble sides and ends using carbolineum on meeting surfaces to check mites

8. Joint, square and cut to length the boards for the bottom.

8

113

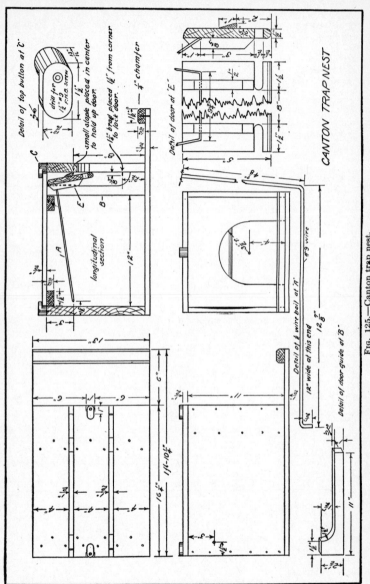

Fig. 125.—Canton trap nest.

9. By jointing, gauging, and ripping prepare a piece of material $^{13}/_{16}''$ x 1-½'', for perch and cover cleats.

10. Square and cut a piece of this material 13'' long for perch. Chamfer ¼'' on upper edges.

11. Nail bottom and perch in position, using carbolineum on all meeting surfaces.

12. Prepare 2 pieces of $^{13}/_{16}''$ material, 2-½'' wide by 11'' long with jointed edges and squared ends for door guides.

13. Set the gauge at 1-½'' and gauge a line down one side.

14. Set the compasses with a 1-½'' radius and using a point on the edge of the piece 3'' up from one end as a center, describe an arc meeting the line just gauged.

15. Cut along this line with the compass saw and finish curve, smooth with rasp and sand paper.

16. Fasten door guides in position on inside of side pieces as shown in longitudinal section by nailing.

17. Drive two 1-¼'' brads in the front 2-½'' up from the bottom and 1-½'' in from each corner as shown in longitudinal section to lock door in position when it drops.

18. Joint, square and cut to length 3 pieces of ½'' material 4'' x 16-¼'' for the top.

19. Cut 2 pieces of $^{13}/_{16}''$ x 1-½'' material previously prepared 11-¾'' long for top cleats.

20. Mark and assemble top, placing front cleat just back of the upright door guides as indicated in longitudinal section.

21. Locate center line of top and bore a 1'' hole in this line, ⅝'' from each end. Remove the waste wood between the hole and the end forming slots for top buttons.

22. By jointing, prepare a short piece of maple $^{13}/_{16}''$ x $^{13}/_{16}''$ for top buttons. Drill and countersink holes for 1-½'' No. 9 F. H. B. screws cut to length and with sharp knife or chisel, finish to shape shown in detail.

23. Attach buttons to top.

24. Joint and square a piece of ½'' material 5'' wide and 11'' long for door.

25. Gauge a line ¾'' from lower edge.

26. 1-¼'' in from each end bore a ½'' hole in this gauge line.

27. Gauge lines ½'' and 1'' respectively from this edge and rip along these lines to the holes just bored, forming the slots in the ends of the door.

28. Round lower edge of door with plane.

29. Prepare 2 pieces of ½'' x ⅝'' material 4'' long with beveled ends for door cleats as shown in door detail.

30. 1'' down from the top cut a freely-fitting notch for No. 9 wire used to support door.

31. Bend No. 9 wire to size and shape shown in detail of one-half wire bail at " A ". Place in position on back of door and nail cross cleats in position as shown in detail of door.

32. Cut a piece of maple $^{5}/_{16}''$ x 1'' x 4'' and plane to a knife edge for door catch.

33. Drill and countersink for two ⅝'' No. 5 F. H. B. screws and attach to center of door 2'' above lower edge.

34. Drill $^{3}/_{16}''$ hole in each side of nest box 1-½'' from rear end and 3'' down from top.

35. Place door in position with ends of wire supporting it in these holes and adjust until it works easily.

36. With door in raised position as shown in longitudinal section, locate and drive staple at top of door opening, holding door up when open.

37. Adjust door until it works properly and place cover in position.

Job 2.—**A well made egg crate** is necessary in the shipping, handling and storage of eggs as a protection against breakage. When lettered with the owner's name and address it is also a good advertisement. The crate shown is a double one of thirty dozen capacity and takes standard fillers. It may be made in a single unit of fifteen dozen capacity, or shallower to take any quantity desired (Fig. 126).

Stock List

No. Pieces	Material	Dimensions	Where used
2	Pine or basswood S2S	½″ x 6–⅜″ x 2′ 2″	Top.
4	Pine or basswood S2S	½″ x 2″ x 11–½″	Top cleats.
4	Pine or basswood S2S	½″ x 6–⅜″ x 2′ 2″	Front and back.
2	Pine or basswood S2S	½″ x 6–⅜″ x 2′ 2″	Bottom.
6	Pine or basswood S2S	½″ x 6–⅜″ x 11–¾″	Ends and center partition.
4	Pine or basswood S2S	½″ x 2″ x 11–¾″	Ends.
4	Pine or basswood S2S	½″ x 2″ x 8–¾″	Ends.

Hardware

2	Box hinges	for ½″ material	Top.
1	Chest lock	for ½″ material	Top.
2	Tin or galvanized iron	2–½″ x 5″	Ends.
5	Doz. F.H.B screws	⅞″ No. 6	Cover and ends.
3	Doz. F.H.B. screws	1–¼″ No. 8	Fastening sides and bottom to ends.
1	Doz. F.H.B. screws	⅜″ No. 4	Fastening metal inside of handle openings.

Small quantity of liquid glue.
Small quantity of paint.

Construction.—1. Joint to width, square and cut to length, 4 pieces ½″ x 6–⅜″ x 2′ 2″, for top and bottom.

2. In same way, prepare 4 pieces ½″ x 6–⅜″ x 2′ 2″ for front and rear of crate.

3. Joint to width, square and cut to length 4 pieces ½″ x 6–⅜″ x 11–¾″ for ends.

4. Gauge, rip and joint a piece of ½″ material to 2″ wide.

5. From material so prepared, square and cut 4 pieces 11–¾″ long and 4 pieces 8–¾″ long for end bindings. Dimensions may vary slightly due to inaccuracy in workmanship and a better fit will be secured by obtaining the lengths of these pieces directly from the ends to be fitted.

6. Set the gauge at 2–¼″ and gauge horizontal center line of the handle opening on the end.

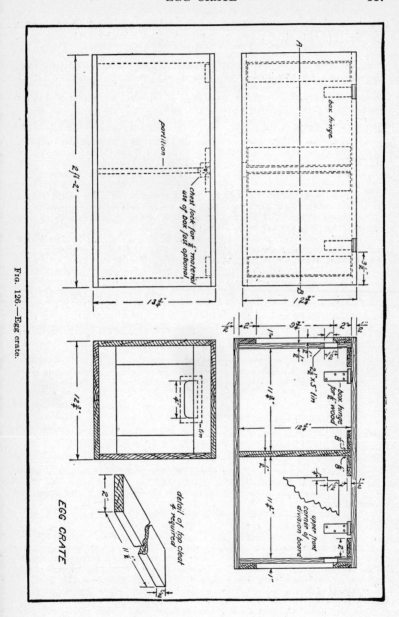

Fig. 126.—Egg crate.

7. Measure in 4–⅝″ from each end in this line and with the points so located as centers, bore holes with the expansive bit set at 1–½″, forming the ends of the handle opening.

8. Gauge lines at tops and bottoms of holes so bored and cut out waste wood with compass saw, forming handle opening of shape shown in end view. Smooth up inner surface with rasp.

9. Assemble ends using glue on meeting surfaces and screws turned in from the inside. Round up lower edge of top cleat over handle opening as indicated in longitudinal section.

10. Cut piece of tin 2–½″ x 5″ and fasten inside of handle openings with ⅝″ No. 4 F. H. B. screws.

11. Assemble bottom sides and ends using screws listed for the purpose.

12. Fit chest lock to center of upper edge of front side of crate.

13. Prepare 4 cleats for the cover ½″ x 2″ x 11–½″.

14. Square lines across cover 1–⅛″ from each end and ⅜″ from the center.

15. Set the gauge at ⅝″ and guage lines along the sides of the cover.

16. Assemble cover locating cross piece by the lines gauged and squared on underside of cover. Fasten cross pieces to cover by means of glue and screws listed, driving the screws from the underside.

17. Cut upper front corner of center partition as shown in detail and fasten in place, using screws listed.

18. Attach cover to crate with box hinges.

19. Smooth up surfaces and apply a lead priming coat.

20. When dry, apply finish coat and letter, if desired.

Job 3.—**Egg Candler.**—To insure the sale of fresh eggs only and to determine fertility in hatching, a means of examining an egg against a light is necessary. The candler shown permits such examination and is easily made (Fig. 127).

Stock List

No. Pieces	Material	Dimensions	Where used
2	Pine or basswood S2S	½″ x 6″ x 1′ 6″	Sides.
1	Pine or basswood S2S	½″ x 7″ x 1′ 6″	Back.
1	Pine or basswood S2S	½″ x 2″ x 7″	Top.
1	Pine or basswood S2S	½″ x 7″ x 1′ 4″	Door.
1	Pine or basswood S2S	¹³/₁₆″ x 9″ x 9″	Base.
1	Pine or basswood S2S	¹³/₁₆″ x 6″ x 6″	Base.

Hardware

1	Bright tin	9″ x 10″	Reflector.
6	Steel tacks	8 oz.	Reflector.
1 pr.	Butts	1″ x 1″	Door.
1	Hook with screw	Small	Door.
1	Sheet packing rubber	3″ x 3″	Egg opening in door.
3 doz.	Box nails	4d	Bottom and sides.

Construction.—1. Square and cut from ¹³/₁₆″ material S2S a piece 9″ x 9″.

2. Set the gauge at 1–½″ and gauge a line around edge.

3. Run a ¼″ chamfer all around.

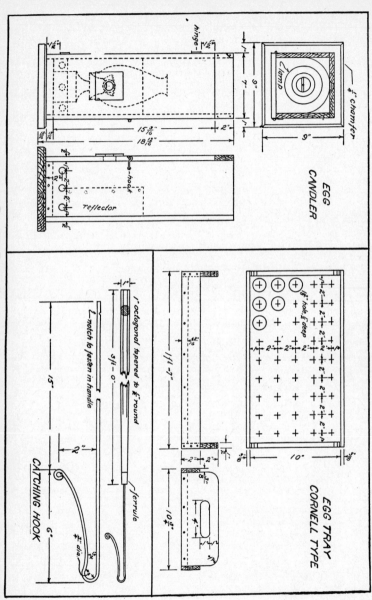

FIG. 127.—Egg candler; egg tray; catching hook.

4. Square and cut from $^{13}/_{16}''$ material a piece 6'' x 6''.

5. Nail to first piece inside the gauge line with grain at right angles, forming base.

6. Using $\frac{1}{2}''$ material joint, square and cut 2 sides $\frac{1}{2}''$ x 6'' x 1' 6''.

7. Two inches from the lower end square a line across, and with $\frac{3}{4}''$ bit bore 3 holes in this line, as indicated in the drawing.

8. Joint, square and cut a back $\frac{1}{2}''$ x 7'' x 1' 6''.

9. Square a line across 2'' from the lower edge and bore three $\frac{3}{4}''$ holes in this line, one in the center and other two, $1-\frac{1}{2}''$ from the edge.

10. Square and cut the piece for across the top of the door openings $\frac{1}{2}''$ x 2'' x 7''.

11. Assemble sides, back and base.

12. Cut a piece of bright tin 9'' x 10'' and bend to semicircular shape and fasten in box above ventilating holes for reflector, with tacks listed.

13. From $\frac{1}{2}''$ material, cut a door 7'' x 1' 4'', and fit to opening.

14. Set lamp inside candler and holding door in position, make a mark at the height of the approximate center of the flame.

15. Square across the door at this point and with the expansive bit bore a $1-\frac{1}{2}''$ hole in the center of this line.

16. Cut a piece of sheet rubber packing, 3'' x 3''. Locate center by means of intersecting diagonals and cut a 1'' hole in the center. Hole may be bored with sharp, wet bit.

17. Tack this in place over openings in door to place eggs against.

18. Attach hinges and hang door.

19. Smooth up outside and paint with flat black paint.

Job 4.—**Egg Tray, Cornell Type.**—A tray of the type shown is useful in gathering and temporarily storing eggs. Racks may be arranged in the packing room into which the trays slide as drawers (Fig. 127).

Stock List

No. Pieces	Material	Dimensions	Where used
1	Pine or basswood S2S	$^{13}/_{16}''$ x 10'' x 1' 6''	Bottom.
2	Pine or basswood S2S	$\frac{3}{8}''$ x 2'' x 1' 7''	Sides.
2	Pine or basswood S2S	$\frac{1}{2}''$ x 4'' x 10''	Ends.
30	Barbed box nails	4d	Sides and ends.

Construction.—1. Joint and rip to width, and square and cut to length, a piece of pine or basswood, $^{13}/_{16}''$ x 10'' x 1' 6'' long, for the bottom.

2. Square a line across 1'' from each end and at 2'' intervals.

3. Gauge a line 1'' from each side and at 2'' intervals. The lines squared and gauged across the bottom, divide it into 2'' squares as shown in drawing.

4. Set expansive bit for $1-\frac{3}{8}''$ hole and bore a hole $\frac{1}{2}''$ deep at each intersection, as indicated. These holes support the eggs on end.

5. Using $\frac{3}{8}''$ material, joint to 2'' wide and square and cut two pieces 1' 7'' long for sides.

6. From $\frac{1}{2}''$ material 4'' wide, square and cut two pieces, each 10'' long for ends.

7. Set the gauge at $1-\frac{1}{2}''$ and gauge a line $1-\frac{1}{2}''$ from the top forming the center line of the handle opening.

8. $3-\frac{1}{2}''$ from each end bore a 1'' hole in this line forming the ends of the handle opening.

9. Run gauge lines 1″ and 2″, respectively, from the upper edge of the end piece laying out the top and bottom edges of the handle opening.

10. Rip along these lines with the compass saw forming the handle opening.

11. Measure in 1″ from each end, locating a point in the line just gauged 1″ from top edge.

12. With these points as centers and a radius of 1″ describe arcs, rounding off the upper corners of ends as shown. Top corners may be cut at 45 degrees instead, if desired.

13. Pare rounded corners to shape with sharp chisel.

14. Assemble parts with 4d box nails, nailing ends to bottom first.

Job 5.—**A poultry catching hook** is useful in taking birds from a flock without frightening the remainder (Fig. 127).

Stock List

No. Pieces	Material	Dimensions	Where used
1	Ash or hickory	1″ x 1″ x 3′ 0″	Handle.
1	Steel wire	No. 9—2′ 6″	Hook.
1	Ferrule	½″ inside diameter	Handle.
1	Brad	¾″	Handle.

Construction.—1. By splitting or ripping, secure a piece of straight grained ash or hickory and joint to 1″ x 1″ square.

2. Applying the rule diagonally across the stick with the 0″ and 12″ points coinciding with the sides of the stick, as directed in laying out octagon, mark at the 3-½″ and 8-½″ divisions.

3. Set the gauge to coincide with one of these points and gauge lines the whole length of the stick.

4. With the jointer plane to these lines, making the stick octagonal.

5. Taper the end upon which the ferrule is to be placed to ½″ across flats and by removing the corners with the plane work to a round cross section. A ferrule from a discarded screw driver or other tool, an old cartridge shell or a section of small brass piping may be used for a ferrule and wood should be reduced to size to fit it. If no ferrule is available, wrap the end with friction tape or soft iron or copper wire.

6. Fit end to ferrule and drive ferrule in place.

7. Cut a piece of stiff, No. 9 steel wire to 2′ 6″ long and bend to shape shown. If necessary wire may be softened for bending by gasoline blow torch.

8. File notch near end, as shown, to engage brad driven through handle and prevent pulling out.

9. Select Syracuse twist drill or gimlet of proper size to fit wire used and bore hole in end of handle for wire.

10. Lay wire in place against lower end of handle and with awl point locate notch in wire on the handle. With wire still held in same position, make a scratch on the wire at lower end of handle.

11. Insert wire into handle until scratch is flush with end and drive brad through the notch filed in the wire at the point marked on the handle.

12. Smooth up handle with No. 1 sand paper and apply oil.

Job 6.—**Poultry Shipping Crate.**—Where live poultry is to be shipped, a crate affording comfort and safety to the birds and convenience to the shipper is a necessity. The crate shown has these features, and if well made presents a good appearance, adding to the selling value of the birds confined (Fig. 128).

Stock List

No. Pieces	Material	Dimensions	Where used
6	N. C. pine S2S	$^{13}/_{16}''$ x 1-½'' x 1' 10-⅜''	Top and bottom members of end frame and cross pieces of top.
4	N. C. pine S2S	$^{13}/_{16}''$ x 1-½'' x 3'	Top and bottom members of side.
6	N. C. pine S2S	$^{13}/_{16}''$ x 1-½'' x 1'	Corner and center posts.
3	White ash	⅜'' x 1'' x 3'	Top.
6	White ash	⅜'' x 1'' x 2' 11-¼''	Sides.
8	White ash	⅜'' x 1'' x 1' 2''	Top.
6	White ash	⅜'' x 1'' x 1' 10-⅜''	Ends.
1	Pine S2S	$^{13}/_{16}''$ x 7-½'' x 11-½''	Door.
2	Pine	½'' x $^{3}/_{16}''$ x 7-¼''	Door stops.
6	Pine S2S	⅜'' x 6'' x 2'	Floor.
4	Pine S2S	⅜'' x 1-$^{9}/_{16}''$ x 9''	Corner casings.
4	Pine S2S	⅜'' x 1-⅞'' x 9''	Corner casings.
2	Pine S2S	⅜'' x 1-½'' x 3'	Top corner strip.

Hardware

52	F. H. B. screws	1½'' No. 9	Frame.
2	F. H. B. screws	2'' No. 10	Door.
2	Door buttons with screws		Door.
48	F. H. B. screws	1'' No. 7	Bottom.
½	lb. Common nails	3d	Slats.

Construction.—1. By jointing, gauging and ripping, prepare a quantity of $^{13}/_{16}''$ N. C. pine 1-½'' wide.

2. Square and cut to length 6 pieces for corner posts and middle posts.

3. Square and cut to length 6 pieces 1' 10-⅜'' for top and bottom members of end frames and top cross pieces.

4. Drill and countersink the ends as shown in " Detail of Corner Construction " and assemble corner of frame. Maintain a right-angle while assembling.

5. From the same material square and cut 4 pieces 3' long for top and bottom side members.

6. Drill and countersink for 1-½'' No. 9 F. H. B. screws indicated in corner detail and assemble with end frames, being careful to secure square corners.

7. Place and fasten middle posts and center cross pieces in frame.

8. See that frame is square, and tack temporary brace from corner to corner diagonally across top to hold it in this position.

9. Using ⅜'' material S2S, square and cut floor boards. Fasten in place crosswise of frame with 1'' No. 7 F. H. B. screws.

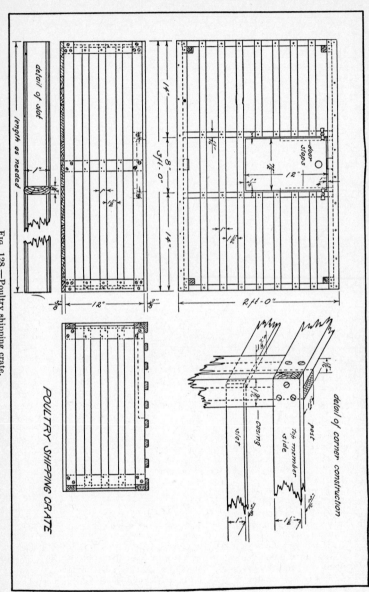

FIG. 128.—Poultry shipping crate.

10. Cut and nail top corner strips in place, making them $\frac{3}{8}''$ x $1-\frac{1}{2}''$ x $3'$.

11. From $\frac{13}{16}''$ pine, S2S, square and cut door $7-\frac{1}{2}''$ x $11-\frac{1}{2}''$. Bore a $1''$ hole in the center of one end to serve as a handle in opening as shown.

12. Set the gauge at $\frac{13}{16}''$ and, using it against the top edge of the center cross pieces, gauge lines on their inner surface.

13. Make two strips $\frac{1}{2}''$ x $\frac{13}{16}''$ x $7-\frac{1}{4}''$ and tack them in place with their upper surface flush with these gauge marks to serve as door stops.

14. Drill the center cross pieces as shown, place the door in position and insert two $2''$ No. 10. F. H. B. screws to serve as hinges.

15. Attach buttons to cross pieces to hold door closed, as shown.

16. Prepare many pieces of ash $\frac{3}{8}''$ x $1''$ with rounded edges. Square and cut to lengths required for strips and nail to side, ends and top with spacing shown.

17. From $\frac{3}{8}''$ material $1-\frac{7}{8}''$ in width, square and cut 4 corner boards fitting and nailing them in position between top and bottom end frame members as shown in corner detail.

18. From $\frac{3}{8}''$ material, $1-\frac{9}{16}''$ wide, square and cut 4 pieces to fit between top and bottom side members at the corners on top of the slat ends and nail in place as shown in detail of corner construction.

19. Give priming coat of paint and when dry finish with coat of durable outdoor paint. Letter, if desired.

Job 7.—Brood Coop.—Chickens in care of the hen require a shelter for nights and rainy weather. This should have a tight roof and permit easy cleaning. The coop shown presents a much better appearance than the barrels and boxes so often used for the same purpose. It affords good protection and the removable bottom permits easy cleaning (Fig. 129).

Stock List

No. Pieces	Material	Dimensions	Where used
2	Spruce S2S	$\frac{13}{16}''$ x $1-\frac{1}{2}''$ x $28''$	Bottom.
5	Spruce D and M	$\frac{13}{16}''$ x $6''$ x 28 ''	Bottom.
2	Spruce S2S	$\frac{13}{16}''$ x $1-\frac{1}{2}''$ x $28-\frac{3}{8}''$	Sills of end frames.
4	Spruce S2S	$\frac{13}{16}''$ x $1-\frac{1}{2}''$ x $21-\frac{1}{2}''$	Rafters.
1	Spruce S2S	$\frac{13}{16}''$ x $1-\frac{1}{2}''$ x $12''$	Front end frame.
1	Spruce S2S	$\frac{13}{16}''$ x $2''$ x $26-\frac{3}{4}''$	Ridge.
2	Spruce S2S	$\frac{13}{16}''$ x $6''$ x $30''$	Sides.
2	Spruce S2S	$\frac{13}{16}''$ x $1-\frac{1}{2}''$ x $25-\frac{3}{8}$	Side sills.
12	Spruce D and M	$\frac{13}{16}''$ x $6''$ x $23-\frac{1}{2}''$	Roof.
2	Spruce S2S	$\frac{13}{16}''$ x $8-\frac{1}{4}''$ x $14-\frac{1}{4}''$	Front end.
1	Spruce S2S	$\frac{13}{16}''$ x $11-\frac{3}{4}''$ x $8-\frac{1}{2}''$	Front end.
2	Spruce S2S	$1''$ x $1-\frac{1}{2}''$ x $15-\frac{1}{2}''$	Door guides.
1	Spruce S2S	$\frac{13}{16}''$ x $1-\frac{1}{2}''$ x $12-\frac{3}{4}''$	Top cross piece of door.
1	Spruce S2S	$\frac{13}{16}''$ x $1-\frac{1}{2}''$ x $11-\frac{3}{4}''$	Bottom cross piece of door.
4	Spruce S2S	$\frac{1}{2}''$ x $1-\frac{3}{4}''$ x $23''$	Upright slats of door.
4	Spruce D and M	$\frac{13}{16}''$ x $6''$ x $28-\frac{3}{4}''$	Rear end.

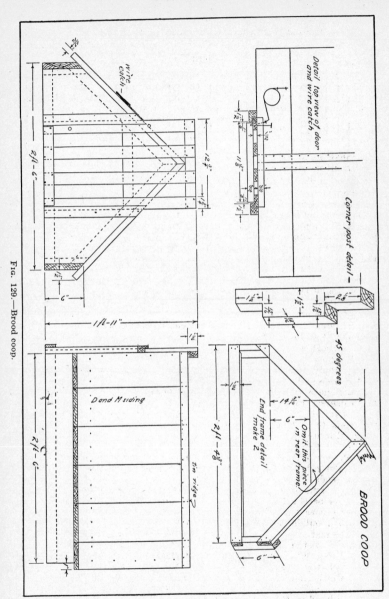

FIG. 129.—Brood coop.

No. Pieces	Material	Dimensions	Where used

Hardware

No. Pieces	Material	Dimensions	Where used
1 lb.	Box nails	6d	Floor, sides, roof and ends.
¼ lb.	Common nails	3d	Door and ridge.
3	Chicken wire staples	¾″	Wire catch.
1	Wire	No. 12	Wire catch.
1	Roofing tin	3″ x 33″	Ridge.

Small quantity creosote wood preservative.
Small quantity lead paint for priming.
Small quantity outdoor paint for finishing.

Construction.—1. Joint the edge of a straight-grained board to secure working edge. Set the gauge at 1-½″ and gauge line full length.

2. Rip along this line. Support the material on the bench top to prevent springing and joint to width.

3. Cut 4 rafters from this material. Secure length and angle by using the square with the 14-3/16″ graduation on both the tongue and blade coinciding with the edge of the stick. Cut both ends of rafter at the same angle.

4. Using the same material, square and cut two sills, 28-3/8″ long.

5. Make 4 corner posts as shown in detail. Set sliding tee bevel at 6″ on tongue and 6″ on blade of steel square to cut the angle at the top.

6. Assemble end frames. In front end frame cut and nail in a piece as shown, 12″ above sill to form top of door opening. Give all meeting surfaces a brush coating of creosote wood preservative when assembling.

7. Apply boards horizontally to rear end frame.

8. Apply boards vertically to front end frame, leaving door opening 11-¾″ wide and 12″ high in the center.

9. Square and cut side pieces 6″ wide by 30″ long. Bevel top edges to 45 degrees to fit angle of roof.

10. Nail side pieces in place. By means of steel square bring sides and ends to a true rectangle and hold in this position by temporary diagonal brace nailed across the bottom from corner to corner.

11. Cut two pieces 13/16″ x 1-½″ x 25-3/8″ long for side sills and nail between corner posts along bottom edges of side pieces.

12. Cut ridge board 2″ wide by 26-¾″ long and nail in place between the two ends.

13. Cut and apply roof boards. Bevel at the top is secured by using sliding tee bevel set at 6″ on both the tongue and blade of the steel square. Remove groove from first board by jointing and nail in place with edge flush with outside surface of front end. Permit roof boards to project 1″ at the rear.

14. Cut a strip of roofing tin 3″ x 33″ and nail over ridge as shown.

15. From ½″ material, S2S, cut 4 slats 1-¾″ x 23″ long for door.

16. Cut top cross bar 13/16″ x 1-¾″ x 12-¾″ long.

17. Cut bottom cross piece for door 13/16″ x 1-¾″ x 11-¾″ long.

18. Assemble door 12-¾″ wide, spacing the four slats equally. Top cross piece is placed on the inside and bottom cross piece is placed on the outside of door.

19. Cut 2 pieces 1″ x 1-½ ″ x 15-½″ long for door guides.

20. Cut a ½″ x ⅝″ rabbet on inside edges of guide, and nail in place over door, making sure that the door has a free sliding fit. Cut tops of guides off flush with roof surface.

21. By bending No. 12 wire about an inch and one-quarter pipe, form coil spring door catch as shown in " Detail top view door and wire catch." Attach to roof with staples as indicated. The top staple is not driven down tight, but forms a guide for the movable part of the latch.

22. Bore two holes in door for latch to enter when door is open and when closed.

23. Make floor 28″ x 28″ from ¹³/₁₆″ material with cross pieces ¹³/₁₆″ x 1-½″ x 28″ across under side.

24. Apply priming coat of lead paint.

25. Follow when dry with finish coat of outdoor paint of color desired. White makes a good color as it reflects sunlight and does not become excessively hot.

26. Letter sides with farm name if desired.

Supplementary Devices for the Poultry House and Yard

1. Water fountain.
2. Stand for water fountain.
3. Guard for water fountain.
4. Feeding trough.
5. Chick feeder.
6. Feed scoop.
7. Feed bin.
8. Feed mixer.
9. Oyster-shell hopper.
10. Oat germinator.
11. Dropping-board scraper.
12. Medicine cabinet.
13. Catching crate.
14. Caponizing board.
15. Holding device for bleeding and picking.
16. Killing tank.
17. Range house.
18. Brooder house.
19. Sun porch.
20. Wire-floored run.
21. Window screen.
22. Metal light reflector.
23. Mouse-trap burglar alarm.
24. Alarm-clock lighting device.
25. Trap-nest record case.

26. Outdoor feed hopper.

CHAPTER XI

DEVICES FOR SURVEYING AND FIELD WORK

Job 1.—An accurate ten foot pole forms a convenient means of measuring when doing repair and construction work about the farm buildings. It is especially useful in laying out foundations, as with it a right angle can be quickly laid out using sides of six feet, eight feet, and ten feet (Fig. 130).

Stock List

No. Pieces	Material	Dimensions	Where used
1	Pine, basswood or spruce	$^{13}/_{16}''$ x 1-½″ x 10′	Body.
2	Galvanized iron	1-$^{3}/_{16}''$ x 1-½″	Ends.
4	F. H. B. screws	½″ No. 5	Ends.

Construction.—1. Select a straight grained pine, basswood or spruce board, S2S, and joint one edge to establish a working edge.

2. Set the gauge at 1½″ and gauge line the full length.

3. Rip along this line and supporting it on the bench top, joint to exact width.

4. Smooth plane sides lightly to remove planer marks.

5. Measure accurately, square and cut to length. Most accurate measurements can be made with steel tape, if available.

6. With steel square and marking awl, lay out on galvanized iron or sheet brass, 2 pieces, 1½″ x 1$^{3}/_{16}''$, and cut to shape with snips, for end plates.

7. Lay off lines $^{3}/_{16}''$ from each end and locate, drill or punch and countersink holes for ½″ No. 5 F.H.B. screws.

8. Clamp in vise and bend to shape indicated in detail of end plate. Exact position of bends will depend upon thickness of metal used. Locate bends so that dimension of detail marked $^{13}/_{16}''$ will equal thickness of 10 foot pole.

9. Rabbet ends of pole to thickness of metal used for end plates so that plates will fit flush to side and leave no projecting edges. Fasten end plates to pole with screws listed, first checking to see that pole will be 10′ in length after end plates are in place and making such adjustments as are necessary to secure this result.

10. Smooth up work with No. 1 or 1½ sand paper.

11. Lay off foot divisions and, with try square and knife point, square across both faces of the pole at each division.

12. Lay off 6″ divisions and with try square and knife point square half way across both faces of the pole at each division.

13. Go over division marks with try square and pencil, working the mark down into the knife mark.

14. Mark the figures 1, 2, 3, etc., at the foot divisions on both sides, reading from left to right in each case. Figures can be applied with stencil, small brush, lead pencil or burned into wood with wire branding irons bent to proper shape and heated red.

15. Apply two coats of weather-proof varnish.

128

Job 2.—**Range Pole.**—In running lines for fences, laying out fields for plowing and similar work, light straight poles, shod with a metal point, to permit setting in the ground, and painted contrasting colors to make them clearly visible are a great convenience (Fig. 130).

Stock List

No. Pieces	Material	Dimensions	Where used
1	Pine	1–⅛″ x 1–⅛″ x 9′ 8–½″	Pole.
1	Black iron pipe	¾″ x 6″	Shoe.
1	F. H. B. screw	¾″ No. 5	Shoe.

Construction.—1. Select a straight grained pine board 1–⅛″ thick and at least 10′ long.

2. Joint one edge to secure working edge.

3. Set gauge at 1–⅛″ and gauge full length.

4. Rip along gauge line, support work on bench top to prevent springing and joint to 1–⅛″ x 1–⅛″.

5. Apply square diagonally across stick and mark at 7″ and 17″ division as described for laying out octagonal stick.

6. Set gauge and gauge lines through these points and also equally distant from the other corners.

7. Support stick on bench top to prevent springing and with the jointer plane to gauge marks making the stick octagonal.

8. Taper the pole to ¾″ across flats at the top end as indicated in turned section.

9. Prepare shoe as described under Job 17 of forge shop work.

10. Fit shoe to pole and cut to 10′ long, over all.

11. Lay off in 1 foot divisions.

12. Smooth up work with No. 1 or 1–½ sand paper and apply priming coat of paint.

13. When dry, apply finishing coat of auto enamel or other hard drying gloss paint. Beginning with the bottom, paint in alternating 1 foot bands of red and white.

Job. 3.—**Folding Rod Pole.**—Farm field measurements are usually made with the rod (16½ feet) as the unit of linear measurement. A single pole of this length is inconvenient to carry and store, making the jointed pole shown convenient (Fig. 130).

Stock List

No. Pieces	Material	Dimensions	Where used
1	Pine S2S	½″ x 1–½″ x 5′ 11–½″	Middle section.
2	Pine S2S	½″ x 1–½″ x 5′ 8–¾″	End sections.
		Hardware	
4	Galvanized iron	1–½″ x 2–½″	Joint plates.
2	Round head stove bolts	¼″ x 1–¼″	Joints.
16	F. H. B. screws	¾″ No. 5	Joint plates.

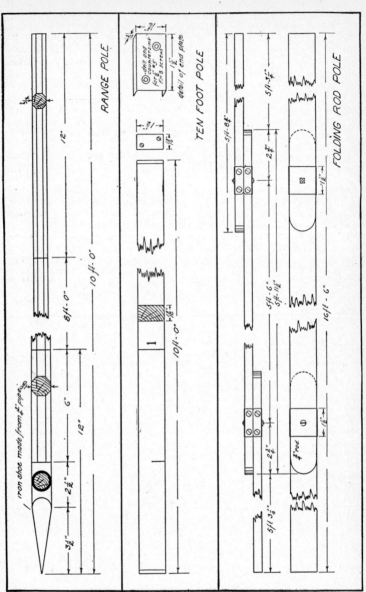

FIG. 130.—Range pole, ten foot pole, folding rod pole.

Construction.—1. Select a straight grained pine board, S2S, of sufficient length and joint one edge to establish working edge.

2. Set the gauge at 1–½″ and gauge a line full length.

3. Rip and joint to width. Prepare 3 sections as above.

4. Square and cut one end of end section.

5. Measure 5′ 6″ from this end and square around the stick at this point.

6. Set the gauge at ½″ the width of the material being used and gauge a light center line intersecting this line.

7. Bore a ¼″ hole at this intersection for the stove bolt used as a joint pin.

8. Locate a point in the center line 2″ from the line squared around the end section and with the dividers set at ¾″ and this point as a center, lay out an arc cutting the end of the section.

9. Cut along this curved edge with compass saw or sharp chisel. Two end sections are to be made as above and the work may be hastened by laying them side by side and cutting them out together.

10. In a similar manner lay out and construct the center section.

11. Square and cut 4 pieces of galvanized iron 1–½″ x 2½″. Smooth up edges and remove corners with file.

12. With try square and marking awl, lay out marks for bends.

13. Punch or drill holes ¼″ from edge. Countersink for ¾″ No. 5 F. H. B. screws. Holes may be punched easily using cup pointed nail set of size desired. Hold metal to be punched on end of hard wood block.

14. Bend up ½″ at each edge to fit over end and center sections. Locate center of each joint plate by means of intersecting diagonals and drill a ¼″ hole in each for stove bolt used as joint pin.

15. Place joint plates in position and fasten as indicated with ¾″ No. 5 F. H. B. screws.

16. Assemble the 3 sections of the pole, using ¼″ x 1–¼″ round head stove bolts as joint pins.

17. Lay off one side of pole with foot and half-foot divisions marking them with knife point and lead pencil worked well into the knife cut. The other side of the pole may be divided into 25 equal parts, if desired, each representing one link.

18. Finish pole with weather-proof varnish.

Job. 4.—**Target Rod.**—When taking levels with a carpenter's level some means of measuring from the projected line of sight to the ground is necessary. The target rod illustrated serves for this purpose. When used with an instrument carrying a telescope, the adjustable target may be removed and the rod read directly from the instrument (Fig. 131).

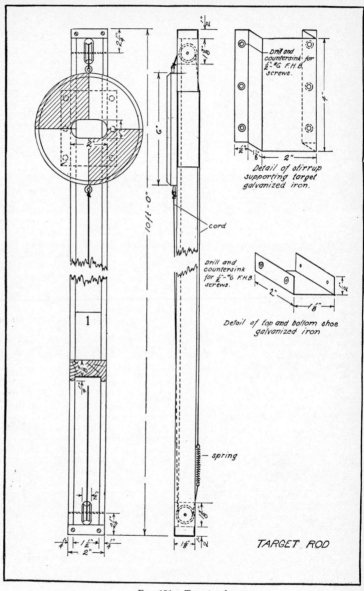

FIG. 131.—Target rod.

Stock List

No. Pieces	Material	Dimensions	Where used
1	Pine S2S	1-⅛″ x 2″ x 10′ 0″	Rod.
1	Pine S2S	½″ x 6″ diameter	Target.
		Hardware	
1	Coil tension spring	⅜″ x 3″	Used to maintain tension in cord.
1	Chalk line	20 ft. long	Used to adjust target.
2	Screw eyes	⅞″	Target.
14	F. H. B. screws	½″ No. 6	Target and ends of rod.
2	Awning pulleys	1″ diameter	Top and bottom of rod.
1	Flexible rod	10′ x 1-½″	Rod face.
2	Common wire nails	8d	Axles for pulleys at rod ends.
2	Galvanized irons	2-⅛″ x 2″	Rod ends.
1	Galvanized iron	4″ x 5-⅛″	Supporting strip for target.

Construction.—1. Select a straight grained pine board S2S, 1-⅛″ thick 10′ long and establish a working edge by jointing.

2. Set the gauge at 2″ and using it against the working edge, gauge a line the full length.

3. Rip along this line.

4. Support stock ripped off on edge on bench top to prevent springing and joint 2″ wide.

5. Set gauge at ¼″ and gauge lines down each side.

6. Rabbet out the portion between these lines ¼″ deep. This can be most easily done by running over a circular saw, set to project required distance above the table. If circular saw is not available the work can be done with a rabbeting plane.

7. With try square and marking awl, lay out galvanized iron 2″ x 2-⅛″ for top and bottom ends of rod.

8. Punch or drill and countersink holes for ½″ No. 6 F. H. B. screws and bend as indicated in detail of top and bottom shoe. Make two.

9. Cut two pieces of pine ¼″ x ½″ x 1-½″ to fill rabbet beneath shoe on front of rod at top and bottom ends of rod.

10. Square and cut rod to length.

11. Apply glue to rabbet and to back of flexible rod. Glue flexible rod in place and fasten ends by two pieces described in No. 9. Press flexible rod firmly in place with clamps and set aside to dry.

12. When dry remove clamps and fit top and bottom shoes described in Nos. 7 and 8.

13. In center of each end lay out and work a ½″ x 1-⅜″ mortise ½″ from the end to house pulleys as shown in front and side views.

14. Set the compasses with a 3″ radius and lay out target 6″ in diameter using ½″ pine.

15. Draw vertical and horizontal diameters.

16. Locate points $\frac{1}{2}''$ on each side of the center and using these points as centers bore $1''$ holes. Remove the wood between these holes with the compass saw as indicated in drawing of target.

17. Run a $\frac{1}{4}''$ chamfer around edge of target as shown in front view.

18. Lay out a piece of galvanized iron $4'' \times 5\text{-}\frac{1}{4}''$. Punch or drill holes and countersink for $\frac{1}{2}''$ No. 6 F. H. B. screws and bend as indicated in the detail of stirrup, forming the stirrup which carries the target. This should be a free sliding fit on the rod.

19. Paint alternating quarters of target red and white as indicated.

20. Lay out and drill $\frac{1}{8}''$ hole through center of rod edgewise, $2\text{-}\frac{1}{4}''$ from each end for 8d nail serving as pulley axle. Lay out and bore hole from each side to center.

21. Remove sheaves from awning pulleys and put in position using section cut from 8d nail, or wire of proper size for axle. Plug holes to prevent axle from working out.

22. Apply coat of shellac to rod with oiled pad.

23. Turn screw eyes into upper and lower sides of target and assemble with rod.

24. Tie cord into screw eyes on target, thread through pulleys and fasten to tension spring at the back. Tension should be adjusted until cord is sufficiently taut to hold target in position. Spring should be at lowest position at the back of the rod when target is at highest position at the front as shown. Target is raised or lowered to line of sight by pulling on the cord. Flexible rod can be purchased for a nominal sum from dealers in engineering supplies and should be secured before construction of rod is begun so that the rabbet protecting it can be made to fit. If desired, the rod can be divided into feet and tenths and the use of the flexible rod dispensed with.

Job. 5.—Adjustable Ditcher's Square.—When digging ditch for laying tile some means is necessary for measuring down from the overhead line to the ditch bottom in order that a smooth tile base may be prepared, parallel with the line (Fig. 132).

The adjustable square shown is convenient, as it may be set to varying heights. The horizontal arm projects beneath the line stretched up at the side of the ditch, parallel with its length, while the upright part serves as a depth gauge.

Stock List

No. Pieces	Material	Dimensions	Where used
1	Pine S2S	$\frac{13}{16}'' \times 1\text{-}\frac{1}{2}'' \times 8'\ 0''$	Upright.
2	Pine S2S	$\frac{1}{2}'' \times 2\text{-}\frac{1}{2}'' \times 2'\ 3''$	Arm.
3	F. H. B. screws	$1''$ No. 8	Arm.

Construction.—1. Select a straight grained pine board and joint edge to secure working edge.

2. Set the gauge at $1\text{-}\frac{1}{2}''$ and using it against working edge, gauge line the full length.

3. Rip along the gauge line and joint to width, supporting stick while jointing.

4. Square and cut to length desired. Seven feet is sufficiently long for ordinary ditching. Ten feet makes a good length as it can be used through

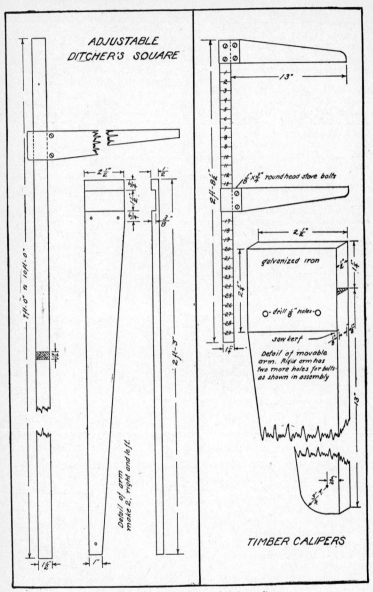

ADJUSTABLE
DITCHER'S SQUARE

TIMBER CALIPERS

FIG. 132.—Ditcher's square and timber calipers.

most cuts and in addition is useful in measuring. The horizontal arm may be made to fit the ten foot pole described in Job 1, if desired.

5. Joint edge of ½″ pine board. Set gauge at 2–½″ and gauge line at this distance from working edge.

6. Rip along this line and joint to 2–½″ wide.

7. Square and cut off 2′ 3″ long.

8. Square two lines across the face of this piece ¾″ and 2–¼″ from the end respectively.

9. Set the gauge at ⅜″ and gauge lines on the edges of the pieces, connecting the lines squared across in 8.

10. With saw cut along the squared lines down to the gauge marks and remove wood down to gauge marks by paring with chisel.

11. Measure down 1″ from the top edge of the piece at one end and draw a diagonal line from this point to a point on the opposite edge 3″ from the end.

12. Rip along this line and smooth up with plane.

13. Make a second piece for the arm as outlined in 5–12, being careful to make them left and right.

14. Drill and countersink one of these pieces for 1″ No. 7 F. H. B. wood screws, as shown in detail.

11. Assemble as shown in drawing. Arm should slide freely on upright when screws are loosened but should grip it tightly when the screws are drawn up.

Job. 6.—**Timber Calipers.**—When estimating the possible amount of lumber obtainable from a stand of trees some method of determining the diameter is necessary. It is also desirable to know the yearly growth made by trees in farm forestry operations. The calipers shown are convenient for these purposes and will measure trees from 1 inch up to 2 feet in diameter (Fig. 132).

Stock List

No. Pieces	Material	Dimensions	Where used
1	Maple	½″ x 1–¼″ x 2′ 8–½″	Beam.
2	Maple	½″ x 2–½″ x 1′ 1″	Arms.
2	Galvanized iron	2–½″ x 5–¼″	Clamps for arms.
6	Round head stove bolts	⅛″ x ¾″	Clamps for arms.

Construction.—1. Joint edges of ½″ maple board S2S to prepare working edge.

2. Set gauge at 1–¼″ and gauge line full length.

3. Support strip on bench top and joint to width.

4. Smooth plane sides lightly to remove planer marks.

5. Square and cut to length.

6. Lay off 1″ divisions and square lines across with knife point as shown. Mark numbers with steel stamp, if available, otherwise use pencil.

7. Prepare a working edge on a second piece of ½″ maple S2S.

8. Set gauge at 2–½″ and gauge a line full length.

9. Rip along this line and joint to width.

10. Square and cut to length 13″.

11. Locate a point at one end 1″ down from the edge and draw a diagonal line to a point 1″ from the end of the opposite side.

12. Rip along this line and plane edge smooth.

13. Round off corner to ¾″ radius by paring with chisel, as shown in detail of movable arm.

14. Lay out with square and marking awl and cut two pieces of galvanized iron or sheet brass to 2-½″ x 5-¼″.

15. Bend up ⅛″ of each end at right angles in vise.

16. 2-¼″ from each end square lines across and bend in vise to fit around ½″ beam.

17. Place arm in position against beam, slip metal slides in place and mark position of ends.

18. Square across arms at these points and make ⅛″ saw kerfs to house ends of metal slides which have been turned down as shown in detail.

19. Mark and drill holes for ⅛″ x ¾″ round head stove bolts as shown.

20. Insert bolts, tighten up and file projecting ends flush with nuts.

21. Smooth with fine sand paper and apply shellac with oiled pad. Light machine oil or floor oil may be used as dressing, if desired.

Stock List for Tripod for Carpenter's Level (p. 138.)

No. Pieces	Material	Dimensions	Where used
3	White ash	1″ x 1-¾″ x 4′ 7″	Legs.
3	White ash	¹³/₁₆″ x 2″ x 1-¾″	Spacing blocks in legs.
2	Pine S2S	½″ x 7″ diameter	Tripod head.
3	Maple	¹³/₁₆″ x 2″ x 3″	Blocks beneath head.
2	Pine S2S	½″ x 6″ diameter	Base of swinging head.
1	Maple	¹³/₁₆″ x 1-⅜″ x 4-⅞″	Block between uprights, swinging head.
2	Maple	¹³/₁₆″ x 4-⅞″ x 5″	Uprights, swinging head.

Hardware

3	Common nails	20d	Ends of legs.
6	F. H. B. screws	1″ No. 8	Middle of legs.
6	Round head stove bolts	¼″ x 2-¼″	Spacing blocks and top of legs.
6	F. H. B. screws	2″ No. 10	Tripod head.
1	Galvanized iron	3-¼″ diameter	Reinforcing plate beneath head.
6	Common nails	3d	
6	F. H. B. screws	1-¾″ No. 10	Swinging head.
1	Carriage bolt with washer and thumb-nut	¼″ x 3-½″	Swinging head.
1	Carriage bolt with washer and thumb-nut	¼″ x 4-½″	Swinging head.

Small quantity of glue and shellac.

Job. 7.—**Tripod for Carpenter's Level.**—When laying out foundations or establishing grades with a carpenter's level, some means by which it can be quickly and securely set up and held in position for sighting is essential. The tripod shown is convenient for this purpose. The swinging head permits the level to be turned in any direction and quickly brought to a level position (Fig. 133) (Stock list p. 137).

Construction.—1. Select a straight grained white ash board 1″ in thickness S2S, and establish working edge by jointing.

2. Set gauge at 1-¾″ and gauge line full length.

3. Rip along gauge line and supporting the piece on the bench top to prevent springing, joint to 1-¾″ wide.

4. Square and cut to length, 4′ 7″.

5. Gauge a light center line along each edge of the piece prepared as above.

6. Set the gauge at half the width of the material in use and gauge a light center line along each side.

7. Set the dividers at 1″ radius and using a point in the center line mentioned in No. 6, one inch from the end as a center, describe an arc outlining the top of the leg.

8. With a sharp chisel pare to this outline.

9. Bore a ¼″ hole at the center used to take hinge pin at top of leg.

10. 1′ down from this hole bore another ¼″ hole in the same center line.

11. 2′ from the top end drill and countersink two holes as shown in leg detail for 1″ No. 8 F. H. B. wood screws.

12. With draw knife roughly taper leg for a distance of 2′ 7″ as shown. Finish taper to 1″ square at the lower end with plane. Remove corners of lower portion of leg with plane making it octagonal.

13. Select drill making a tight fit for 20d common nail and drill endwise into center of leg for 3″.

14. With draw knife point leg as indicated in drawing.

15. Drive 20d nail in place and cut off with hacksaw or bolt clippers.

16. Dress end of leg and nail to blunt point with file. Tripod shoes may be made from gas pipe if desired as directed for range pole, Job 2.

17. From top end rip along center line gauged along edge to a point 2′ from the top end. This can best be done on the combination saw if available.

18. Drive the two screws in the holes previously drilled and countersunk in the center of the leg.

19. Prepare a block $^{13}/_{16}″$ x 2″ x 1-¾″ and dress lower edge slightly wedge shape to fit between the two upper parts of the leg as a spreader.

20. When fitted apply glue, set in place and drill ¼″ hole to coincide with the one already drilled in the leg.

21. Insert stove bolt and draw up snug. Cut off projecting end of stove bolt with hack saw or bolt cutter and smooth up end with file. Make 3 legs as above.

22. Using ½″ pine S2S lay out and cut with the compass saw two circles, each 7″ in diameter.

23. Apply glue to the meeting surfaces and clamp up tightly with grain crossed at right angles to prevent warping. Set aside to dry.

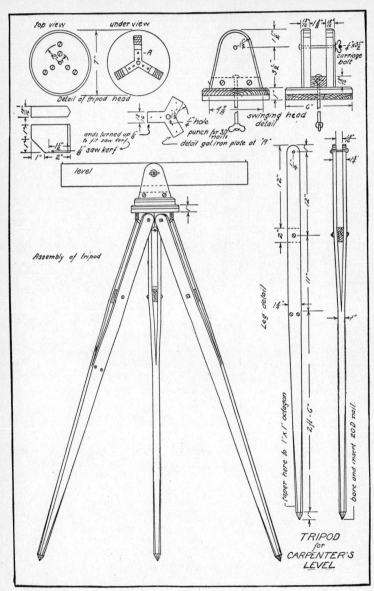

top view

under view

Detail of tripod head

swinging head detail

carriage bolt

¼" hole punch for 30 nails

detail gal.iron plate at "A"

ends turned up to fit saw kerf

⅛" saw kerf

level

Assembly of tripod

Leg detail

taper here to 1"x1" octagon

2'1'-6"

bore and insert 20D nail.

TRIPOD for CARPENTER'S LEVEL

FIG. 133.—Tripod for carpenter's level.

24. When dry smooth up edge with spoke shave and run a ¼" chamfer around the top edge.

25. Using the same center that was used in laying out the tripod top lay out two other circles with radii of 1" and 2" respectively.

26. With the same radius step around the circle dividing it into 6 equal parts.

27. Through each alternate point draw a line intersecting the center, dividing the top into 3 equal parts.

28. At each of these intersections drill and countersink a hole for a 2" No. 10 F. H. B. wood screw as shown in top view, detail of tripod head.

29. Using ¹³/₁₆" maple or birch, S2S cut three blocks for under side of tripod head as shown in detail of tripod head. Angle for end, 120 degrees, can be obtained by drawing all radii from points stepped off in 26 and fitting end of block to go between two of them.

30. Drill blocks to coincide with holes drilled in tripod head and fasten blocks to head with screws listed, applying glue to meeting surfaces.

31. Apply a piece of galvanized iron or sheet brass, at least 3-¼" in diameter over the blocks described in 29 and 30, and with sharp pointed marking awl scribe a line around them.

32. Cut to this line with snips as shown in detail of iron plate at A.

33. Bend up ends of plate so formed, ⅛" to lock in saw cuts made in blocks.

34. Place in position and mark location of saw cuts on blocks.

35. Make saw cuts and nail metal plate in place with 3d common nails as indicated.

36. Locate center and drill ¼" hole through metal plate and half way through tripod head. Remove the drill and complete the hole from the opposite side to insure having it well centered at both sides.

37. Bolt legs in position on tripod head and cut off and smooth up projecting ends of bolts.

38. Set the compasses with a 3" radius and lay out and cut with the compass saw, two 6" circles, using ½" pine S2S.

39. Apply glue to meeting surfaces and clamp together with grain at right angles. Set aside to dry.

40. When dry smooth up edges with spoke shave and run a ¼" chamfer clear around.

41. Prepare a piece of ¹³/₁₆" maple, S2S, 4-⅞" wide.

42. Set the gauge at one-half the width and gauge a center line along one side.

43. Square and cut off one end.

44. At a point 3-½" from this end mark a point in the center line and with a radius of 1-½" lay out a curve marking the top of the upright part of the swinging head.

45. Draw lines from the lower corners of the piece tangent with the circle just made and cut along these lines.

46. Smooth up edges with plane and spoke shave and run a ¼" chamfer clear around.

47. Bore hole for bolt carrying level at the point indicated in swinging head detail, and drill and countersink holes for F. H. B. screws as shown. Prepare two upright pieces as described in 41–47.

48. Prepare a piece of ¹³/₁₆" maple, 1-⅜" x 4-⅞" to fit between uprights and drill to coincide with holes made in uprights.

49. By means of intersecting diagonals locate center of this piece and bore a ¼″ hole for bolt about which swinging head revolves.

50. Bore ¼″ hole in center of circular portion of swinging top.

51. Apply glue to meeting surfaces and assemble parts. Uprights are attached to circular portion by screws inserted from beneath.

52. Bore ¼″ hole through level stock and mount as indicated. Sights can be purchased for the carpenter's level at the hardware store. On level shown sights consist of fine notch filed in upturned edge of sheet metal fastened to top of level stock with small screws like a rear rifle sight. Front sight consists of small brad driven to proper depth to give it same height as rear sight. Both sights are painted dead black to avoid reflection of light.

53. Apply shellac to tripod with oiled pad after smoothing up with No. 1 sand paper.

Devices to be Made for Use in Farm Engineering

1. Hubs and finders for staking out tile lines.
2. Height-measurer for determining height and contents of standing timber.
3. Tile hook for laying small tile.
4. Form for concrete silt well.
5. Form for concrete outlet for tile drain.
6. Adjustable straight edge for laying tile to grade.
7. Water level for leveling building foundations and determining grades.
8. Plane table for use in farm mapping.
9. Alidade or sighting ruler for plane table.
10. Cross for laying out orchards or right angles.
11. Device for measuring angles.
12. Land-measuring wheel.

CHAPTER XII

DEVICES FOR GENERAL FARM USE

Job. 1.—Bushel Crate, Type 1.—The bushel crates shown in jobs 1 and 2 are designed for the handling of potatoes and root crops. They have a capacity of 2688 cubic inches, which is equal to $1\frac{1}{4}$ standard bushels of 2150.42 cubic inches each, this being the capacity specified by the New York State Department of Farms and Markets. The slatted construction permits the escape of dirt, while the length used fits the standard wagon bed (Fig. 134).

Stock List

No. Pieces	Material	Dimensions	Where used
2	Pine S2S	$^{13}/_{16}''$ x 12'' x 14''	Ends.
16	Pine	$\frac{3}{8}''$ x $1-\frac{3}{4}''$ x $17-\frac{5}{8}''$	Sides and bottom.
64	Cement coated box nails	6d	Ends.

Construction.—1. Joint the edge of a $^{13}/_{16}''$ pine board S2S to secure a working edge.

2. By ripping or jointing as required, reduce to 12'' wide.

3. Square lines across and cut to 14'' long.

4. Five and five-eighths inches from each end, square lines across the piece so obtained.

5. Set the gauge at $1-\frac{7}{8}''$ and gauge a line intersecting the lines squared across in No. 4. The intersections mark the center of the $1-\frac{1}{4}''$ holes forming the ends of the handles.

6. Set the expansive bit at $1-\frac{1}{4}''$ and bore holes at the centers established in No. 5.

7. With the gauge run parallel lines touching the top and bottom of the holes just bored, $1-\frac{1}{4}''$ and $2-\frac{1}{2}''$ from the top edge respectively.

8. With the compass saw cut along these lines, forming the handle. Smooth up the inside of the opening and run a light chamfer around it.

9. Prepare a second end in the same way.

10. Prepare a quantity of material $\frac{3}{8}''$ x $1-\frac{3}{4}''$ sufficient for the side and bottom slats.

11. Square and cut them to $17-\frac{5}{8}''$ long. This can best be done by fitting a measure or stop block in the miter box and cutting them all against this stop.

12. Assemble by nailing with 6d cement coated box nails, using two in each end of each slat. Nail top and bottom side slats in position, and space others equally between them. Test with square when nailing to insure fitting the work together at right angles.

13. Paint, if desired, and stencil name on end.

142

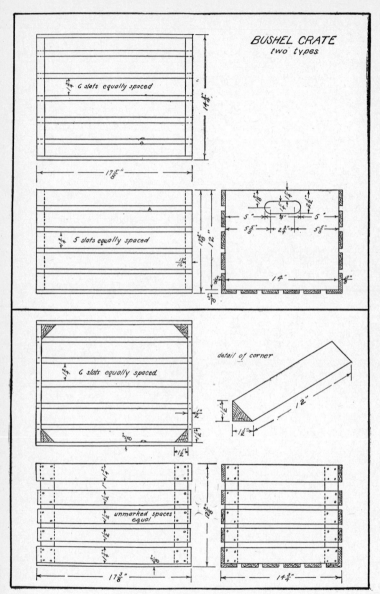

FIG. 134.—Bushel crate, two types.

Job. 2.—Bushel Crate, Type 2.—(Fig. 134).

Stock List

No. Pieces	Material	Dimensions	Where used
4	Elm	1-½″ x 1-½″ triangular x 12″ long	Corners.
10	Elm S2S	⅜″ x 1-¾″ x 17-⅜″	Top and bottom of sides and bottom.
6	Elm S2S	⅜″ x 1-½″ x 17-⅛″	Sides.
4	Elm S2S	½″ x 1-¾″ x 14″	Top and bottom ends.
6	Elm S2S	⅜″ x 1-½″ x 14″	Ends.
164	Cement coated box nails	4d	Ends, sides and bottom.

Construction.—1. By jointing and ripping, prepare corner block material as shown in detail of corner, square and cut to length, making 4. If triangular corner blocks are used and are desired in any quantity, they can best be secured by having them run out in strips at the local mill. If desired corner blocks ¹³/₁₆″ x 1-½″ in cross section may be used as they have practically the same volume as the ones shown.

2. Joint the edge of a ½″ board to secure working edge.

3. Set gauge at 1-¾″ and gauge line full length.

4. Rip along this line and joint to width.

5. From material so prepared, square and cut to length 4 pieces 14″ long for top and bottom slats on ends.

6. Using nails listed, assemble top and bottom end cleats and corner blocks. Use the square while nailing to insure getting a rectangular box.

7. Joint the edge of a ⅜″ board and gauge a line 1-½″ from the edge.

8. Rip along this line and joint to 1-½″ wide preparing material for end and side cleats.

9. Square and cut 6 pieces of this material 14″ long, for end slats. Slats can best be squared and cut to exact length by nailing a gauge block in the miter box.

10. Nail these slats to corner blocks putting the first one down 1″ from the top to provide a hand hold and space the others equally.

11. In the same way, prepare 4 pieces ⅜″ x 1-¾″ x 17-⅜″ for top and bottom side slats and nail them in place. Test with steel square to see that side is kept rectangular while doing this.

12. Measure exact length of side slats and square and cut 6 to this length, using the material prepared in 7 and 8. Nail them in place with ends coinciding with ends of end cleats.

13. Measure length of bottom slats and square and cut 6 slats to this length. Nail these in place as shown in the drawing, keeping sides and ends square while doing it.

Job. 3.—**A light roof ladder** is a necessity when making repairs to the roofs of farm buildings. If stored in a convenient place, it is also a protection against fire loss, as it furnishes a means of getting upon the roof for fire fighting purposes (Fig 135).

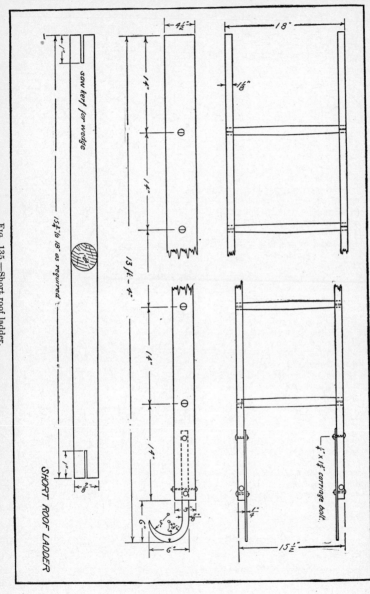

Fig. 135.—Short roof ladder.

10

Stock List

No. Pieces	Material	Dimensions	Where Used
2	Spruce S2S	1–⅛″ x 4–½″ x 12′ 10″	Sides.
10	White ash	1″ x 1″ x 16″ to 18″ long, as required	Rungs.
2	Iron	¼″ x ⅞″ x 1′ 8″	Hooks.
2	Carriage bolts with washers	¼″ x 3–¼″	Top end of sides.
4	Carriage bolts	¼″ x 1–¾″	Hooks.
6	Finishing nails	8d	Sides.
	Small quantity of paint.		

Construction.—1. Select a piece of straight-grained spruce, free from knots.

2. With the chalk line, strike a line through the center of the board.

3. Measure the length of the proposed ladder along this center line and mark the ends.

4. Lay off one-half of the width on each side of this center line at both top and bottom.

5. With the chalk line strike lines between the points so determined locating the tapered sides of the ladder side pieces.

6. Rip or joint to these lines as the case requires. Where the board used is only sufficiently wide for the bottom of the ladder sides, the waste material can be best removed by jointing.

7. Lay off the locations of the holes for the rungs along the center line and bore with a ⅞″ bit.

8. Prepare a second side piece as above.

9. Select a straight grained, air-dried white ash block of sufficient length and split out 10 rungs 1″ x 1″ and ranging in length from 16″ to 18″. The wood will split straight if the piece is split through the center each time.

10. Finish rungs to shape shown with the draw knife, making them first octagonal and then round.

11. Cut rungs to length required. Bottom rung should be 18″ and each succeeding rung ¼″ shorter in ladder shown.

12. Bore ⅞″ hole in hard wood block and fit ends of ladder rungs to it.

13. Make a 1″ saw kerf in each end of each rung.

14. Assemble sides and rungs placing rungs in sides with saw kerfs at right angles to center line of sides. Dip ends of rungs in paint or apply wood preservative before assembling.

15. Drive wedges in rung ends and smooth up with plane.

16. Nail top, middle and bottom rungs at each end to prevent ladder spreading.

17. Bore hole near top end of side pieces as shown and insert bolts to prevent splitting.

18. Make hooks as directed in Chapter XV, Job 2.

19. Place in position and mark and bore holes for bolting them to sides.

20. Bolt in position with bolts listed.

21. Paint with outdoor paint, bright red preferred, and stencil name on sides.

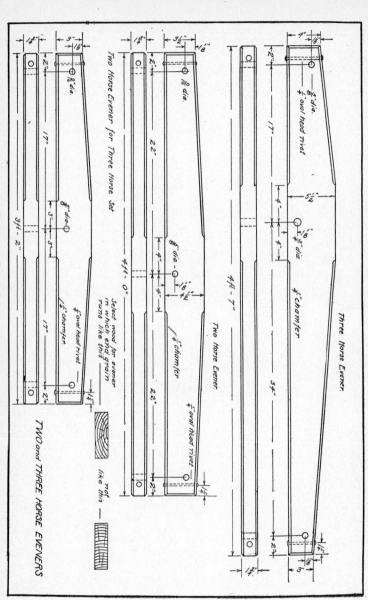

Fig. 136.—Two and three horse eveners.

Job. 4.—**Three-horse Evener.**—The evener forms the connecting link between the load and the horses comprising the team, apportioning the proper share of the load to each horse and spacing them so that they can work to the best advantage (Fig. 136).

Stock List

No. Pieces	Material	Dimensions	Where Used
1	Hickory or white ash	1-¾″ x 5-½″ x 4′ 7″	Evener.
2	Oval head rivets	¼″ x 4-¼″	Ends.

Construction.—1. Select a straight-grained, slash sawed, white ash plank of sufficient length and joint one edge to form working edge.

2. Square and cut to length.

3. Square across the evener at points 15″ and 23″ from the two horse end.

4. Mark points 5-½″ back from the front edge on these lines.

5. Mark a point 4″ back from the front edge on the two horse end of the evener and another 3″ back from the front edge on the one horse end of the evener.

6. Connect the points by diagonal lines with the points located in No. 4.

7. Rip along these lines and smooth up the edges with the jointer forming the back of the evener.

8. Run a ¼″ chamfer with the spoke shave as shown.

9. Square across the evener from the working edge at the points shown and locate and bore holes for clevises.

10. Bore ¼″ holes at points indicated for end rivets.

11. Insert rivets, cut to proper length and head down securely over burr.

12. Smooth up and finish by applying several coats of floor oil or light machine oil, filling the wood to prevent absorption of water. Two horse eveners are made in a similar manner using the dimensions shown.

Job. 5.—**Wagon Jack.**—When greasing a wagon the axle must be supported while the wheel is removed. The jack shown is a convenient one for light wagons, lifting them quickly and holding them securely (Fig. 137).

Stock List

No. Pieces	Material	Dimensions	Where Used
1	Maple S2S	1″ x 4″ x 3′	Front upright.
1	Maple S2S	1″ x 4″ x 2′ 4″	Rear upright.
1	Maple	1-¾″ x 1-½″ x 6″	Step.
1	Maple S2S	1″ x 4″ x 2′ 2″	Handle.
2	Carriage bolts with washers	¼″ x 4-½″	Handle.
1	Carriage bolt with washer	¼″ x 4″	Step.
1	F. H. B. screw	1-½″ No. 12	Step.

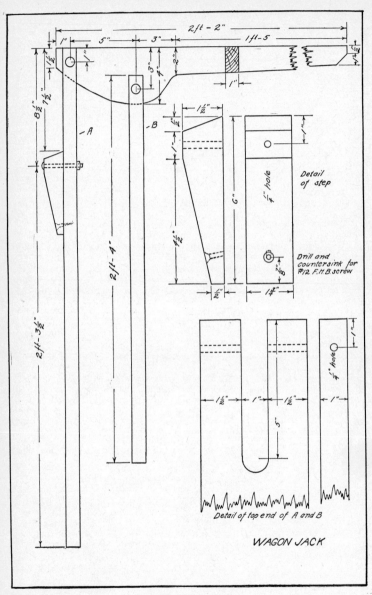

FIG. 137.—Wagon jack.

Construction.—1, Select a piece of straight-grained maple 1″ in thickness and joint one edge to establish working edge.

2. Set gauge at 4″ and gauge a line the full length.

3. Remove the waste wood with the rip saw or jointer as the case requires, finishing by jointing to 4″ in width.

4. Square and cut to length shown in figure, 3′.

5. With gauge establish center line at top end.

6. Five inches down from top bore a 1″ hole in this center line. See detail; A and B.

7. With gauge draw lines connecting the edges of this hole with the top end.

8. Rip along these lines forming a 1″ slot for the handle.

9. Using a piece of 1-¾″ maple, lay out and cut to shape a step to support the axle as shown in detail of step.

10. Fasten to front upright in position shown with bolt and screw listed. Center line of step should coincide with center line of upright.

11. Bore a ¼″ hole through the center of the edge of the upper end of the upright 1″ below the top end. Lay out work on both sides and bore from both sides meeting in the center.

12. In a similar way, minus the step, make the rear upright.

13. Lay out the handle to the dimensions shown in the drawing and cut to shape. Use the compass saw or jig saw for the curved portion and the rip saw for the handle.

14. Locate and bore ¼″ hole at the points indicated.

15. Assemble handle and uprights with bolts listed.

Job. 6.—A light, secure stepladder of the type shown is useful about the farm buildings in putting on and removing storm sash and similar work. The shelf shown for supporting a pail makes it particularly useful in painting and cleaning (Fig. 138).

Stock List

No. Pieces	Material	Dimensions	Where Used
2	Spruce S2S	$^{13}/_{16}$″ x 3″ x 5′ 2″	Front sides.
2	Spruce S2S	$^{13}/_{16}$″ x 2″ x 5′ 1-½″	Rear legs.
1	Spruce S2S	$^{13}/_{16}$″ x 4-½″ x 17-⅛″	Bottom step.
1	Spruce S2S	$^{13}/_{16}$″ x 4-½″ x 15-⁹/₁₆″	Second step.
1	Spruce S2S	$^{13}/_{16}$″ x 4½″ x 13-¹⁵/₁₆″	Third step.
1	Spruce S2S	$^{13}/_{16}$″ x4-½″ x 12-⅜″	Fourth step.
1	Spruce S2S	$^{13}/_{16}$″ x 7″ x 16″	Top.
2	Spruce S2S	$^{13}/_{16}$″ x 2″ x 6″	Cleats beneath top.
2	Spruce S2S	$^{13}/_{16}$″ x 1-¼″ x 19″	Shelf supports.
2	Spruce S2S	½″ x 1-¼″ x 2″	Spacing blocks on sides of shelf supports.
1	Spruce S2S	½″ x 6″ x 10-½″	Shelf.
2	Spruce S2S	½″ x 12″ x 3′ 9″	Diagonal braces.

No. Pieces	Material	Dimensions	Where Used
	Hardware		
1	Iron rod threaded at both ends and provided w i t h n u t s a n d washers	¼″ x 19–¼″	Rod beneath bottom step.
1	Iron rod threaded at both ends and provided w i t h n u t s a n d washers	¼″ x 16″	Rod beneath third step.
1	Iron rod	¼″ x 15″	Shelf support.
2	Carriage b o l t s with washers	¼″ x 2″	Top of rear legs.
2	Carriage b o l t s with washers	¼″ x 2–¾″	Shelf support.
16	F. H. B. screws	2″ No. 12	Steps.
6	F. H. B. screws	2″ No. 10	Top.
6	F. H. B. screws	1–½″ No. 9	Shelf.
8	F. H. B. screws	1–½″ No. 9	Diagonal braces.
6	F. H. B. screws	1–½″ No. 9	Joint b e t w e e n cleats and side pieces.
8	Common nails	3d	Spacing blocks on shelf supports.

Small quantity of glue.
Small quantity of paint.

Construction.—1. Joint the edge of a straight-grained spruce board to prepare a working edge.

2. Set the gauge at 3″ and gauge full length.

3. Rip along gauge line and joint piece to width.

4. Place the square with 3–⅛″ on the tongue and 12″ on the blade coinciding with the working edge of the piece prepared and mark along the tongue for the angle of cut at the bottom. Mark at 12 on the blade for the top of bottom step.

5. Cut at angle laid out for the bottom.

6. Apply the square a second time 3–⅛″ on the tongue coinciding with the point marked in No. 4 for the top of the bottom step. Bring the 12″ division on the blade to coincide with the working edge. Mark along the tongue for the top of the lower step and mark a point at 12 on the blade to locate the top of the second step.

7. Continue in this manner until top edges of all steps are laid out. Measure down $^{13}/_{16}$″ from top mark made and cut off at same angle as at the bottom as shown in drawing.

8. Using a piece of material to be used for the steps as a gauge, lay off the width of the dadoes for housing the ends of the steps and with the steel square or sliding tee bevel, make lines across the side piece of the ladder locating the under side of the step.

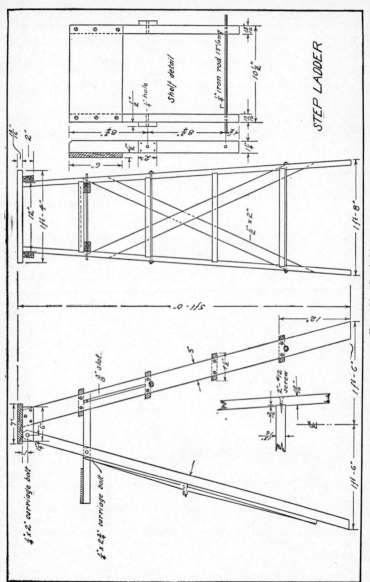

Fig. 138.—Stepladder.

9. Set the gauge at $3/16''$ and gauge depth lines on each edge of the side piece of the ladder at the points where the steps are to be housed.

10. Cut down to the gauge mark on the lines locating the upper and lower edges of the steps.

11. Pare out the waste wood with the chisel.

12. Gauge a center line down the side of the side piece.

13. Bore a $3/8''$ hole in this line at the upper edge of the third step and at the lower edge of the fourth step.

14. With the gauge, lay out a $3/8''$ slot connecting these two holes and remove the wood between them with the compass saw.

15. In the same way, construct a second side piece making them right and left.

16. Set sliding tee bevel to angle of cut at bottom of side piece and with jointer bevel $4-1/2''$ material to this angle for steps.

17. Secure lengths of steps by laying out drawing full size, symmetrically on each side of a center line, by means of a straight-edge and steel square. Drawing may be laid out on the floor or on wall board.

18. Hold the sliding tee bevel with the beam against the blade of the square and set it at $1''$ on the beam and $15''$ on the square to secure bevel for ends of steps.

19. Mark and cut the steps to the lengths as shown by the full size lay out using the bevel found in No. 18 for the end, as shown in detail.

20. Drill and countersink screw holes in side pieces and assemble side pieces and steps. Use glue in joints. Tack a temporary stay across it to hold it in position while drying.

21. Cut and thread $1/4''$ rods, bore holes and place in position indicated.

22. Cut out the two cleats for the underside of top. Bevel the top edge at same angle as step ends. Bore and countersink as shown and attach to top ends of side pieces with screws listed. Use glue on meeting surfaces.

23. From $13/16''$ material, make a top $7'' \times 16''$ and fasten to top of side pieces with screws listed.

24. Joint the edge of a $13/16$ board and with the gauge run a line $2''$ from the edge.

25. Rip along this line and joint to width forming material for rear legs.

26. Cut bottom end to same angle as side pieces.

27. Measure off $5'$ $1-1/2''$ and square and cut off. Round the top end to a $1''$ radius, and bore a $1/4''$ hole in the center line $1''$ down from the top end.

28. Bore holes in top cleats and bolt rear legs in position.

29. Joint the edge of a $1/2''$ board and rip out two pieces $2''$ wide and $3'$ $9''$ long.

30. Fold rear legs down upon side pieces. Place diagonal braces in the position shown and mark angle for cuts at top and bottom or diagonal braces.

31. Place diagonal braces in position and fasten with screws listed.

32. Prepare two pieces $13/16'' \times 1-1/4'' \times 19''$ as supporting arms for shelf.

33. Make two blocks $1/2'' \times 1-1/4'' \times 2''$ and attach to supporting arms at point shown. Bore for $1/4''$ bolts.

34. Make a shelf $1/2'' \times 6'' \times 10-1/2''$ and attach supporting arms as shown in shelf detail.

35. Bore holes for $1/4''$ iron rod as shown in detail. Cut rod, put shelf in place and insert rod.

36. Mark location for bolt holes in rear legs where shelf supports are fastened and put bolts in position.

37. Test ladder to see if it works satisfactorily; if not, make necessary adjustments, clean up with sand paper and apply a coat of paint or varnish.

Job. 7.—Seed Corn Rack.—To insure satisfactory germination, seed corn should be stored in a dry place in such a way that the air is free to circulate about each ear. It should also be protected against rats and mice. The rack shown meets these conditions, and by a simple system of numbering, permits keeping a record of each ear if it is desired to conduct breeding and germination tests (Fig. 139).

Stock List

No Pieces	Material	Dimensions	Where Used
2	Pine or Spruce S4S	1–¾″ x 3–¾″ x 5′ 9″	Side members.
2	Pine or Spruce S4S	1–¾″ x 3–¾″ x 4′ 4¾″	Top and bottom members.
2	Pine or Spruce S4S	1–¾″ x 3–¾″ x 4′ 4–¾″	Cross members.
2	Pine or Spruce S4S	1–¾″ x 3–¾″ x 1′ 6″	Feet.

Hardware

4	Carriage bolts with washers	¼″ x 2–¼″	Feet.
16	Common nails	20d	Frame joints.
3 lbs.	Fence staples	1″	Fastening wire to frame.
72	Iron wire	No. 12, 4′ 8″ long	Ear supports.
2	Galvanized irons	12″ diameter	Mouse guards.
8	Common nails	4d	Mouse guards.

Construction.—1. Select a straight 2″ x 4″ S4S and joint to width if necessary. If two by fours used are all sized to the same width, adapt measurements shown on the drawing to the actual width of the material.

2. Square and cut to 5′ 9″ long.

3. Square across the stick at the points indicated in the drawing, laying out the dadoes for the top, bottom, and center members, making the width to correspond to the exact thickness of the material used.

4. Set the gauge at ½″ and gauge depth lines for these dadoes.

5. Cut down to depth lines with saw and pare them out with sharp chisel.

6. Square and cut two pieces 1′ 6″ long for foot pieces and cut off the corners as shown in the detail.

7. With gauge and square lay out halved joint in center of foot piece, making the depth and width correspond to the material used.

8. Lay out and cut halved joint on lower end of side to fit joint cut in foot piece.

9. Square and cut four pieces 4′ 4–¾″ long for top, bottom and cross members of frame.

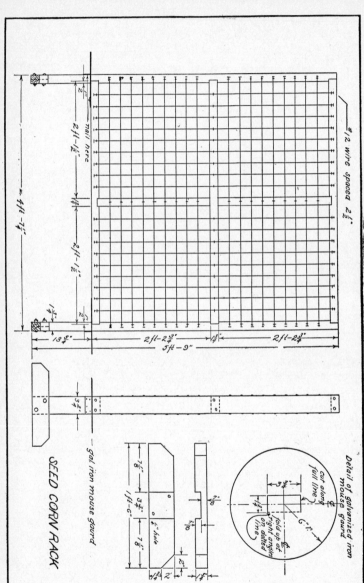

FIG. 139.—Seed corn rack.

10. Lay out and cut dadoes in top and bottom members ½″ deep to receive ends of vertical cross member.

11. Lay out and cut cross lap joint in center of cross members.

12. Assemble frame and nail with 20d nails.

13. Square up frame and tack temporary diagonal brace across the back.

14. Divide each quarter of the frame into 10 equal parts on each side.

15. Fasten end of wire at one of these divisions with 1″ staple placed 1″ from end of wire. Bend wire back over staple and drive a second staple ¾″ from first, covering wire and the bent over end.

16. Apply lever stretcher, pliers or hammer claws to wire and stretch up taut. Staple to opposite side of frame. Bend up to a form hook at staple, cut off and bend over and apply a second staple as at first end.

17. Continue this until one side of frame is covered with parallel wires equally spaced. Wire running at right angles to first course of wires should be interwoven basket fashion.

18. Apply wires to the other side of the frame in the same way.

19. Lay out and cut with the snips two 12″ circles from galvanized iron for mouse guards.

20. In the center of each, lay out a 1-¾″ x 3-¾″ rectangle. Cut around one side and two ends with sharp, cold chisel and bend up at right angles on the other side.

21. Slip these guards over the bottom ends of the side pieces with the rectangular flap to the outside and down and nail in position as indicated in the drawing.

22. Place foot pieces in position, bore holes as shown in detail and bolt to uprights.

23. Apply coat of paint, if desired.

Job. 8.—**Adjustable Bag-holder.**—The use of grain as feed is universal on farms regardless of the type of farming carried on. In feeding, it is seldom fed as bought, but is mixed to form the ration in use and then rebagged for more convenient handling. The bag-holder described is very convenient for this purpose, as it holds all bags securely, regardless of shape (Fig. 140).

Stock List

Pieces No.	Material	Dimensions	Where Used
2	N. C pine S2S	1-¾″ x 2-¾″ x 15″	Sills Nos. 11 and 12.
2	N. C. pine S2S	$^{13}/_{16}$″ x 7-¼″ x 18″	Floor boards No. 7.
2	White ash	½″ x 6″ x 4′	Uprights, No. 8.
2	Maple	$^{13}/_{16}$″ x 1-½″ x 6″	Cross pieces at base of uprights, No. 10.
1	Pine	$^{13}/_{16}$″ x 1-½″ x 6″	Cross piece on extension bar No. 14.
1	Pine	$^{13}/_{16}$″ x 6″ x 18″	Extension bar, No. 2.

No. Pieces	Material	Dimensions	Where Used
1	Maple	1-¾" x 1-¾" x 6"	Support for right hand upright, No. 13.
2	Pine	¹³/₁₆" x ¹³/₁₆" x 14-½"	Guides for extension bar, No. 1.
2	Maple	1-¾" x 3" x 5-½"	Guides for holding jaws, No. 6.
2	Maple	1-¾" x 3-¼" x 9"	Holding jaws, No. 5.
		Hardware	
4	Carriage bolts with washers	¼" x 3-¼"	For bolting uprights to base.
2	Carriage bolts with washers	¼" x 2-¾"	For joining support block, No. 13 to extension bar, No. 2.
1	Carriage bolt with washer	⅜" x 3"	Left hand end of extension board, No. 3.
10	F H. B. screws	2" No. 10	Base.
12	F. H. B. screws	1" No. 7	J a w assembly, Nos. 5 and 6.
6	F. H. B. screws	1" No. 7	For fastening upper cross cleats to uprights, (10).
10	Common nails	6d	Points for holding bag.

Small quantity light machine oil or floor oil, for finishing.

Construction.—1. Select a piece of ½" ash or other springy material that will dress 6" wide for uprights.

2. Joint one edge to establish working edge.

3. Set gauge at 6" and gauge line full length. Rip along this line and joint to 6" wide.

4. Square and cut off bottom end and 2' 8" above this square a second line across locating the upper edge of center cross cleat, No. 10.

5. Square a third line across the piece 1' 4" above the second locating the top of the uprights.

6. Gauge a center line from the top down to the top of the upper cross piece.

7. With a 2" radius and a point in this center line, 2" from the top as a center, describe a half circle outlining the top of the upright.

8. With a point in the center line as a center, bore a 1" hole whose circumference will just touch the line locating the upper side of the cross piece.

9. With the gauge lay out a 1" slot from this hole to the end.

10. Draw lines from the extremities of the lines locating top edge of cross piece No. 10 tangent to half circle drawn at upper end of upright.

11. With compass saw cut curve at top of upright.

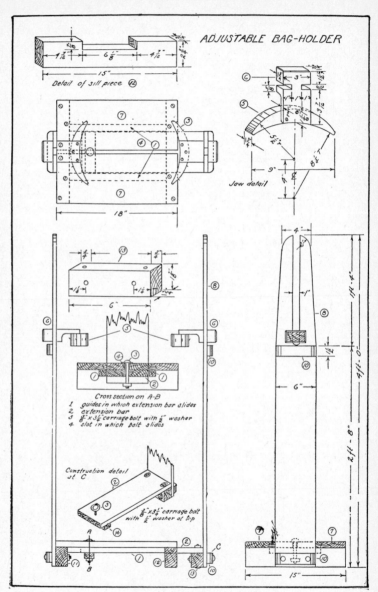

Fig. 140.—Adjustable bag-holder.

12. Rip along gauge lines forming 1″ slot and rip along diagonal lines at the side forming taper shown at top end of upright.

13. Make cross cleat No 10, $^{13}/_{16}$″ x 1–½″ x 6″ with rounded end and fasten in position on upright with three screws driven from the inside.

14. Make a second upright like the one just constructed.

15. Square and cut two pieces of N. C. pine 1–¾″ x 3–¾″ x 15″ long for cross sills Nos. 11 and 12.

16. Construct No. 12 as shown in detail of sill piece.

17. Square and cut two pieces of $^{13}/_{16}$″ pine S2S 7–¼″ x 18″ long for floor pieces. Bore and countersink and fasten to sill pieces as shown in plan with screws listed.

18. Square and cut an extension bar, No. 2, from $^{13}/_{16}$″ pine S2S, 6″ x 18″.

19. Cut block No. 13, 1–¾″ x 1–¾″ x 6″.

20. Cut two lower cross cleats, No. 10, from maple $^{13}/_{16}$″ x 1–½″ x 6″.

21. Bore holes (detail No. 13) and bolt to outer end of extension bar, No. 2, with bolts listed.

22. Bore holes and bolt lower cross cleat, No. 10, and lower end of right hand upright No. 8, to end of extension bar as shown at C, using bolts listed.

23. Bore holes and bolt left hand upright No. 6 to sill piece No. 11, as shown in side end view, using cross cleat, No. 10 to prevent splitting.

24. Slip assembled extension bar No. 2 and right-hand upright No. 6 through opening in top of sill piece No. 12.

25. Clamp in position, attach cross piece No. 14, bore hole and insert ⅜″ x 3–¼″ carriage bolt as shown in detail at C.

26. Cut two pieces $^{13}/_{16}$″ x $^{13}/_{16}$″ x 14–½″ and attach to under side of floor boards on either side of extension bar to serve as guide as shown on cross section on B. Extension bar should work freely between the guides.

27. Using stiff paper or light cardboard, construct a template for cutting the holding jaws, using the centers and radii shown in jaw detail.

28. Using the pattern as made, lay out the holding jaws on 1–¾″ maple with grain running lengthwise of jaw.

29. Cut to shape with jig saw or by a series of saw cuts made at right angles to the edge, cutting down to the curved outline and paring out the waste wood with a chisel. Smooth up with spoke shave and rasp.

30. Square and cut two pieces of maple 1–¾″ x 3″ x 5–½″ for No. 6.

31. At a point 1–½″ from the end lay out and cut $^{9}/_{16}$″ grooves 1″ in depth as shown in jaw detail, to fit in fork on top end of upright.

32. Two and eleven-sixteenths inches from the end, square a line around the block and locate points in this line ⅞″ from the top edge of the block on each side.

33. Using these points as centers bore with a ¾″ bit until the holes meet in the center.

34. Gauge a line on each side ½″ from top surfaces, from the end until it meets the hole, and rip along this line.

35. Square around the block 2–$^{11}/_{16}$″ from the back end and make a saw cut across the under side extending in until it meets the ¾″ hole bored edgewise through the block forming guide for holding jaw.

36. Attach finished guide for holding jaw to jaw with three screws listed as shown in jaw detail, using glue on meeting surfaces.

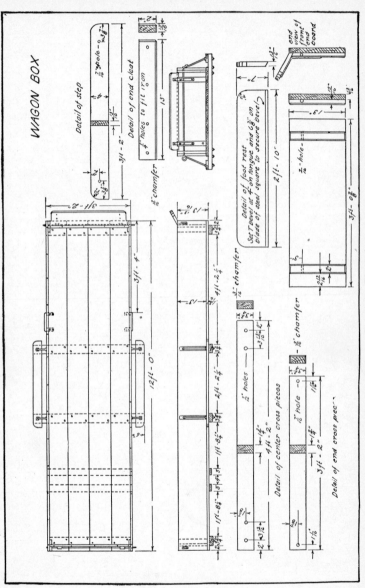

FIG. 141.—Wagon box.

37. Drill holes and insert five 6d nails in each jaw as shown in plan driving them from the inside with points inclined upwards. Cut to about ½″ projection and file to point for holding bags.

38. Make second jaw like first.

39. Place jaws in position and adjust until they work freely.

40. Smooth up work and give finished bagger several coats of floor oil or light machine oil.

Job. 9.—**Wagon Box.**—A substantial wagon box of good appearance is necessary on every farm for handling potatoes, ear-corn and similar material. The one shown permits of the addition of top box and stock rack (Fig. 141).

Stock List

No. Pieces	Material	Dimensions	Where Used
2	Pine or basswood S2S	$^{13}/_{16}''$ x 13″ x 12′	Sides.
2	Pine or basswood S2S	$^{13}/_{16}''$ x 13″ x 3′ 0-⅜″	End boards.
1	Pine or basswood S2S	$^{13}/_{16}''$ x 7″ x 2′ 10″	Foot rest.
2	White ash S2S	$^{13}/_{16}''$ x 4″ x 3′ 2″	Steps.
2	N. C. pine S4S	1-¾″ x 3-¾″ x 3′ 2″	End cross pieces.
2	N. C. pine S4S	1-¾″ x 3-¾″ x 4′ 2″	Center cross pieces.
2	N. C. pine S2S	$^{13}/_{16}''$ x 3″ x 3′ 2″	Cleats on each side rear bolster.
12	Maple S2S	$^{13}/_{16}''$ x 2″ x 13″	Cleats across end boards and box end.
4 50′	Spruce or B. M. matched spruce S2S	} $^{13}/_{16}''$ x 9-½″ x 12′	Box bottom.

Hardware

8	Wagon box strap bolts	15-½″ shank $^{7}/_{16}''$ x 3-¼″	Sides.
2	Tail rods complete with washers and nuts	⅜″ x 3′ 2-¾″	Ends.
2	Rub irons, round iron	¾″ diameter	Sides of box.
4	Brace bolts	$^{7}/_{16}''$ x 12″	Sides of box.
2	Iron braces	¼″ x ⅞″ x 11-½″	Foot rest.
2	Beveled box binding iron	⅛″ x ¾″ x 12′	Top sides.
2	Beveled box binding iron	⅛″ x ¾″ x 3′	Top ends.
12	Oval head box rivets	¼″ x 1-¼″	Center strap bolts, 3 each.
8	Oval head box rivets	¼″ x 2″	Front strap bolts, 2 each.
8	Oval head box rivets	¼″ x 2″	Rear strap bolts, 4 each.

11

No. Pieces	Material	Dimensions	Where Used
4	Oval head box rivets	¼″ x 2″	Front end board.
4	Oval head box rivets	¼″ x 1-¼″	Foot rest.
4	Oval head box rivets	¼″ x 1-⅝″	Side braces.
42	F.H.B. screws	1″ No. 7	Top binding sides and ends.
24	F.H.B. screws	1-½″ No. 10	Cleats on end board.
6	F.H.B. screws	1-½″ No. 10	Foot rest.
24	F.H.B. screws	1-½″ No. 10	Cleats on side boards.
80	F.H.B screws	1-½″ No. 10	Bottom and steps.
8	Carriage bolts	¼″ x 1-½″	Rub irons.

Small quantity of white lead, color, linseed oil and turpentine for priming coat.

1 quart auto enamel for finishing coat.

Construction.—1. Using 1-¾″ x 3-¾″ N. C. pine (2″ x 4″ nominal size) square and cut two end cross pieces and two center cross pieces as shown in details of cross piece.

2. Bore holes and chamfer ends as indicated in details.

3. Joint the edge of one of the boards to be used as floor boards and with the square lay out the positions of the center and cross pieces and end cuts using spacing as shown in side view of box.

4. Fasten center and end cross pieces in position temporarily on the under side of the board. The ends of center cross pieces should project 6″ and end cross pieces should be placed flush with edge. Use the steel square to insure placing the cross piece at right angles with edge of bottom.

5. Complete the bottom, square and cut off ends. Line across over the cross pieces, drill holes and drive screws for permanent fastening, and place on saw horses for further work.

6. Square and cut two side boards ¹³/₁₆″ x 13″ x 12′ long.

7. Using ¹³/₁₆″ x 2″ maple, square and cut eight pieces 13″ long for end cleats. Chamfer top end and outside edge as shown in detail.

8. Square lines across the ends of side pieces and fasten end cleats in position as shown in side view. Leave opening for end board a loose fit for the end board.

9. Make strap bolts as described in Chapter XV and place in position in cross pieces.

10. Place sides in position against strap bolts and mark positions of rivet holes on side boards.

11. Bore holes, remove strap bolts from box bottom and rivet to sides.

12. Place sides in position on box bottom.

13. Using ¹³/₁₆″ x 4″ ash, construct step as shown in detail.

14. Make four wagon box side braces as described in Chapter XV and place in position through step. Drill hole through strap bolt and box at top end and fasten with rivet listed.

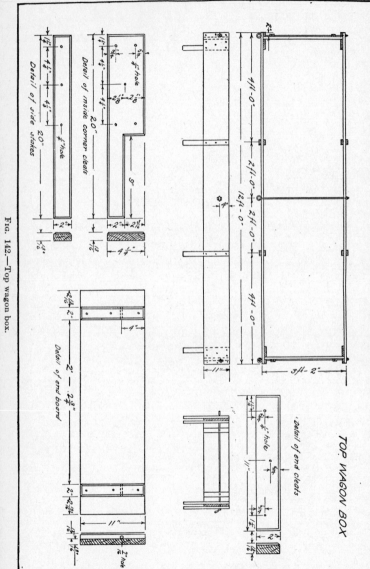

Fig. 142.—Top wagon box.

15. Tighten nuts on strap bolts and braces and using square as guide adjust the box side until it stands at right angles with the bottom.

16. Make rear end board complete with cross cleats as shown in detail of end board and adjust to free sliding fit.

17. Make front end board to same dimensions.

18. Construct foot rest as shown in detail and bevel lower edge to angle indicated.

19. Using the sliding tee bevel set at the same angle mark and cut the tops of the front end board cleats to fit foot rest.

20. Fasten foot rest in place with screws driven from the inside.

21. Make foot rest braces as described in Chapter XV and place in position beneath foot rest. Mark and drill holes in foot rest and end board and rivet braces in place with rivets listed.

22. Make tail rods, nuts and washers as described in Chapter XV, Jobs 9, 10 and 11.

23. Place end boards in position and bore holes for tail rods. Place tail rod washers in position on box sides, insert tail rods and tighten up.

24. Make two rub irons as directed in Chapter XV, Job 12. Place box in position on wagon and locate proper position for rub irons. Bore holes and bolt rub irons in place.

25. Locate position for cross cleats straddling rear bolster and fasten them in position.

26. Cut to length, mark with center punch, and drill and countersink holes in box binding. Holes should be spaced about 10″ apart.

27. Fasten binding to top edge of wagon box with screws listed.

28. With the bolt clippers or hack saw, cut off all projecting ends of bolts.

29. Smooth up work, shellac knots and sappy places if any, and apply priming coat of lead paint with pigment added to secure approximate color desired.

30. When dry sand lightly, putty defects, dust off and apply coat of auto enamel of the color desired. Inside of box may be painted contrasting color, using lead and oil paint.

31. Stencil farm name on box side, if desired.

Job. 10.—**Top Wagon Box.**—The top box is used to place on top of the ordinary wagon box, making it deeper, when hauling light but bulky material (Fig. 142).

Stock List

No. Pieces	Material	Dimensions	Where Used
2	Pine or basswood S2S	$^{13}/_{16}″$ x 11″ x 12′	Sides.
2	Pine or basswood S2S	$^{13}/_{16}″$ x 11″ x 3′ 0–⅜″	End boards.
4	Maple S2S	$^{13}/_{16}″$ x 2″ x 11″	End cleats.
4	Maple S2S	$^{13}/_{16}″$ x 2″ x 11″	Cleats on end boards.
8	White ash S2S	$^{13}/_{16}″$ x 2″ x 20″	Side stakes.
4	White ash S2S	$^{13}/_{16}″$ x4-¼″ x 20″	Corner stakes.

No. Pieces	Material	Dimensions	Where Used
		Hardware	
3	Tail rods complete	⅜" x 3' 2–¾"	Ends and middle.
2	Beveled box binding iron	⅛" x ¾" x 12'	Top sides.
2	Beveled box binding iron	⅛" x ¾" x 3'	Top ends.
20	Oval head wagon box rivets with burrs	¼" x 2"	Corner stakes.
12	Oval head wagon box rivets with burrs	¼" x 2"	End cleats.
12	Oval head wagon box rivets with burrs	¼" x 2–¾"	Side stakes.
12	F. H. B. screws	1–½" No. 10	End boards.
12	F. H. B. screws	1" No. 8	Tail rod washers.
42	F. H. B. screws	1" No. 7	Top binding.

Lead, oil, turpentine and pigment for priming coat.
One pint auto enamel for finishing coat.

Construction.—1. Select two straight-grained pine or basswood boards S2S. By jointing or ripping reduce to width and square and cut off to length indicated.

2. Using maple make four end cleats as shown in detail of end cleats.

3. Clamp in position on side boards, bore holes and rivet in place.

4. From white ash make four corner stakes to the dimensions shown in detail of inside corner cleats.

5. Clamp in position on side board, leaving a free sliding fit for end board, bore holes and rivet in place, using rivets listed.

6. Make eight side stakes from white ash as shown in detail of side stakes. Clamp in position as shown in plan. Bore holes and rivet in place with the rivets listed.

7. Make two end boards as shown in detail of end boards.

8. Place in position between side boards and mark and bore holes for tail rods.

9. Make three wagon box rods complete with washers and nuts as described in Chapter XV, Jobs 9, 10 and 11.

10. Fasten washers in position with screws listed, insert rods and tighten up.

11. Cut to length, drill and countersink beveled box binding iron for top edges of box. Drill screw holes about 10" apart.

12. Fasten beveled binding iron to top of box with screws listed.

13. Smooth up work. Cover knots and sappy places, if any, with shellac and apply priming coat of lead paint.

14. When dry, sand lightly, putty defects and apply finishing coat of automobile enamel of color desired.

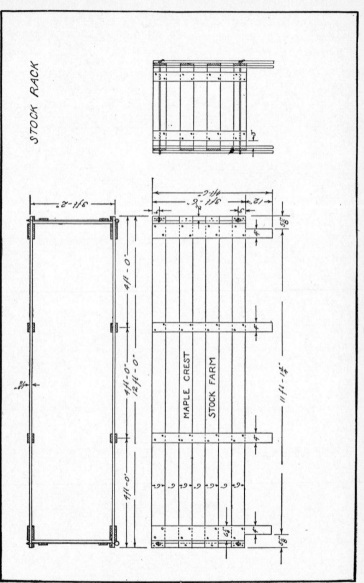

Fig. 143.—Stock rack.

Job. 11.—**Stock Rack.**—The stock rack shown is designed for use on top of an ordinary wagon box for marketing calves and other livestock. It can also be used for hauling light, bulky material (Fig. 143).

Stock List

No. Pieces	Material	Dimensions	Where Used
8	Spruce S2S	$^{13}/_{16}''$ x 6″ x 12′	Sides.
8	Spruce S2S	$^{13}/_{16}''$ x 6″ x 3′ 0–⅜″	Ends.
8	Spruce S2S	$^{13}/_{16}''$ x 6–¼″ x 4′ 6″	End stakes.
8	Spruce S2S	$^{13}/_{16}''$ x 4″ x 4′ 6″	Center stakes.
4	Maple S2S	$^{13}/_{16}''$ x 2″ x 3′ 6″	Cross cleats at ends of sides.
4	Spruce S2S	$^{13}/_{16}''$ x 4″ x 3′ 6″	Cross pieces on end gates.

Hardware

64	Carriage bolts with washers	$^{5}/_{16}''$ x 2–¾″	Fastening for stakes and side pieces.
24	Carriage bolts with washers	$^{5}/_{16}''$ x 1–¾″	Fastening for end cleats and side pieces.
32	Carriage bolts with washers	$^{5}/_{16}''$ x 1–¾″	End gates.
4	Wagon box rods	⅜″ x 3′ 2–¾″	Top and bottom of end gates.
16	F.H.B. screws	1″ No. 8	Fastening for wagon box rod washers.

Small quantity lead, color, oil and turpentine for priming. 1 quart automobile enamel for finishing.

Construction.—1. Select 8 straight-grained spruce boards $^{13}/_{16}''$ in thickness and of a width sufficient to joint to 6″ wide.

2. Joint edges and lay side by side in groups of 4, each group representing one side of the rack.

3. Square the ends of each group of boards and cut to 12′ long.

4. Cut 4 pieces of $^{13}/_{16}''$ x 2″ maple 3′ 6″ long, and bolt to inside surface of side pieces flush with the ends, as shown in drawing, using bolts listed. Keep work at right angles by frequent tests with the steel square and space side boards equally while doing this work.

5. Make 8 end stakes from spruce $^{13}/_{16}''$ x 6–¼″ x 4′ 6″ cutting out the bottom as shown in drawing. Bolt these in position shown 7⅞″ from end cleats forming a groove to hold the end gate.

6. Make 8 center stakes $^{13}/_{16}''$ x 4″ x 4′ 6″ and bolt in position shown using bolts listed for the purpose.

7. Square and cut the other side to length and bore and bolt up in the same way.

8. Square and cut 8 pieces of $^{13}/_{16}''$ x 6″ spruce 3′ 0–⅜″ long for end gates.

9. Square and cut 4 pieces of $^{13}/_{16}''$ x 4″ spruce 3′ 6″ long for cross pieces on end gates.

10. Assemble end gates using bolts listed. Place cross pieces 3'' from ends of end gates. Use square when assembling to maintain right angle and see that spacing of horizontal pieces corresponds to spacing of horizontal pieces in sides.

11. Make 4 gate rods, nuts and washers as described in Chapter XV.

12. Locate position of holes for gate rods. Bore holes in both sides and cross pieces of end gates, attach washers to sides and assemble rack.

13. Adjust parts to fit and cut off projecting bolt ends with bolt clippers or hack saw.

14. Remove gate rods and apply priming coat of lead paint to rack.

15. When dry apply finish coat of auto enamel or other good outdoor gloss paint to match box. Letter, if desired.

Job 12.—Stock Loading Chute.

—It is frequently necessary to load live animals on a wagon for transfer from farm to farm or for marketing. The chute shown, mounted on skids, can be used at different places about the farm, and permits loading with ease to the men and safety to the animals (Fig. 144).

Stock List

No. Pieces	Material	Dimensions	Where Used
2	N. C. Pine S4S	1-¾ '' x 3-¾ '' x 7'	Skids.
3	N. C. Pine S4S	1-¾ '' x 3-¾ '' x 3' 5½ ''	Cross sills.
2	N. C. Pine S4S	1-¾ '' x 3-¾ '' x 5' 6''	Front uprights.
2	N. C. Pine S4S	1-¾ '' x 3-¾ '' x 4' 5-¼ ''	Center uprights.
2	N. C. Pine S4S	1-¾ '' x 3-¾ '' x 3' 4-½ ''	Rear uprights.
2	N. C. Pine S4S	1-¾ '' x 3-¾ '' x 3' 5½ ''	Upper cross sills.
4	N. C. Pine S4S	1-¾ '' x 8-½ '' x 7' 9''	Floor.
9	N. C. Pine S4S	¹³/₁₆ '' x 2'' x 2' 10''	Floor cleats.
6	N. C. Pine S4S	¹³/₁₆ '' x 6'' x 7' 8-⅝ ''	Sides.
2	N. C. Pine S4S	¹³/₁₆ '' x 2'' x 3' 11-¾ ''	Diagonal braces.

Hardware

8	Carriage b o l t s with washers	⅜ '' x 4''	Front and center lower cross sills.
2	Carriage b o l t s with washers	⅜ '' x 6''	Rear cross sills.
8	Carriage b o l t s with washers	⅜ '' x 6''	Bottom end, front and center uprights.
4	Carriage b o l t s with washers	⅜ '' x 4''	Bottom end rear uprights.
8	Carriage b o l t s with washers	⅜ '' x 4''	Upper front and center cross sills.
4	Carriage b o l t s with washers	⅜ '' x 3''	Diagonal braces.
36	Common nails	20d	Floor.
54	Common nails	10d	Side boards.
54	Common nails	8d	Floor cleats.

Small quantity of lead, oil, turpentine, and color for priming.
1 quart of outdoor paint of color desired for finish coat.

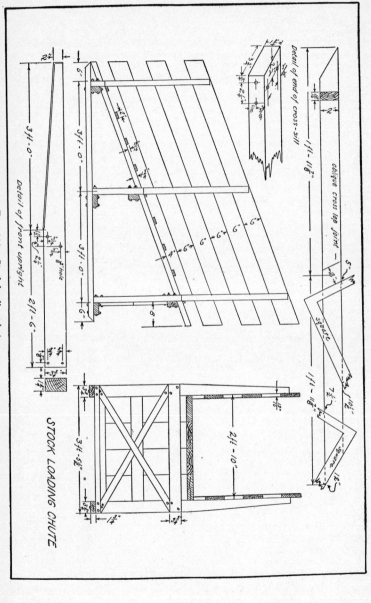

Fig. 144.—Stock loading chute.

Construction.—1. Select two straight 2″ x 4″ pieces S2S (actual size 1-¾″ x 3-¾″), and lay out and cut two skids 7′ in length. Cut angle at front and rear at 45 degrees.

2. Square and cut two pieces 1-¾″ x 3-¾″ x 3′ 5-½″ for front and center lower cross sills and bore ends as shown in detail of ends of cross sills.

3. Mark and bore holes in skids and bolt center and front sills in position. Test with square to see that cross sills are fastened at right angles to skids.

4. Make two uprights to dimensions shown in detail of front uprights. Bolt to lower front cross sill with bolts listed.

5. Make two center uprights 1¾″ x 3′-¾″, 4′ 5-¼″ long. Tapered portion is made the same as shown in detail of front uprights. Square portion at bottom is 1′ 5-¼″ long. Bore and bolt in position on center lower cross sill.

6. Cut two rear uprights 1-¾″ x 3-¾″ x 3′ 4-½″. Taper upper three feet as shown in detail of front upright.

7. Cut rear cross sill 3′ 5-½″ long. Set sliding tee bevel at 3″ on the blade and 8-¼″ on the tongue of the steel square, with the beam of the tee bevel against the blade of the square, and with the jointer, bevel one edge of the cross sill to this angle. Bore and bolt in position with rear uprights as shown.

8. Prepare upper center and front cross sill 1-¾″ x 3-¾″ x 3′ 5-½″ and bevel to same angle as directed for rear sill.

9. Bore and bolt front sill in position with upper edge 2′ 7″ above under side of skid.

10. Lay straight edge or stretch line from top of upper front sill to top rear sill and adjust center sill to this line. Bore holes and bolt in place.

11. Make sure that uprights are perpendicular to skids; place floor in position and nail to cross sills with 20d nails.

12. Make two diagonal braces to go across front end as shown in detail, cross lap joint in center should be half the depth of material used for braces. Bore holes and fasten in place with bolts listed.

13. Square across ends of floor and cut to same angle used to bevel upper edges of cross sills.

14 Joint edges of boards used for sides and nail in place with spacing shown. Use 10d nails.

15. Mark ends at same angle used for beveling top edges of sills and cut off.

16. Prepare floor cleats and nail in place with 8d nails.

17. Clip off projecting bolt ends.

18. Apply priming coat of lead paint.

19. When dry apply finish coat of outdoor paint of color desired.

Job 13.—Hay Rack.

The rack shown is designed for hauling loose hay and grain. The tail board is made low, permitting its use with the loader while the flat upper surface adapts it to handling baled hay and similar material (Fig. 145).

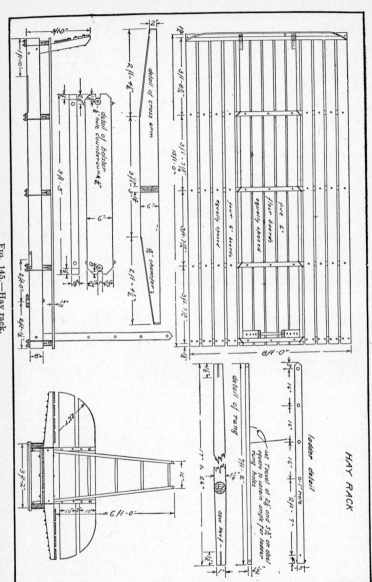

FIG. 145.—Hay rack.

Stock List

No. Pieces	Material	Dimensions	Where Used
2	N. C. pine S4S	1-¾″ x 8″ x 15′	Sills.
5	N. C. pine S4S	1-¾″ x 6″ x 8′	Cross arms.
13	Spruce S2S	¹³/₁₆″ x 6″ x 15′	Floor boards.
2	White ash S4S	1-½″ x 3″ x 7′ 2″	Ladder.
4	Split white ash	1-¼″ x 1-¼″ x 17″ to 26″	Ladder rungs.
2	Spruce S2S	¹³/₁₆″ x 10″ x 8′	Tail board.
2	White ash	1-½″ x 3″ x 3′	Tail board.
1	Oak or maple S4S	1-¾″ x 6″ x 3′ 3″	Bolster.
5	White ash	¹³/₁₆″ x 3″ x 3′ 4″	Cross pieces beneath sills.
5	White ash	¹³/₁₆″ x 2″ x 2′ 11-½″	Supports beneath floor.

Hardware

No. Pieces	Material	Dimensions	Where Used
10	Clip bolts complete	⅜″ x 15-½″	Fastening for cross arms and sills.
15	Carriage bolts with washers	⅜″ x 8-½″	Center floor.
4	Carriage bolts with washers	⅜″ x 3-½″	Outside floor boards.
10	Carriage bolts with washers	⅜″ x 4″	
4	Carriage bolts with washers	⅜″ x 4-½″	Second row of floor boards.
10	Carriage bolts with washers	⅜″ x 5″	
4	Carriage bolts with washers	⅜″ x 5-½″	Third row of floor boards.
10	Carriage bolts with washers	⅜″ x 6″	
4	Carriage bolts with washers	⅜″ x 6-½″	Fourth row of floor boards.
10	Carriage bolts with washers	⅜″ x 7″	
8	Carriage bolts with washers	⅜″ x 4-½″	Tail board.
4	Carriage bolts with washers	⅜″ x 3-½″	Tail board supports.
2	Carriage bolts with washers	½″ x 9-¾″	Bolster.
2	Carriage bolts with washers	⅜″ x 6-½″	Bolster.
2	Carriage bolts with washers	⅜″ x 3-½″	Bottom of front ladder.
2	Carriage bolts with washers	⅜″ x 5-¼″	Fastening between ladder and front cross arm.

No. Pieces	Material	Dimensions	Where Used
2	Carriage bolts with washers	$5/16''$ x 3-1/2''	Bottom of ladder sides.
4	Carriage bolts	$5/16''$ x 2-1/2''	Rub irons.
8	F.H.B. screws	2'' No. 14	Wear irons over rear bolster.

Small quantity of lead paint for priming coat.
1 quart of outdoor paint of color desired for finish coat.

Construction.—1. Select five straight-grained pieces of 2'' x 6'' N. C. pine, or spruce S4S, and lay out and work to shape shown in detail of cross arm.

2. Square and cut two pieces of straight-grained 2'' x 8'' N. C. pine S4S, 15' in length for sills.

3. Place sills in position on wagon. Place cross arms on top and adjust to position where they will not interfere with wheels. Make spaces between as nearly equal as possible.

4. Make clip bolts for fastening cross arms to sills as directed in Chapter XV, Job 7.

5. Place clip bolts in position over cross arms.

6. Using $13/16''$ white ash, make five pieces 3'' wide by 3' 4'' long. Place beneath sill, allowing 1'' projection at each end and mark and bore holes for clip bolts.

7. Place end of clip bolts through the holes so bored, see that cross arms are in position at right angles to bed of rack and tighten up bolts.

8. Joint edges of $13/16''$ spruce boards S2S to 6'' wide. Square and cut to 15' long, and bolt to sides of rack as shown. Fasten boards temporarily with nails, boring holes and bolting after assembly is complete.

9. Using 1-1/2'' x 3'' white ash, lay out and construct two ladder sides as shown in ladder detail.

10. Make four ladder rungs as shown in detail of rung, from split white ash. Split out and reduce to 1-1/4'' square, remove corners with draw knife, making the stick octagonal and finally finish round. Taper from middle to 1'' diameter at ends and make saw kerf for wedge as shown. Exact lengths of rungs may be obtained by laying the drawing of the ladder out full size on wall board or smooth floor and taking measurements direct.

11. Assemble ladder. Bore holes and bolt in position with bolts listed.

12. Construct two tail board supports of white ash 1-1/2'' x 3'' x 3' long and bolt to rear ends of sills in position shown.

13. Fasten tail boards temporarily in place and bore holes and bolt in position.

14. Using radius shown, round off end and cut to shape with compass saw.

15. Cut five boards $13/16''$ x 6'' x 15' for center floor boards. Match two outer boards to fit around tail board supports and front ladder, and nail boards temporarily in place, spacing them equally.

16. Cut five pieces of $13/16''$ ash 2' 11-1/2'' long to fit between sill pieces on under side of cross arms. Fasten them temporarily in place and bore three holes through each cross arm as shown. Insert bolts and fasten in place.

17. Bore holes for bolts in side floor, using two bolts at the end of each board and one through the center cross arms. Bolt in place with bolts listed.

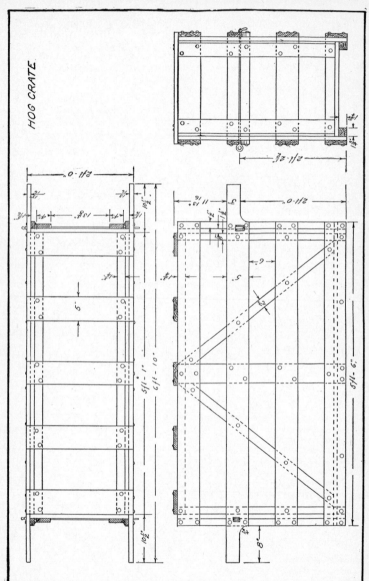

Fig. 146.—Hog crate.

18. Make rub irons as directed in Chapter XV. Locate position, bore holes and bolt in place.

19. Make wear irons for rear bolster as directed in Chapter XV, Job 6. Locate position and fasten in place with screws listed, setting the iron flush with the lower edge of the sill.

20. Locate front bolster and bolt in position. Countersink bolts in bolster so that smooth surface is presented to top of wagon bolster.

21. Cut off projecting bolt ends and smooth up work.

22. Apply coat of lead paint for priming.

23. When dry apply finish coat of outdoor paint of color desired.

Job 14.—**Hog Crate.**—It is frequently necessary to move breeding stock about the farm or to ship such animals by rail. The hog crate shown provides a convenient method of handling such animals in shipment (Fig. 146).

Stock List

No. Pieces	Material	Dimensions	Where Used
6	Spruce S2S	$^{13}/_{16}''$ x 5'' x 5' 6''	Sides.
2	Spruce S2S	$^{13}/_{16}''$ x 5'' x 6' 10''	Handles.
2	Spruce S2S	1-¾'' x 1-¾'' x 5' 6''	Sills.
2	Spruce S2S	1-¾'' x 1-¾'' x 5' 1''	Top frame members.
13	D and M Spruce	$^{13}/_{16}''$ x 3-½'' x 1' 10-⅜''	Floor.
2	Spruce S2S	$^{13}/_{16}''$ x 5'' x 3' 2''	Center upright.
4	Spruce S2S	$^{13}/_{16}''$ x 2'' x 3' 8-½''	Diagonal braces.
8	White ash S2S	$^{13}/_{16}''$ x 1-½'' x 3' 2''	Door guides.
4	Spruce S2S	$^{13}/_{16}''$ x 3'' x 2' 11-½''	Upright pieces in doors.
6	Spruce S2S	$^{13}/_{16}''$ x 5'' x 1' 10-¼''	Cross pieces of door.
2	Spruce S2S	$^{13}/_{16}''$ x 2-$^{7}/_{16}''$ x 1' 10-¼''	Lower cross pieces of doors.
5	Spruce S2S	$^{13}/_{16}''$ x 5'' x 2'	Top.

Hardware

22	Carriage bolts with washers	$^{5}/_{16}''$ x 3-¾''	Sills and top frame.
92	Carriage bolts with washers	$^{5}/_{16}''$ x 2''	Sides and doors.
20	Carriage bolts with washers	$^{5}/_{16}''$ x 3''	Top.
2	End gate rods complete with washers and nuts	⅜'' x 2' 1''	Ends.
16	F.H.B. screws	⅞'' No. 7	End gate rod washers.

1 lb. Common nails 8d Floor.
1 Pint lead paint for priming.
1 Pint outdoor paint of color desired, for finish coat.

Construction.—1. Rip and joint $^{13}/_{16}''$ ash to 1-½'' wide. Square and cut eight pieces of this material 3' 2'' long for door guides.

2. Using $^{13}/_{16}''$ spruce 5'' wide, square and cut two pieces 3' 2'' long for center uprights.

3. Using same material as for uprights, square and cut six pieces for sides.

4. From same material, lay out and make two handles using dimensions shown in side view.

5. Using 1-¾'' x 1-¾'' N. C. pine, square and cut two pieces 5' 6'' long for sills.

6. From same material, square and cut two pieces 5' 1'' long for top frame members.

7. Assemble side temporarily with small nails left with heads projecting for easy removal. See that proper spacing is secured and that cross pieces are at right angles to horizontal side pieces by tests with steel square while assembling.

8. Bore holes and fasten sides together with bolts listed. Use spacing blocks between sill and side pieces at the bottom.

9. Joint, gauge to width, and rip out 2'' material for diagonal braces.

10. Cut the diagonal braces. Use 13-⅛'' on the tongue and 17-¾'' on the blade to secure these cuts. Cut along tongue for bottom cut and along blade for plumb or top cut. Both length and angle of cut can be obtained by placing brace in position and marking direct, if desired.

11. Fasten diagonal braces in position.

12. Make two doors as shown in end view. Space cross pieces to coincide.

13. Make two end gate rods as directed in Chapter XV, bore holes, attach washers, and put rods in place.

14. Cut the top boards and bolt in place spacing them equally.

15. Smooth up work and give crate priming coat of lead paint.

16. When dry, give finishing coat of outdoor paint of color desired.

17. Letter with farm name if desired.

Job 15.—Sliding Farm Gate.—To protect crops, openings in farm fences must be protected by gates strong enough to resist stock, and of such design that they are not easily opened by cattle rubbing against them. A neat appearance and convenience in opening are other desirable features (Fig. 147).

Stock List

No. Pieces	Material	Dimensions	Where Used
5	N. C. pine or spruce	$^{13}/_{16}''$ x 5'' x 15'	Horizontal members.
1	N. C. pine or spruce	$^{13}/_{16}''$ x 4'' x 15'	Top.
6	N. C. pine or spruce	$^{13}/_{16}''$ x 5'' x 4' 5-¼''	Uprights.
2	N. C. pine or spruce	$^{13}/_{16}''$ x 3'' x 8' 2''	Diagonal braces.

Hardware

35	Carriage bolts with washers	¼'' x 3''	Uprights and diagonal braces.
1 lb.	Common nails	8d	Top.
4	Staples	6-½'' x 6-½''	Gate posts.
1	Quart lead paint		

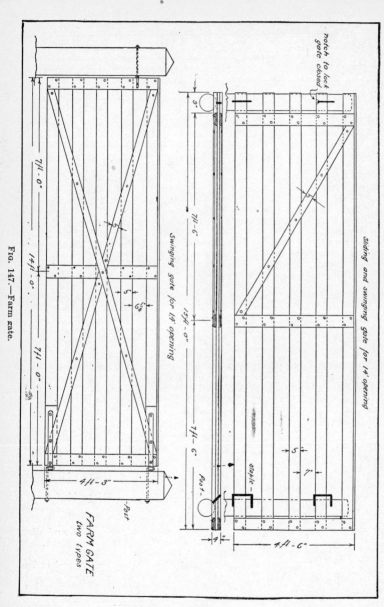

Fig. 147.—Farm gate.

Construction.—1. Select five pieces of $^{13}/_{16}''$ N. C. pine or spruce, 5″ wide and smooth edges with jointer. Square and cut to 15′ long.

2. Square and cut six pieces of the same material for center and end uprights.

3. Arrange in position shown on floor and nail temporarily in place making sure that spacing between boards is correct and that uprights are perpendicular to horizontal pieces by testing with steel square.

4. Bore holes for bolts.

5. Draw nails and coat meeting surfaces with lead paint or wood preservative.

6. Replace, insert bolts, and tighten nuts.

7. Prepare material for diagonal braces. Obtain length and angle of cut by laying it in place upon gate and marking along edge of upright. Cut to shape and bolt in place, coating meeting surfaces with lead paint or wood preservative.

8. Cut top piece to length, apply paint or preservative to meeting surfaces and nail in place.

9. Cut notch in lower side of one of the horizontal bars to engage staple and prevent opening by rubbing.

10. Make staples as directed in Chapter XV, Job 3.

11. Clip off projecting bolt ends and apply priming coat of paint.

12. When dry, apply finish coat of lead paint with pigment of desired color added.

Job 16.—**The Swinging gate** is used about the farm buildings, where its better appearance makes it more desirable. It is not adapted for use where much loose snow is encountered (Fig. 147).

Stock List

No. Pieces	Material	Dimensions	Where Used
5	N. C. pine or spruce	$^{13}/_{16}''$ x 5″ x 14′	Horizontal bars.
1	N. C. pine or spruce	$^{13}/_{16}''$ x 4″ x 14′	Top.
4	N. C. pine or spruce	$^{13}/_{16}''$ x 5″ x 4′ 2–¼″	End uprights.
4	N. C. pine or spruce	$^{13}/_{16}''$ x 5″ x 1′ 11–¾″	Center uprights.
2	N. C. pine or spruce	$^{13}/_{16}''$ x 3″ x 13′ 10″	Diagonal braces.
4	N. C. pine or spruce	$^{13}/_{16}''$ x 3″ x 6′ 10″	Diagonal braces.
4	N. C. pine or spruce	$^{13}/_{16}''$ x 5″ x 1′ 9″	Hinge blocks.
Hardware			
35	Carriage bolts with washers	¼″ x 3″	Upright and diagonal braces.
6	Carriage bolts	⅜″ x 3–½″	Hinges.
2	Strap hinges, complete	⅜″ x 2″ x 2′ 3″	Right hand end of gate.
1	Gate latch, complete	5–½″	Left hand end of gate.

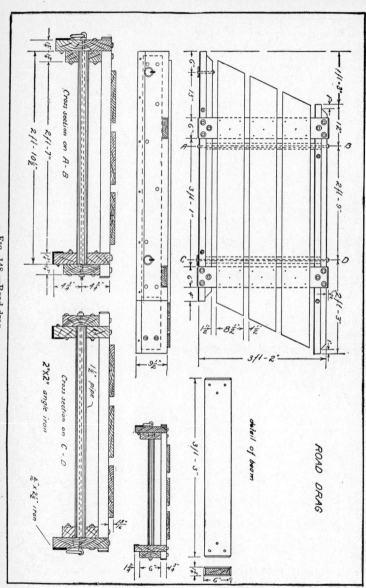

Fig. 148—Road drag.

Construction.—1. Smooth up edges of boards selected for horizontal members of gate with jointer and square and cut to length 14'.

2. From same material, square and cut four pieces 4' 2-¼" long for end uprights.

3. Apply paint or wood preservative to meeting surfaces and assemble end uprights and horizontal members. Fasten temporarily, with nails, adjust to square position and correct spacing, bore holes, insert bolts and tighten up.

4. Prepare material ¹³/₁₆" x 3" wide for diagonal brace. Obtain length and angle of cut for diagonal brace by placing it in position on the gate and marking along uprights. Cut to size, apply paint or preservative to meeting surfaces and fasten temporarily in place with small nails.

5. In the same way cut and apply the short diagonal braces.

6. Using 5" material, cut 2 short pieces for the center upright and fasten in position after painting or applying preservative.

7. Turn the gate over and in the same way cut and apply braces and center uprights to this side. Full length diagonal brace should cross the first one put on forming a letter x, rather than running parallel with it.

8. Prepare top piece 4" wide and nail in place after coating meeting surfaces with paint or preservative.

9. Bore holes, insert bolts and tighten up.

10. Make strap hinges as directed in Chapter XV, Job 4, and attach to gate with bolts listed.

11. Clip off projecting bolt ends and smooth up work.

12. Apply a priming coat of lead paint.

13. When dry, apply finish coat of lead paint colored as desired.

Job 17.—**The King road drag,** by its scraping and compressing action, preserves a well crowned, smooth and impervious surface upon dirt roads, lessening both mud and dust. If used at intervals following rains during the summer, dirt road surfaces are much improved. The one shown is designed for use upon the roads of the farm. A chain is hitched between the two rings and the team attached to them at such point as gives the angle desired to the drag (Fig. 148).

Stock List

No. Pieces	Material	Dimensions	Where Used
2	White oak S2S	1-¾" x 9-½" x 6'	Front and rear scrapers.
2	White oak S2S	1-¾" x 6" x 5'-10"	Reinforcement for front and rear scrapers.
2	White oak S2S	1-¾" x 6" x 3' 3"	Beams.
3	N. C. pine S2S	¹³/₁₆" x 8-½" x 6' 2"	Floor boards.

No. Pieces	Material	Dimensions	Where Used
		Hardware	
16	Carriage b o l t s with washers	$^7/_{16}''$ x 4''	Front and rear reinforcement.
4	Carriage b o l t s with washers	$^7/_{16}''$ x 9–½''	Front and rear scrapers.
12	Lag screws with washers	$^7/_{16}''$ x 6''	Beams.
12	Sleigh shoe bolts with washers	⅜'' x 2–½''	Front and rear iron plates.
2	Galvanized i r o n pipe	1–½'' dia. x 2' 10–½''	Cross braces.
1	Eye bolt with ring and washers	½'' x 3' –3''	Tension rod at C–D.
1	Eye bolt with ring and washers	$^7/_{16}''$ x 5''	Inside end, front scraper.
1	Rod threaded both ends with nut and washers	½'' x 3' 3–½''	Tension rod- at A–B.
1	Flat iron bar	$^5/_{16}''$ x 2–½'' x 6'	Front scraper.
1	Angle iron	2'' x 2'' x 6'	Rear scraper.
30	Common nails	8d	Floor.

Construction.—1. Joint edges of oak planks to be used as scrapers and square and cut to length, 6'.

2. Joint the edges of 6'' oak plank and lay out and construct two beams as shown in detail. Run a ¼'' chamfer around each end.

3. Gauge a line 1–¾'' from the top edge along the inside surface of both front and rear scrapers.

4. With square lay out gains, housing ends of beams at intervals shown. Obtain width of gains directly from ends of beams to insure a snug fit.

5. Cut reinforcing planks from 1–¾'' x 6'' oak 5' 10'' long. Cut ends beveled at 45 degrees.

6. Bore holes and bolt in position with upper edge coinciding with gauge line.

7. With calipers obtain outside diameter of 1–½'' pipe. Set expansive bit to this diameter and bore holes housing ends of pipe in rear scraper and front reinforcing plank. Continue holes clear through with half-inch bit for tension rod as indicated in cross section.

8. Make rods and eye bolts for road drag as directed in Chapter XV, Job 16.

9. Assemble front and rear scrapers with pipe braces and rods.

10. Place beams in position with chamfered ends projecting ½'' front and rear. Mark and bore holes for lag screws, making portion of hole in scrapers and reinforcing planks small enough to grip thread of lag bolt. Apply grease to lag screws, put in place with washer beneath head and turn up tightly.

11. Cut to length, drill and countersink flat iron bar used as front scraping edge and angle iron used for pulverizer as shown in Chapter XV, Job 15.

12. Mark holes on front and rear scraper, bore holes and bolt in place with bolts listed. Cutting edge should be dropped ¼″ at outer end of scraper.

13. Bore hole and place short eye bolt in position at outer end of drag.

14. Place floor boards in position and nail in place with 8d nails.

15. Lay a straight edge across from corner to corner, mark and cut at the angle shown.

16. Clean up work and apply a coat of lead priming paint.

17. When dry apply finish coat, using outdoor paint of color desired.

Supplementary Projects and Repairs

1. Making new slats for hayloader.
2. Making new slats for binder reel.
3. Making new arms for binder reel.
4. Putting new handle in fork or shovel.
5. Grinding mowing machine sections.
6. Removing old sections.
7. Putting on new sections.
8. Making and fitting new pitman.
9. Making and fitting new swath board.
10. Putting a new reach in a wagon.
11. Repairing wagon or implement tongue.
12. Making a new wagon or implement tongue.
13. Putting new slats in a manure spreader.
14. Putting new sill in manure spreader.
15. Construction of wood-hauling rack for sled.
16. Construction of wood-measuring rack.
17. Repair of truck stake body.
18. Marker for row crops.
19. Construction of hotbed.
20. Construction of cold frame.
21. Construction of grapevine trellis.
22. Construction of wire fence.
23. Repair of fence.
24. Repair of roof.
25. Shingling a roof.
26. Hanging a screen or storm door.
27. Applying weather strips.
28. Fitting storm sash or screens.
29. Construction of storm house.
30. Repair of steps.
31. Construction of new steps.
32. Repair of porch railing.
33. Construction of a feed bin.
34. Construction of a stone boat or jumper.
35. Construction of hog-scalding device.
36. Construction of derrick for hay stacking.

CHAPTER XIII

PAINTING AND GLAZING

THE barn and outbuildings of the modern farm represent a considerable investment, upon which depreciation should be reduced to a minimum. A large sum is also invested in machines and implements for field work. The present yearly depreciation is estimated at 10 per cent, and is largely due to weathering rather than wear. A protective coating of paint lessens this depreciation.

Effects of Paint.—A frequent use of a well selected paint forms a waterproof covering, which tends to prevent rusting and decay caused by moisture. The operator will also give a well painted implement better care.

Painted surfaces are more easily kept clean, improving sanitation. Lighting is improved by the use of light colored paints.

Composition of Paints.—A paint consists of a combination of a base, vehicle, and pigment, designed to give protection and to beautify the object to which it is applied. A solvent and drier is sometimes added.

Base.—The base is the portion of the paint designed to give body and covering capacity to the paint. White lead is the standard base for out-of-door paints.

Vehicle.—The liquid in which the base is carried is called the vehicle. Linseed oil is the vehicle used in first-class grades of commercial paints, because it has the property of absorbing oxygen and hardening to a tough, horn-like surface.

Linseed oil is obtainable in two conditions: " raw oil " and " boiled oil." The latter is prepared by heating and adding certain chemicals, making it darker, thicker, and more rapid in drying. Boiled oil is generally used in inside work. Raw oil is lighter colored and somewhat slower in drying. It is considered more durable and is usually specified for outside work.

Pigment is the finely ground color used in paint to give it the color desired. It may be either in powder or paste form. The paste colors are most easily mixed with the paint. They should be mixed smoothly with turpentine before being added to the paint.

Solvent.—Turpentine, a product of the southern pine, is used in paint for the purpose of softening up the surface resins of the wood, making the paint more penetrating. It also gives the paint certain desirable properties of spreading, handling, and drying. An excess lessens durability.

Drier.—This is a thin, varnish-like liquid, called japan drier. It is mixed with paint in proportions varying from 5 to 10 per cent of the quantity of vehicle used when it is desired to make the paint dry rapidly. Certain metallic oxides are contained which serve as carriers of oxygen and hasten the oxidation of the oil with which it is mixed.

Adulterations.—The nature of paint makes the detection of an adulterant difficult without the aid of chemical analysis. For this reason only good brands should be used, and these should have the analysis plainly printed on the container. When offered paint much below the market price it is an indication of adulteration.

Mixing Paint.—A satisfactory paint for general outside use can be made by mixing fifteen pounds of paste white lead with about four-fifths of a gallon of raw oil to which drier has been added at the rate of about 5 per cent of the vehicle used. This can be considered as a standard paint and can be modified by the addition of more oil, more lead, pigment, and turpentine to meet the requirements of priming or of finishing coats. Color pigments vary and should be tried carefully.

Common Colors and Pigment Required To Make Them*

Color	Pigment to add to 100 pounds of white lead
Light Terra Cotta	40 to 50 pounds French ochre and 4 to 5 pounds Venetian red.
Tan	30 to 35 pounds raw sienna.
Bedford Stone	3 pounds raw sienna. Shade with lamp black.
Buff	15 to 20 pounds French ochre and 2 to 3 pounds medium chrome yellow.
French Gray	2 pounds raw umber. Shade with lamp black.
Ivory White	¼ pound medium chrome yellow.
Apple Green	4 to 6 pounds medium chrome green and 5 to 7 pounds medium chrome yellow.
Medium Olive	25 pounds French ochre, 6 to 7 pounds medium chrome green and a very little lamp black.
Slate	¼ pound lamp black for lightest shade. Increase black for darker shades.
Warm Drab	1–½ pounds raw umber and 2 to 3 pounds French ochre.
Cream	2 to 3 pounds of French ochre.

* Carter White Lead Company.

The white lead and oil are measured out and the lead mixed to a thin paste with a part of the oil, stirred until smooth, and the remainder of the oil is then added. After the paint has been prepared the pigment is mixed with turpentine and slowly stirred into the paint until the desired tint is obtained (Fig. 149).

Selection of Paint.—Paint for outside use can be purchased in three forms.

1. Ready prepared paste which is ready for use upon the addition of more oil.
2. Ready prepared liquid.
3. The base, vehicle, and pigment can be purchased separately and mixed on the job.

Covering Capacity.—The covering capacity of paint will vary with (1) the porosity of the surface, (2) the purity of the paint, (3) the amount of rubbing. Under average conditions a gallon of properly mixed paint will cover about 250 square feet, two coats.

Equipment for Painting.— Equipment for painting consists of suitable containers, which in the case of the prepared paints may consist of the cans in which the paint was purchased, brushes

FIG. 149.—Adding pigment to paint to tint it. The color is first mixed with turpentine and then added to paint by pouring a small quantity on a piece of cheesecloth and straining it through by twisting the ends.

for spreading, a putty knife, scraper, wire brushes, sand-paper, and dust brush for preparing the surface (Fig. 150). Where the surface to be painted is the side of a building, suitable staging and ladders are also required.

Brushes.—A round or oval brush of the size known as 6-0, gives good results in applying body colors. A 5-0 brush of the same type is used for trim. Paint may be applied faster with a flat brush, but it cannot be applied as evenly as with a round brush. Select one with long, springy bristles, securely fastened. A good dry brush is carried to dust the work before applying paint.

Smoothing the Surface.—A scraper or broad blade is used to remove paint scales that hold too closely to be removed with the dust brush. An assortment of sandpaper ranging from fine to coarse should be provided. Where an extremely smooth surface is desired, as in finishing a varnished surface, finer polishing mediums as steel wool and curled hair should be used. A putty knife should have a thin, flexible blade. It is used for filling imperfections with putty after the priming coat has been applied.

Ladders.—A light and strong extension ladder of sufficient length to reach the highest points of the gable is necessary in house

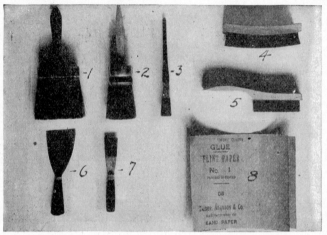

Fig. 150.—Equipment for painting: 1, dust-brush; 2, 6-0 oval paint-brush; 3, sash tool; 4 and 5, wire brushes; 6, scraper; 7, putty knife; 8, sandpaper.

painting. Short ladders, step ladders, and staging trestles are conveniences in painting the side walls lower down.

Time to Paint.—Outside painting should be done in warm weather. The paint is more liquid when warm and permits better working into the wood. If too hot, paint will " crawl." The surface to be painted must be dry. Avoid a time when insects or fuzzy materials from plants are flying about to stick in the fresh paint.

The Priming Coat.—Coat all knots and sappy places with orange shellac before putting on the priming coat of paint, to prevent pitch coming through. A relatively thin paint that will have good penetration and will dry with a flat surface is best for priming. This condition can be secured by adding a small quantity of turpentine. Never use ochre in priming.

Spreading the Paint.—Apply the paint lengthwise of the wood, working it well into all interstices and brushing it out thin and evenly. The paint should be spread in strips the whole length of the building or between vertical divisions, as doors and windows, to avoid showing a lap where the new work joins the old. When painting a clapboarded surface draw the brush along the under edge of the clapboard when first taken from the paint to insure covering the edge (Fig. 151).

Second Coat.—Permit the first coat to stand until thoroughly dry, usually from 4 to 6 days. Fill the nail holes and other imperfections with a good grade of putty, by pressing it in well.

Paint for the second coat may be somewhat thicker and should contain less turpentine. Where but two coats are to be used the turpentine should be omitted. Apply this coat as directed for the priming coat, brushing it out thin and evenly. Where the trim and body colors are different apply the light color first and work the dark color up to it, carrying both along together.

FIG. 151.—Spreading paint. The first stroke of the brush is made along the under edge of the clapboard to insure that the lower edge is painted.

The third coat should be applied after the preceding coats have become thoroughly hard. A smooth, horn-like surface is desired for the finishing coat to resist weathering, and to give a glossy appearance, therefore, no turpentine is used. It is applied in the same manner as directed for the first and second coats.

Inside Work.—The purpose of inside painting is largely decorative. The vehicle used contains a larger proportion of turpentine than should be used out-of-doors, resulting in a quick drying paint that hardens with a "flat" or dull finish. Where a porcelain-like finish is desired the so-called enamels are used. These consist of a pigment ground in varnish, which gives the brilliant surface wanted. Directions given by the manufacturer should be closely followed.

Painting Farm Equipment.—Automobile and carriage paints put out by reputable varnish companies are well suited for this work. They are obtainable in desirable colors and economical sizes, and are durable.

Preparation for Painting.—Wash the implement first with sal soda and water, using scrapers and wire brushes to remove all of the accumulated dirt possible. When dry, remove as many parts of the machine as it is convenient to do, and clean them completely of

Fig. 152.—Brush treatment of timber with wood preservative. The preservative is heated to about 200 degrees F. and applied to the dry timber with a brush. (U. S. Forest Service.)

grease, using a stiff brush and kerosene or gasoline in a tub. Do not do this work near an open flame of any kind, because of the danger of fire.

Remove all loose paint and rust by scraping, sandpapering, or by the use of a stiff wire brush, and smooth the surfaces with fine sandpaper. The dust should now be removed with a damp, lintless cloth, and the priming coat applied.

Painting.—For the primer any good oil paint can be used, and the finishing coat can be applied as soon as it has dried. If an oil paint is used for the primer the gloss can be removed and a better foothold secured for the finishing coat by sandpapering lightly.

Wood Preservation.—In farm practice much lumber is used in direct contact with the earth or in damp places, as fence posts and the sills of buildings, making the most favorable conditions for decay. Decay of lumber is produced by low forms of plant life called fungi which must have moisture, air, warmth, and food to grow. A wood preservative acts in one of the following ways or through a combination of both: (1) seals the wood, keeping out air and moisture; (2) poisons the food supply of the fungi.

Under the methods of application available on the farm coal tar creosote seems to give the best results as a wood preservative. Three methods of application are commonly used: (1) the brush treatment, (2) the dipping process, (3) the open tank process.

Brush Treatment.—This method is applicable to the sills and joists of buildings which are too large to be treated by dipping. The preservative is heated to about 200 degrees F., and applied with a

FIG. 153.—Applying wood preservative by the dipping process. The wood is placed in a bath of hot preservative maintained at about 200 degrees F. and allowed to remain for a short period of time. (U. S. Forest Service.)

brush (Fig. 152). It should be flowed on, taking care to see that all checks and other inperfections are filled.

The dipping process is adapted to the smaller timbers, such as fence posts. The wood to be treated is placed in a hot tar or creosote bath (200 degrees F.), and allowed to remain there from 5 to 15 minutes or longer (Fig. 153). It is then removed and allowed to drain. Checks and imperfections are filled if timber is seasoned.

The open tank process utilizes two tanks, in one of which the creosote or tar is maintained at a temperature of about 200 degrees F. The timbers to be treated are placed in the hot bath and allowed to stay for an hour or more, when they are removed, and placed in the cooled bath for an equal length of time (Fig. 154). This method secures the deepest penetration of any method available for farm use. To secure the best penetration possible, wood to be treated should be peeled and thoroughly seasoned.

Whitewash and Color Washes.—Whitewash is a paint made with lime as a base and water as a vehicle. It may be tinted with a pigment, and may also be given other characteristics of weather resistance, gloss, etc., by the addition of certain other ingredients.

Because of its sanitary effect, light deflecting qualities and cheapness, it is a very satisfactory paint for cellars, stables, poultry

Fig. 154.—Open tank process. (U.S. Forest Service.)

houses and other like interiors. It can be applied rapidly with broad, flat brushes, or by means of a sprayer. The following are recipes for whitewash selected from *U. S. Farmers' Bulletin 474.*

Ordinary Whitewash.—Place 10 pounds of quicklime in a pail and pour over it 2 gallons of water. Cover with an old carpet and allow to stand for an hour. Add water to bring to a proper consistency for application, the amount depending upon whether the wash is to be spread with a brush or used as a spray.

Factory Whitewash (Interiors).—(1) Place 62 pounds (1 bushel) of quicklime in a tight barrel and slake with 15 gallons of water. Keep barrel covered until steam ceases to rise. Stir occasionally to prevent scorching.

2. Stir up 2–½ pounds of rye flour in ½ gallon of cold water and add two gallons of boiling water.

3. Dissolve 2–½ pounds of rock salt in 2–½ gallons of hot water.

4. Mix (2) and (3) and pour into (1), stirring until well mixed.

Weatherproof Whitewash (Exteriors).—(1) Slake 62 pounds quicklime in 12 gallons of hot water.

2. Dissolve two pounds common table salt and one pound sulfate of zinc in two gallons of boiling water.

3. Pour (2) into (1) and add two gallons of skimmed milk and mix thoroughly.

Molasses renders the lime more soluble and causes it to better penetrate the surface to which it is applied. It is added in the proportion of one pint to five gallons of whitewash.

A gloss resembling that of oil paint can be obtained by dissolving

FIG. 155.—Cutting glass.

a pound of cheap bar soap in a gallon of boiling water and adding it to five gallons of thick whitewash.

Glazing.—The windows of farm buildings should be kept in repair. A broken light wastes heat, interferes with proper ventilation, and detracts greatly from the appearance of the building.

The necessary equipment for glazing consists of a putty knife, a glass cutter, glazier's points, and supply of glass large enough to permit cutting the largest lights needed. Small lights can be cut from the broken pieces taken from the larger windows. A smooth bench top and a yard stick can be used as a surface upon which to do the cutting, and a guide for the glass cutter. A 1½ or 2-inch chisel is used for removing the old putty, and for setting the glazier's points.

Cutting Glass.—A cheap steel disc cutter is satisfactory for farm repair work. It should be frequently dipped in kerosene while in use to improve its cutting qualities. Make a full-sized drawing on paper of the light that it is desired to cut. This is placed beneath the glass, and used as a pattern. Adjust the straight edge over a line, and draw the cutter clear across the glass along the straight edge (Fig. 155), using sufficient pressure to cause it to make a scratch on the surface of the glass. The glass should crack along this line by grasping it with both hands firmly on each side of the line and bending it backward. If it fails to do so with reasonable pressure, support it with one hand, as shown in figure 156, and tap lightly along the scratch on the under side of the glass with the

Fig. 156.—Tapping a glass with head of glass-cutter to make it crack along scratch.

glass cutter. Very narrow and small pieces can be broken off with the notches on the side of the cutter.

Glass should be cut at least ⅛ inch smaller than the opening it is to fill, because of the slightly irregular edge secured.

Putty is used for making a weather-tight joint between the glass and the sash (Fig. 157), and also for filling imperfections in wood work. It can be purchased at paint and hardware stores. Better putty can be made, however, by mixing dry whiting and white lead paste in about equal weights. It can be colored to match the surface upon which it is used by the addition of the proper pigment, and should be used about as soft as it can be conveniently handled.

After mixing, it should be stored in a tight container or kept covered with oil or water.

Putty must not be applied to bare wood, as the oil contained in it is absorbed, leaving the putty as a soft dry powder on the surface. The pores of the wood must first be " filled " by painting or by a coat of shellac.

QUESTIONS AND EXERCISES

1. In what way does paint protect the surface to which it is applied?

2. Name the chief materials used in paint making and give the purpose of each.

3. How would you prepare a new surface for painting? An old surface?

FIG. 157.—Puttying glass in sash. The putty is placed with the left hand and smoothed with the putty knife. The glass is first fastened in place with glazier's "points" driven with the side of a chisel.

4. What precautions can be taken to avoid adulterations in paint?

5. Give the proportions of lead and oil used in making paint for general outside use.

6. How should ready mixed paint be prepared for use?

7. What advantages does ready mixed paint possess?

8. Determine how much lead and oil will be necessary to paint your house.

9. Determine the probable quantity of ready mixed paint needed to paint your house.

10. Using present prices determine the difference in cost between painting with lead and oil or ready mixed paint.

11. Secure a color card and select colors for body and trim for your house. Are the colors selected suitable for your type of house?

12. Try to find out whether the colors selected in (11) are permanent.

13. How can the colors selected be secured?

13

14. Why should a window sash be primed before the glass is puttied in?

15. What portion of a fence post decays most rapidly? Why?

16. How can fence posts be treated to lessen decay?

17. Why does creosote oil act as a wood preservative?

18. Why could not a solution of copper sulfate be used for the same purpose?

19. What difficulties have you had in cutting glass? Can you suggest any way by which these difficulties can be overcome?

20. How can grease be removed from farm machinery preparatory to painting?

Job 1.—Repainting the Farm House.—Tools and materials required for the work: Numbers 5-0 and 6-0 round or oval brushes, sash tool, dust brush, wire brush, scraper, putty knife, hammer, white lead paste, raw linseed oil, turpentine, japan drier, pigment, shellac, putty, sandpaper, ladders, staging planks, and brackets.

Operations.—1. Determine body and trim to be used by a study and comparison of color cards in connection with surroundings.

2. Measure the exterior of the house and determine area.

3. Order sufficient paint, oil, turpentine, etc., for the job.

4. Clean the walls thoroughly, removing all scaling paint with scraper and wire brush. Smooth rough spots with sandpaper and remove dust with dust brush.

5. Drive all loose nails and make necessary repairs.

6. Coat knots and sappy places with shellac.

7. Mix sufficient paint for the priming coat. Use but little turpentine if the wood is porous and absorbent. More turpentine is required for resinous woods. Where existing paint is in good condition, the first coat may be made more of the nature of the second coat and the second coat omitted, finishing the building with the priming and finishing coats.

8. Apply the priming coat, beginning at the top and working downward. Brush it on smoothly and evenly lengthwise of the grain and rub it well into the wood. A good job depends upon a well laid priming coat.

9. Permit priming coat to dry and then fill nail holes and imperfections with putty, mixed as directed.

10. Mix and apply second coat, working from the top downward as in priming coat and painting both trim and body at one operation. Apply the lighter color first and lay the others up next to it to avoid smears showing.

11. Mix third coat without turpentine. Brush on smoothly as in preceding coats when second coat has become hard and dry.

12. Clean the sash, removing all loose putty and any broken lights.

13. Prime the sash. When dry replace broken lights and apply putty to places where missing.

14. Paint the sash.

15. Eaves troughs and down spouts, if new, should be cleaned with a cloth wet in gasoline or turpentine before painting to remove grease. The same applies to metal roofs. When painting piazza railings the work is facilitated by two working in unison, one on each side.

Job 2.—Painting the Farm Car.—Tools and materials needed for the work. Soap and brushes for washing, small metal wash tub or dish pan for cleaning, supply of gasoline for cleaning; one quart turpentine for cleaning, stiff-bristled paint brush for cleaning, putty knife, sandpaper, assorted sizes 00 to 1½; steel wool, curled hair, chamois skin, two soft 2-inch badger hair brushes for body and chassis, 2-inch bristle brush for applying top and seat dressing, small quantity of aluminum bronze for rims, small quantity shellac to seal crevices, ground coat, color varnish, clear varnish, and top dressing. About one quart of each is required for the average small car. Avoid the use of fancy colors. The average small car presents a better appearance when painted black.

Operations.—1. Wash the car thoroughly with soap, water and brush to remove mud.

2. Remove tires, wheels and fenders and thoroughly clean chassis and all parts with gasoline. Use stiff brush, wire brush or putty knife to remove encrusted grease.

3. Sandpaper body lightly with fine sandpaper to remove gloss. Clean rust from chipped places and smooth with sandpaper.

4. Remove road tar from underside of fenders with putty knife. Smooth with sandpaper.

5. Clean top, seats and side curtains with cloth dampened with turpentine. Make necessary repairs to these parts.

6. Clean and smooth wheels with sandpaper. The use of a paint remover or scraper may be resorted to if in very bad condition. They must be made clean and smooth.

7. Wipe off top, seats, body and chassis to remove dust.

8. Apply top dressing to top, seats and curtains, following directions on can.

9. Apply undercoating or primer to body and chassis. Follow directions given by manufacturer. Spread both horizontally and vertically to secure an even coating. Run shellac in crevices with small brush to seal dust particles and to prevent getting dust into finish.

10. When dry (24 to 36 hours) sandpaper lightly and after wiping off dust apply first coat of color varnish. Spread horizontally first and finish vertically. Use soft badger hair brush and work as little as required to spread it to avoid the formation of bubbles.

11. When dry rub lightly with fine sandpaper to remove gloss. Assemble the car and wipe off with chamois skin dampened with turpentine to remove dust particles.

12. Apply second coat of body color, flowing it on with soft badger hair brush.

13. When thoroughly dry rub over the surface with curled hair to remove any dust nibs that may appear.

14. Again wipe off with chamois skin moistened with turpentine and flow on a coat of clear auto finish.

15. Clean the rims thoroughly and give them a coat of rim paint or aluminum bronze.

Clean garage thoroughly after the first cleaning of the car and dampen floor and side walls before applying finishes to keep down the dust. Use separate brushes for body and chassis. Choose a period of bright, warm weather for car painting unless the garage is provided with artificial heat. Do not attempt to paint car in the open air because of the dust particles.

Job 3.—**Replacing a Broken Window Light.**—Tools and materials needed for the work: Sash tool for applying paint; paint for priming and painting sash, or for emergency job shellac for priming sash beneath putty; putty knife; glazier's points; one- and one-half or two-inch chisel; glass cutter; glass of sufficient size to cut light desired.

Operations.—1. Remove putty from broken light with chisel and clean sash thoroughly.

2. Prime sash with paint or if emergency job use shellac beneath putty,

3. Obtain dimensions of broken light, lay out size on paper with steel square and cut light.

4. Apply light coating of putty to sash and set glass in place, bedding it down firmly and evenly.

5. Fasten in place with glazier's points driven with the edge of the chisel.

6. Apply putty to outside of glass, smoothing it down neatly with the putty knife and taking care to see that it does not project beyond the sash.

7. Remove all excess putty with the putty knife.

8. Cover with sash paint to match the remainder of the window.

9. When dry clean glass with ammonia or alcohol.

Factors Affecting Quantities of Paint and Labor.—The problem of quantity of paint used and the time required to apply it, is affected greatly by the character of the surface and the quality of work desired. The following table may be used in estimating the paint and labor required for typical farm jobs.

Material and Labor Required for Painting[1]

Surface covered	Kind of material used	Number of coats	Materials used per 100 square feet of surface		Hours of labor per 100 sq. ft. of surface
			Gallons	Pounds	
Plastered wall	Varnish size	1	.29		.56
Plastered wall	Lead and oil paint	2	.64		1.57
Wood floor	Filler	1		2.36	1.00
Wood floor	Varnish	2	.52		1.50
Interior woodwork	Varnish	2	.51		2.24
Interior woodwork	Lead and oil paint	3	.91		3.04
Exterior woodwork	Lead and oil paint	3	.93		2.85
Shingles	Dipped in stain ⅔ length	1	1.00 per M		.92 per M

[1] From *Estimating and Appraising of Buildings*, by C. E. Barnes, McGraw-Hill Company.

CHAPTER XIV

FARM FORGE SHOP WORK

MODERN farm machinery is largely of iron and steel construction, making an equipment of metal working tools necessary if satisfactory repairs are to be made.

Tools Required.—The tools shown in figure 158 are considered necessary, although much repair work can be done with the forge,

FIG. 158.—Equipment for forge work: 1, forge with 14-inch fan; 2, anvil; 3, 2-lb. ball pene hammer; 4, 16-inch bolt tongs; 5, 16-inch straight jaw tongs; 6, post drill; 7, steel vise; 8, stock and dies; 9, hardie; 10, knife-handle wrench; 11, 12-inch flat file; 12, hack saw; 15, punch; 16, cold chisel; 17, bolt cutters; 18, steel square.

anvil, hammer and tongs, alone. An assortment of round, square and flat iron should also be acquired, together with a supply of bolts and rivets. Punches, tongs and hot and cold chisels of various shapes can be made as soon as a little experience is gained.

Arrangement of Forge, Anvil, and Tools.—The anvil should be placed with the horn pointing diagonally toward the forge (Fig. 159). The proper height for the average man is about 30 inches.

197

Where but one pair of tongs is available they must be heated and the jaws fitted to the iron being used, causing them to fit down

Fig. 159.—Arrangement of forge and anvil. Water bucket behind anvil block.

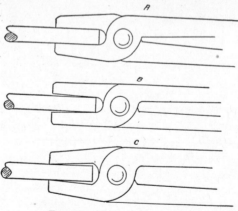

Fig. 160.—Fitting tongs to work.

upon the iron full length (Fig. 160A). When in this shape the iron can be held securely with but little effort. If open at the point or heel of the jaw, as at B and C, it is impossible to hold the work, no matter how tightly gripped.

Work should be grasped at the end. This permits handling it easily upon the anvil face. When it is necessary to change ends with a piece of work or to secure a fresh grip with the tongs, hold the heated iron with the hammer and swing it about with the tongs.

The fuel used in forge work is coke, a spongy, grayish black material that compacts closely and forms a dense, hot fire. It is nearly pure carbon and contains few impurities to attack the iron being heated. Coke is made directly in the forge from smithing coal, a high-grade bituminous coal that contains little sulfur or earthy matter, packs closely about the fire and forms coke rapidly under the action of heat.

Requirements of a Forge Fire.—It is difficult or impossible to do good work with a poor fire. To secure the best results the fire

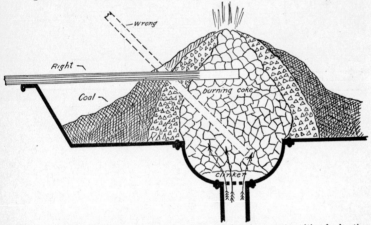

Fig. 161.—Cross-section of properly built forge fire with iron in correct position for heating.

must be: (1) deep, (2) clean, (3) compact. A cross section of a properly built fire is shown in figure 161.

Coke uses oxygen when burning, and if a deep, clean, compact fire is provided, much of the oxygen of the entering air blast will be exhausted before reaching the iron. This lessens the formation of scale and permits heating the iron to a higher temperature without burning.

Forging operations consist of bending, upsetting, drawing out, welding, punching, drilling, riveting, thread-cutting, hardening, tempering, and annealing. Heat makes iron soft and ductile. Practically all forging operations on iron can be done more rapidly when it is at a high heat. Steel will not stand as high a temperature.

Bending.—Curves may be bent cold in light work. The iron should be heated when an angular bend is desired, to prevent breaking. A bend of this kind is usually desired at some definite point, and its location should be marked with a center punch before heating the iron. Avoid marking with a cold chisel as it tends to cause the iron to crack when the bend is made. Heat to a bright red heat for bending.

Upsetting is making an iron shorter and thicker, as at the end of a brace where the hole is to be punched. This is done by giving

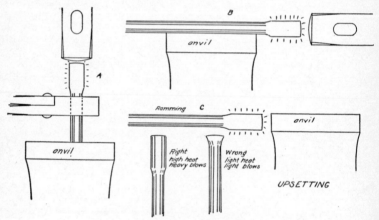

FIG. 162.—Methods of upsetting iron.

the portion of the iron that it is desired to upset, a high heat, and driving back upon it with the hammer (Fig. 162). Short pieces are upset, as shown at A or B. Larger pieces are often upset by ramming the heated end against the side of the anvil, as shown in figure 162C. Keep the iron straight while upsetting, and maintain a high heat, making the material soft and easily worked. Strike heavy blows. Light blows have little upsetting effect, simply forming a burr or rivet head on the end of the iron (Fig. 162). To lessen the trouble from bending confine the heat in the iron to the portion that it is desired to enlarge. If the heated part becomes too long shorten it by dipping in water to the point desired.

Drawing out is used to make an iron longer and thinner, and is most readily accomplished across the horn of the anvil (Fig. 163). The rounded surface of the horn acts as a blunt wedge which tends to stretch the iron lengthwise as it is pounded from above. Keep the

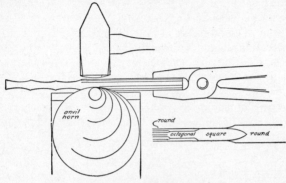

Fig. 163.—Method of drawing out iron.

iron at a white heat, and turn backward and forward, one-quarter of a revolution, between alternate blows. When reduced to the approximate cross-section desired finish to a uniform square cross-section on the face of the anvil. If the finished iron is to be round, work

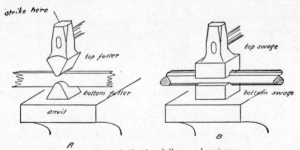

Fig. 164.—Method of using fullers and swages.

down the corners, making it octagonal; next make it sixteen-sided, and finally round. It may be finished in the swages (Fig. 164B), or by draw filing (Fig. 165), if a smooth surface is desired.

Punching.—The iron is brought to a white heat and the punch is driven about half-way through as it lays on the face of the anvil in the same way that a nail is driven into a board (Fig. 166). It is then removed and driven in from the other side, the raised, blackened spot on the iron locating the hole as the iron is turned over. As the punch is driven down it is brought over the pritchel hole in the

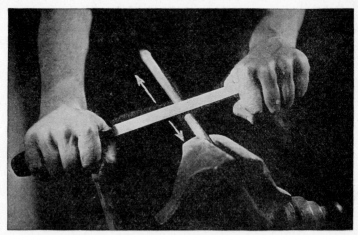

Fig. 165.—Drawfiling a heated iron to give it a round cross-section. File is grasped at both ends and pulled back and forth as indicated by arrow.

heel of the anvil and the little pellet driven out, making a hole with clean-cut edges. If the punch had been started over the

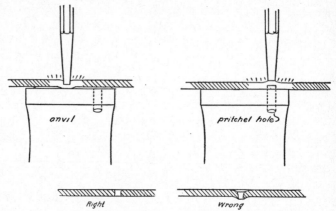

Fig. 166.—Method of punching holes in iron.

pritchel hole and driven clear through at the first operation, the hole would have had raised and roughened edges like one punched through tin with a nail. The punch should be dipped frequently while in use to prevent its temper being destroyed, and the edges should be kept sharp and square by frequent fitting.

To punch a large hole in a small piece of metal, use a small punch first and stretch the hole so formed by following with larger punches. Square holes can be made by the use of a small round punch followed by a square one of the size desired.

Where a hole is being punched in an iron of considerable thickness a pinch of coal dust dropped in the hole will prevent the punch from sticking.

Welding.—Wrought iron and mild steel have a considerable temperature range through which they are pasty and will unite if

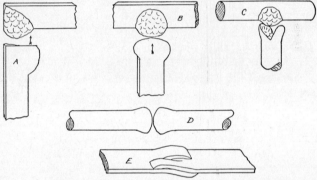

Fig. 167.—Welds for special purposes: *A*, angle weld for flat stock; *B*, T weld for flat stock; *C*, T weld for round stock; *D*, butt weld for large irons. Weld is started in the fire by sledging on end when iron is at welding heat; *E*, split weld for thin flat stock.

brought together and hammered, but the higher carbon steels present difficulties in welding that make a higher degree of skill necessary for a successful union. There are a number of forms of welds in use, as the lap weld, butt weld, and jump weld (Fig. 167), used for special purposes. The lap weld is the principal one used in farm practice.

Scarfing.—Before welding, the ends of the irons to be joined must be shaped for the purpose or "scarfed" (Fig. 168). The ends are first upset, as at A. The upset end is then held as shown at B, and by striking backward and downward, it is given a blunt wedge shape. Next lay the iron flat across the face of the anvil with the edge of this wedge vertical, as at C, and form the scarf or meeting surface by striking in the same manner used for forming the wedge. This brings the iron down to a blunt point of the shape shown at D. The scarf is finished by giving it a slightly convex surface by a few light blows from the hammer. The convex shape insures that the irons will meet first in the center of the weld and squeeze out any scale or other impurities from between them as the welding progresses, resulting in a strong weld. The upsetting is

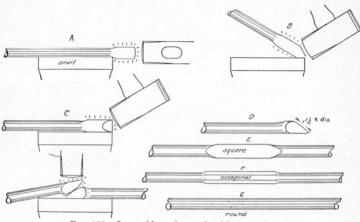

FIG. 168.—Lap weld scarfing and welding round stock.

done to provide sufficient material for the drawing out and waste due to hammering and scale.

The length of the scarf should be about 1½ times the diameter of the iron being welded, a ¾-inch rod requiring a scarf about 1⅛ inches in length. A common mistake of beginners is to make too long and pointed a scarf, due to pounding at too flat an angle when forming it. This results in a weak weld of poor appearance.

The fire for welding must be deep, clean, and compact, and free from fresh coal. Fresh coal contains a certain amount of sulfur, which makes the iron slippery at welding heat, and prevents a weld being made. Welding requires a high temperature, and a sufficient heat cannot be obtained in a loose, shallow, and dirty fire without excessive scaling or burning of the iron.

Heating the Iron.—The irons should be placed in the upper part of the fire, with the scarfed sides up. Use a light blast in heating. This prevents excess air being forced into the fire, lessens scaling and permits the iron to be heated uniformly clear through. A heavy blast may result in a surface heat only. Watch the work closely and secure an equal heat on the pieces being welded by changing their positions in the fire if necessary. The pieces must be heated equally to weld. Dip the points of the scarfs in water if they heat too rapidly, to prevent burning. When a bright red heat has been reached a flux may be applied. This lessens the formation of scale and permits a weld to be made at a somewhat lower heat.

The Welding Heat.—At this heat the iron becomes the same color as the glowing fire and seems to disappear in it. The heated portions are white and wet appearing, like a snowball that has been carried for a long time in the hands, and if the irons are touched together in the fire a portion of the surface will flow from one to the other, causing them to stick. If heated much beyond this point white, explosive sparks will appear, indicating that the iron is burning. With steel this high temperature cannot always be reached because of its higher carbon content. In general, welding should be done at the highest heat possible; a common trouble with beginners is attempting to weld when the iron is too cold. If the irons do not stick at the first blow, reheat them, as further pounding is useless.

Taking the Irons from the Fire.—Just before the welding heat

FIG. 169.—Position of hands when taking irons from fire for welding. Scarfed sides of irons are down, little finger of right hand and thumb of left hand are toward fire, both hands held with backs uppermost.

is reached the irons should be turned over in the fire with the scarfed sides down, exposing the meeting surfaces to the highest heat. Take the irons from the fire with the backs of the hands uppermost, the little finger of the right hand and the thumb of the left hand toward the fire (Fig. 169). As the irons are pulled from

Fig. 170.—Right hand turned over as irons are to be laid across anvil. Iron in right hand is laid across anvil and held in place by iron in left hand, leaving right hand free to grasp hammer, which is shown in place on anvil.

the fire rap them smartly upon the forge or anvil to remove adhering slag, turn the right hand over so that the scarfed end of the iron held by it points toward the body (Fig. 170), and lay it across the anvil

Fig. 171.—Irons on anvil in position for welding. Iron marked "A" was formerly held in right hand.

in this position with the scarfed side up. Bring the iron held in the left hand down upon it, as shown in figure 171, by first resting it across the corner of the anvil and using this as a fulcrum. The right hand is now free, and the hammer, which should have been in place on the anvil, is picked up and a blow struck uniting the two pieces. After the first blow the points of the scarfs should be welded down, as because of their small size they will be the first to drop below the welding heat.

When stuck together the weld is reheated to the welding point, and worked down square to the size desired (Fig. 168), next it is made octagonal, and round as described under drawing out. Whatever the finished shape is to be it should first be made square; attempting to work the weld round at once will result in opening it. Where the pieces of iron are both short, necessitating the use of two pair of tongs, the tongs held by the right hand are released and dropped when the left hand iron is brought down on top of the iron held by them.

Fluxes.—A flux is a powder or paste used to make welding easier. It accomplishes this result in two ways: 1. It melts on the heated iron and flows over it, providing a protective coating that

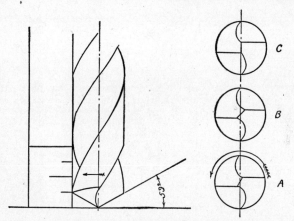

Fig. 172.—Twist drills should be given clearance when grinding, that is, the portion of the drill back of the cutting edge should be ground away, leaving the cutting edge as the only part to touch the work. This can be tested by standing the drill on the point on a plane surface and turning in the direction of the arrow, at the same time holding a scale beside it. The line beneath the arrow should incline upward as shown, indicating that the cutting edge is lower. *A*, *B*, and *C* represent the cutting end of drills. A properly ground drill will appear as *A*, with the angle of the straight central part at the point as indicated.

tends to prevent burning and the formation of scale (oxide). 2. It unites with the scale already formed and lowers its melting point, making it possible to weld at a lower temperature. The ordinary

melting point of iron oxide or ˙scale is higher than that required
for welding. Wrought iron can be heated high enough to melt
this oxide; most steels, except the very mild ones, will burn,
however, before this tempera-
ture is reached, making a flux
a necessity in welding them.

**Materials Used for
Fluxes.**—Patent fluxes can be
obtained from hardware stores
for a few cents per pound, the
chief ingredients being borax,
sal ammoniac, and iron filings.
For ordinary w o r k w i t h
wrought iron and mild steel
clean, white sand may be used
successfully. The action of the
sand is improved if mixed with
borax, which has first been
heated to drive off the water.

For welding steel a flux
made of 1 part sal ammoniac
and 4 parts borax, treated as
above, gives good results. The
flux should be applied to the
iron when it has reached a
yellow heat. This temperature
is necessary to cause it to stick.

Drilling.—The drill should
be kept sharp and well lubricated to prevent heating while
in use. When grinding, the
original shape (Fig. 172)
should be preserved, giving
some clearance back of the cutting edge. Squeaking and hard
running indicate a lack of clearance or lubricant. Common machine
oil makes a satisfactory lubricant for farm shop use. A center punch
mark should be made (Fig. 173) in which to start the drill. The
work should be held securely (Fig. 174), and the feed eased up as
the drill comes through the metal, as otherwise the drill may be

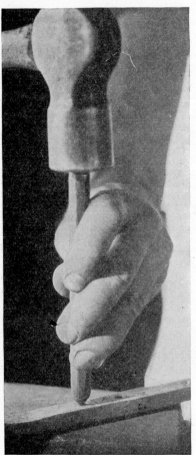

FIG. 173.—Marking with center punch.

broken. Twist drills are very hard and brittle, and break easily when bent.

Thread cutting is done by means of taps and dies. Grip the rod or bolt in the vise, and smooth up the end with the file, permitting the guide of the die to slip over it easily. Apply oil liber-

FIG. 174.—Drilling metal. Hold work securely. FIG. 175.—Cutting a thread on a bolt. Use plenty of oil.

ally and turn the die onto the rod (Fig. 175), using sufficient pressure to start the thread. Nuts are threaded by clamping them in the vise and turning a tap of the proper size into them, running it clear through. The following table gives the size of drill necessary to use with the tap listed:

Taps	Drill diameter	Drill size in nearest 64th
1/4"	.201	13
5/16"	.258	16 or 17
3/8"	.314	20
7/8"	.368	23
1/2"	.425	27

Riveting is done with hot or cold rivets, the former making the tighter joint. A rivet of a size to fill the hole should be used, and

14

one slightly longer than the thickness of the metal being riveted. The rivet is inserted in the hole, the head supported by a sledge or other heavy iron, and the other end swaged down with the pene of the hammer. It can be shaped with a rivet set in finishing to secure a smooth head.

Working Steel.—Steel should be kept at a yellow heat while being worked. This heat should not be exceeded, and the steel should not be worked after it has cooled to a deep red. Too high a temperature results in a coarse-grained steel, while working at too low a heat causes the formation of minute cracks along which the tool will break when in use.

Hardening Steel.—When a piece of steel is heated to a dull red and then cooled suddenly by plunging into water or other cooling agent it becomes very hard and brittle. This is the common method used to give hand-made tools cutting qualities. The proper hardening heat varies. As a general rule it is lowered as the carbon content of the steel is increased. A cherry red heat, judged in the shade, is about right for the steel in common use. This will appear nearly black in the sunlight. A little experimenting and observation will determine the proper hardening heat for any steel. For example, an old cold chisel on which the top end is badly broken indicates a high carbon content, and points to a low heat as the proper one for hardening. One in which the top has mushroomed over would indicate a steel of lower carbon content. Too high a hardening heat makes the steel coarse-grained and brittle, destroying its usefulness. Steel should always be hardened by cooling it quickly, *immediately* it is taken from the fire. It should not be allowed to cool in the air before plunging it in water.

Division Between Hardened and Soft Parts of Steel.— Usually a tool is composed of a hardened steel cutting edge and a softer part upon which the pounding is done as, for example, a cold chisel. Where this is the case the tool should be moved up and down in the water while hardening to avoid forming a sharp division between the hardened and unhardened parts, which is likely to cause breakage when the tool is put to use. Moving the tool about in the water also cools it more quickly and makes it harder.

Tempering.—A piece of steel in this condition is too hard and brittle for ordinary use, and must have this extreme hardness removed to a certain extent, depending upon the use to which the tool is to be put. This is done by reheating and tempering.

Reheating the Steel for Tempering.—The chief method used in farm practice to reheat the steel is to utilize heat remaining in the tool after hardening. The lower portion only is cooled in hardening and the heat remaining in the part above is then allowed to work down until the desired temperature is secured at the cutting edge, when the tool is again plunged in water and cooled.

Determining Tempering Heat.—A piece of polished iron or steel will form a thin scale on the outside that changes in color as the heat is increased. At about 430 degrees F. this scale is a very pale yellow. As the heat increases this changes through shades of yellow to brown, which becomes tinged with red, turning into light purple, dark purple, and finally blue. The following table taken from "Farm Blacksmithing," by J. M. Drew, gives the colors indicating the tempering heat for various tools, and the approximate temperature corresponding to the color:

Color	Temperature, F. degrees	Tools
Very pale straw color	430	Stone drills for hard stone.
Yellow	450	Woodworking tools, ordinary stone drills.
Dark yellow	470	
Brownish yellow	490	Hammer.
Brown	500	Lathe tools.
Brown tinged with purple	520	Drills (hard).
Light purple	525	Drills (ordinary).
Dark purple tinged with blue	550	Hard cold chisels.
Dark blue	565	Cold chisels for soft iron, hand punches and hatchets.
Light blue	605	Screw drivers.

Annealing is the process of softening steel, and is accomplished by heating to the proper hardening heat and cooling very slowly by burying in ashes or some similar heat retainer. It results in a steel of extreme softness, strength and ductility. After forging, steel should always be annealed before hardening, as it relieves internal stresses in the metal and results in a better tool.

Cutting Metal with Chisels.—Cutting should be done on the base of anvil horn (Fig. 176), or on the cutting block immediately back of it. The face of the anvil is hardened and will injure the chisel if driven against it. The cold chisel should be held securely with the left hand and struck heavy blows. Place the chisel before each blow and nick clear around the iron to be cut off; then bring the nicked portion to the edge of the anvil and break off by a blow from the hammer as shown in figure 176. Keep the cold chisel sharpened with the edge slightly convex to give it strength. Avoid cutting with the corners of the chisel, to avoid breakage. When making deep cuts a handful of oil-soaked waste into which the chisel can be dipped occasionally will make it cut better.

The hot chisel is used on hot metal in practically the same way that the cold chisel is used for cold metal. The metal to be cut

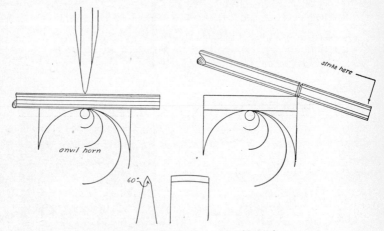

FIG. 176.—Cutting iron with cold chisel.

should be bright red. Dip the hot chisel frequently while using it to retain the temper. The hot chisel may be used in connection with the hardie in cutting hot metal, the hardie forming the lower blade of the shears. Avoid hitting the hardie with the hammer; the last blows struck should be overhanging blows.

Cutting with the Hack-saw.—When using the hack-saw, draw the blade up taut in the frame, avoid twisting or cramping in the cut and use with little pressure to avoid breaking. For economy in the use of blades use the longest stroke possible, making every tooth in the saw do its full share of cutting (Fig. 177).

Filing.—Files are used for leveling and cutting down stock where a degree of accuracy not possible with the cold chisel is

Fig. 177.—Cutting off bolt with hack-saw.

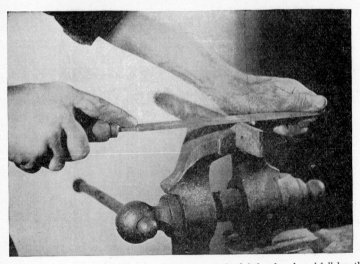

Fig. 178.—Method of using file. File supported at tip by left hand and used full length.

required. An assortment of round, square, triangular, and flat files is desirable. The flat file is the one most used in farm repairs, the size known as 12-inch being the most economical. It should be fitted with a handle permitting it to be grasped firmly. Hold the file steadily and use long strokes (Fig. 178). It should be lifted on the return stroke. It does no cutting on the return stroke and is dulled by contact with the metal.

Care of Files.—A satisfactory way of storing is to provide a shelf on which each file has a groove protecting it from dirt, grease, or injury. When a file becomes worn it may be kept for use on soft or dirty metals and a new file secured for the harder work.

QUESTIONS AND EXERCISES

1. List repair jobs that have come to your attention involving the use of metal working tools.
2. Make a list of the tools that you would consider desirable for the above work. Consult a hardware catalog and determine the cost of the tools selected.
3. Make a sketch floor plan of your shop and show a desirable location for forge, anvil, vise, and drill press.
4. How should tongs be fitted for use? Why is this fitting necessary?
5. How should work be grasped with the tongs?
6. What grade of coal is necessary for forging operations? Why cannot ordinary bituminous or anthracite coal be used for this purpose? Can you suggest a fuel that might be used?
7. What would be the effect on the iron being heated of each of the following: (a) shallow fire? (b) deep fire in which fuel is mixed with ashes and clinker? (c) deep fire but loose and open so that air blast is forced through it easily?
8. What are the chief difficulties encountered in upsetting an iron? How may they be overcome?
9. What objection is there to pounding an iron on all sides when drawing it out?
10. Why is an iron held across the horn of the anvil when drawing it out?
11. Under what conditions may punching be used to make holes in iron?
12. What objection is there to driving the punch clear through a piece of hot metal?
13. What kinds of metals can be welded satisfactorily?
14. Why is it necessary to scarf the ends of the irons before welding?
15. What should be the shape of the scarfed end of the iron and why is this shape desirable?
16. How can the correct welding heat be judged?
17. What trouble is a beginner likely to have when making a weld?
18. What is the purpose of a flux? How does it accomplish this purpose?
19. What materials may be used as fluxes in welding?
20. How should a weld be finished?
21. How can a drill be started at the point desired?
22. What size drill would you select to drill a hole for a ¾″ tap?
23. Why is hot riveting superior to cold riveting?
24. At what heat should steel be worked? What is the effect of (a) working steel when too hot? (b) When too cold?
25. How is steel hardened? How is steel tempered?
26. How can the hardening heat of a cold chisel be determined?
27. How should a cold chisel be sharpened?
28. How should files be used and cared for?

CHAPTER XV

PROBLEMS IN SHOP WORK

Job 1.—Building and Maintaining a Fire.—A clean, deep fire of coke is necessary for satisfactory forge shop work (Fig. 161).

Construction of Fire.—1. Clean out fire pot and blast pipe. Pick out large "clinkers" and remove small "clinkers" and ashes through trap beneath tuyere.

2. Light small handful of shavings and place in fire pot with lighted end down.

3. Select several pieces of coke and place on burning shavings. Start fan slowly to give light blast.

4. When coke ignites increase the blast and add more coke.

5. Complete the fire by banking finely broken coal about it in the form of a hollow mound. Sprinkle this coal to dampen it and make it compact, causing it to form coke rapidly, confining the heat to the center and making the fire comfortable to work about.

6. As fire burns out replenish it by pushing the outside to the center and adding more coal to the outside.

7. Clean fire with poker when "clinker" is felt in the bottom, usually after from one to two hours' steady work. Avoid spreading the fire; keep it deep, clean and compact for the best results.

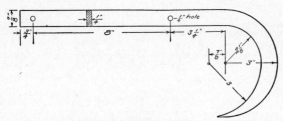

FIG. 179.—Roof ladder iron.

Job 2.—Roof Ladder Iron.—This is bolted to the top of a light ladder, permitting it to be pushed up a roof and hooked over the ridge (Figs. 163, 173, 174, 176, and 179).

Construction.—1. Cut from a ¼″ x ⅞″ bar a piece 20″ long.

2. Heat 3″ of one end to a bright red and draw to a blunt point edgewise. Keep the original thickness.

3. Heat to a uniform bright red for a distance of from 7″ to 8″ back from point and bend edgewise over the horn of the anvil to shape shown in figure 179.

4. Cut with cold chisel to length required.

5. Lay out, center punch and drill ¼″ holes for bolting to ladder.

215

Job 3.—Gate Staples.—Staples of different shapes are used to support sliding gates and bars. Where used for bars made from

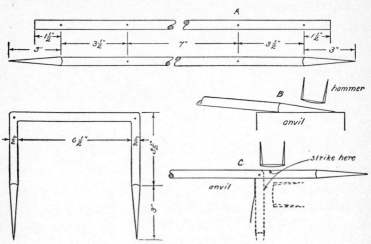

Fig. 180.—Method of making gate staple.

poles, old horse shoes are sometimes pointed and used for staples (Figs. 163, 173, 176, and 180).

Construction.—1. Cut a piece of ½″ round iron, 18″ long.

2. With center punch mark it 1–½″ and 3–½″ from each end. (Fig. 180.)

3. Heat end to a light red heat and draw to a square point 3″ long.

4. Repeat with the other end. If points are more than 3″ long cut off tips with hardie and finish again. Do not work iron after it has cooled below a good red heat or trouble may develop from splitting when drawing to a point.

5. Smooth surface of points at dull red heat with wet hammer. This is below scaling heat and will produce smooth surface.

6. Cool finished points.

7. Heat to bright red at second set of punch marks and bend at right-angles by overhanging blows (Fig. 180), to form staple. Start bend on point of horn and finish over the side of the anvil. Preserve round cross-section and avoid marring inside of bend by holding and striking as indicated. (Fig. 180.)

Job 4.—Gate Hinge.—A heavy hinge of this character is used on swinging gates and heavy doors. It may be changed in construction adapting it to different conditions (Figs. 173, 174, 176, 181, and 182).

Construction of Hinge Strap.—With cold or hot chisel cut from ⅜″ x 1–½″ stock a piece 28″ long.

2. Heat to a bright red for about 1-½" back and upset one end as shown by figure 182A. Keep the width at 1-½" while upsetting.

3. Scarf the end as at B, figure 182, making a scarf 2-½" long. Finish the scarf to a blunt point.

4. Lay off 3" from the shoulder of the scarf and mark on the edge of the iron with the center punch.

5. Take a short heat at the center punch mark and bend at nearly

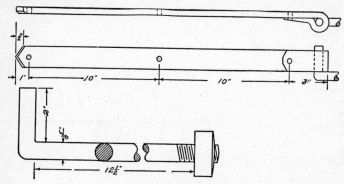

FIG. 181.—Gate hinge.

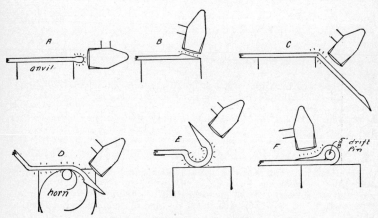

FIG. 182.—Construction of strap hinge.

right-angles by overhanging blows over the side of the anvil. (Fig. 182C.)

6. Heat the part that is to form hinge socket to a uniform light red and with scarfed side down start bending socket over outer end of anvil horn. (Fig. 182D.)

7. Maintain heat in socket end and close on the face of the anvil as shown at figure 182E. Close end around piece of ⅝" rod used for a drift pin.

8. Remove the drift pin, bring hinge to yellow heat, insert drift pin, apply flux, bring to welding heat and weld as shown at figure 182E.

9. Lay out, center punch, and drill holes for bolts.

10. Cut to proper length and shape end. Work chamfer at dull red heat with wet hammer to avoid scale.

Construction of Hinge Pin.—1. With cold chisel cut piece of ⅝″ round iron 16″ long.

2. Heat ends to dull red and work smooth and round.

3. Mark with center punch 2–⅝″ from one end.

4. Heat to bright red at this point and bend at right-angles with overhanging blows as shown for hinge strap. (Fig. 182C.)

5. Again heat to bright red at the bend and cool upright part by dipping in water to the bend.

6. Set the pin upright on the anvil and strike on the top end, upsetting the metal in the bend and forming a right-angled inside corner.

7. Cool the iron and cut a ⅝″ thread as shown.

8. Tap a ⅝″ blank nut to fit thread.

The hinge as shown is made for a 12″ concrete post. If other post is used cut length of horizontal part to fit post. Apply top hinge with pin pointing downward to prevent gate being lifted from hinges by stock.

Lower hinge may be made adjustable, permitting gate to be kept horizontal, by threading entire horizontal length of hinge pin and using two nuts, one on each side of the post.

Job 5.—**Iron Plate for Vise Jaw.**—The utility of a wood vise is increased by iron jaw linings. It can then be used for both wood-

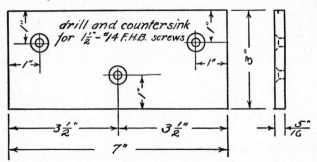

Fɪɢ. 183.—Iron plate for vise jaw.

work and light metal work. A 2″ x 2″ angle iron can be used the whole length of the bench in place of the inner plate if desired (Figs. 173, 174, 177, 178, and 183).

Construction.—1. Square and cut with the hack saw a piece of ⁵/₁₆″ x 3″ iron 7″ long. (Fig 183.)

2. True up the ends with flat file, if necessary.

3. Lay out position of holes and mark with the center punch.

4. Drill with ¼″ drill and countersink for No. 14 F. H. B. screws.

Job 6.—**Rub Iron for Hay Rack.**—This is fastened to side of rack and prevents wear from wheel when turning (Figs. 173, 174, 177, and 185).

Construction.—1. Lay out and cut with hack saw from ½″ x 2″ iron a piece 8″ in length. (Fig. 185.)

2. Lay out position of bolt holes, center punch and drill with ⅜″ drill.

3. Edges may be chamfered if desired by heating to dull red and working with a wet hammer.

Job 7.—**Hay Rack Clamp Bolt.**—It is designed to hold cross sills and bed pieces of hay rack together without weakening them by

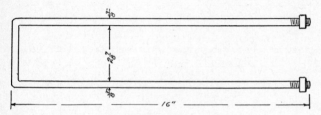

FIG. 184.—Clamp bolt for hay rack.

boring holes. In modified form it may be adapted to other similar conditions (Figs. 173, 175, 176, 182C, and 184).

Construction.—1. Cut from ⅜″ round iron a piece 35–¼″ long.

2. Round up ends, cut threads and tap nuts to fit.

3. Mark lightly with center punch 16″ from each end.

4. Heat to a bright red at punch marks and bend at right-angles in the vise or in pritchel hole of anvil.

Clamp-bolts, U-bolts and other work of this nature are frequently made by shaping first after which they are heated at the top and twisted sufficiently to permit the thread to be cut. They are then reheated and twisted back to place again.

Job 8.—**Wagon-box Strap Bolt.**—It is used to fasten sides of box to bed (Figs. 163, 164, 173, 174, 176, and 185).

Construction.—1. From ¼″ x ⅞″ iron cut a piece 16″ long.

2. Heat end to a dull red and work chamfer, using wet hammer.

3. With center punch mark holes and 12–¼″ from end make punch marks in the edge of the iron to locate shoulders.

4. Heat to a bright red at point where shoulders are to be formed and start shoulders with top and bottom fullers. (Fig. 164.)

5. Heat iron below shoulders to a uniform bright red and draw to ⁷⁄₁₆″ square.

6. Maintain heat and work down corners making heated portion octag-

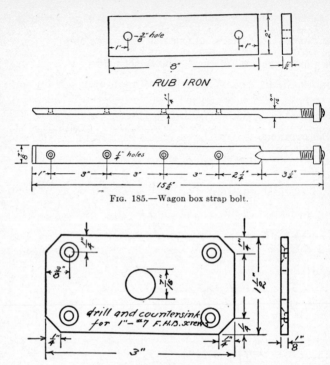

RUB IRON

FIG. 185.—Wagon box strap bolt.

FIG. 186.—Tail rod washer for wagon box.

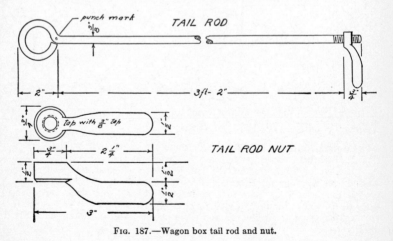

TAIL ROD

TAIL ROD NUT

FIG. 187.—Wagon box tail rod and nut.

onal and finally round, $7/16''$ diameter. Finish between $7/16''$ swages if available. (Fig 164.)

7. Cut to proper length and round up end to take dies.
8. Drill holes and countersink.
9. Cut $7/16''$ thread and tap $7/16''$ blank nut to fit.

Job 9.—Tail Rod Washer for Wagon-box.—It prevents the ring and nut on ends of tail rod from wearing into the wood. Two are required for each rod (Figs. 173, 174, 176, and 186).

Construction.—1. From $1/8'' \times 1-1/2''$ iron cut a piece $3''$ in length.
2. Trim corners with cold chisel as shown.
3. Lay out, center punch, drill and countersink as shown in the drawing. (Fig. 186.)

Job 10.—Wagon-box Tail Rod.—This is used to hold end

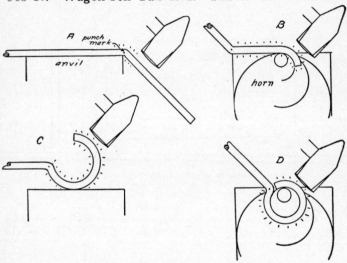

FIG. 188.—Steps in making wagon box tail rod.

gates of wagon-box in place, and to prevent box from spreading (Figs. 173, 175, 176, 187, and 188).

Construction.—1. Cut from $3/8''$ round iron a piece 3' 9'' long.
2. Mark with the center punch $5-3/4''$ from the end.
3. Heat to bright red at the punch mark and bend at nearly right-angles over the edge of the anvil with overhanging blows. (Fig. 188A.)
4. Heat the $5-1/4''$ part to a uniform bright red and work across the horn of the anvil, bending to ring form as shown at figure 188B.
5. Heat ring to bright red and close on the face of the anvil. (Fig. 188C.)

6. Heat ring uniformly and true up the ring over the anvil horn as shown at figure 188D.

7. Cut rod to required length, round up end and cut ⅜″ thread.

Job 11.—Tail Rod Nut.—This is used as fastening on tail rod, as it permits loosening or tightening without the use of wrench, and

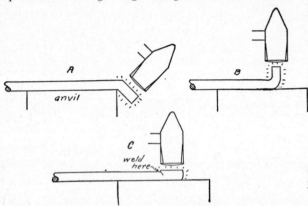

Fig. 189.—Method of upsetting iron for wagon box tail rod nut on brace end.

because of its shape does not easily jar off (Figs. 173, 174, 187, and 189).

Construction.—1. Heat about 1-½″ of end of ½″ rod and bend at right-angles over the side of the anvil by overhanging blows. (Fig. 189A.) The bent up portion should be about ¾″ long.

2. Keep at light red or yellow heat and upset the portion turned up by pounding on the upright end when rod is resting on the anvil face. (Fig. 189B.) Do not let the upright piece fold over while upsetting and be careful to preserve round cross-section.

3. When upset nearly to the point shown at figure 189C, apply flux, bring to a welding heat and weld down.

4. Draw the rod slightly back of the upset portion by working over the horn of the anvil.

5. Cut off to required length and finish end.

6. Heat and bend to shape (Fig. 187).

7. Mark with center punch in center of upset end and drill with ⁹/₃₂″ drill.

8. Tap with ⅜″ tap.

Job 12.—Wagon-box Rub Iron.—Used to protect wagon-box from wear occasioned by contact with front wheels in turning (Figs. 163, 173, 174, 176, 188A, and 190).

Construction.—1. Cut a section of ¾″ round iron 16″ long.

2. Mark with the center punch 4″ from each end.

3. Heat end to center punch mark to a uniform bright red and draw out, working to ⅜″ x 1″ in cross-section.

4. Draw out other end in the same manner.

5. Heat at punch marks and bend at right-angles. Bend over the

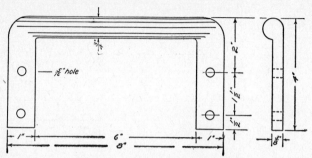

FIG. 190.—Wagon box rub iron.

corner of the anvil with overhanging blows. (Fig. 188A.)

6. Cut flattened parts to proper length, center punch and drill with ⁵/₁₆″ drill.

Job 13.—**Wagon-box Brace.**—Used on the side of wagon-box to prevent spreading (Figs. 166, 175, 176, 189, and 191).

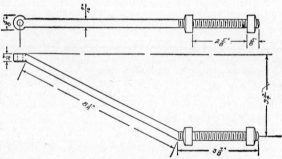

FIG. 191.—Wagon box brace.

Construction.—1. From a ⁷/₁₆″ rod cut a piece 13–½″ long.

2. Heat about 1–½″ of one end to a bright red and turn about ¾″ at right-angles. (Fig. 189A.)

3. Maintain high heat and upset turned up portion as shown at figure 189B. Continue upsetting until nearly at point shown at figure 189C.

4. When nearly down to thickness of the rod, apply flux, bring to a welding heat and weld down at point indicated at figure 189C. Avoid pounding down too thin, keep the thickness at least equal to the thickness of the rod.

5. Reheat to bright red or yellow heat and punch ¼″ hole in the center of upset portion.

6. Lay off position of bends and mark with the center punch.

7. Cut off any excess length, round up end, cut $\frac{7}{16}''$ thread and tap two $\frac{7}{16}''$ blank nuts.

8. Heat at points indicated by center punch marks and bend to proper angles. Bend so that welded side comes next to box.

9. Heat brace end to dull red and work light chamfer around top with hammer.

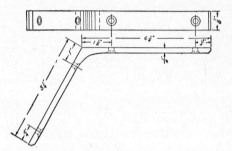

FIG. 192.—End gate brace.

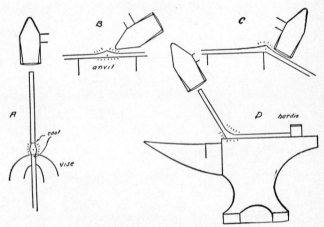

FIG. 193.—Method of making end gate brace.

Job 14.—**End Gate Brace.**—Used to support foot rest on the front end gate of wagon-box (Figs. 173, 174, 192, and 193).

Construction.—1. Cut a piece of $\frac{1}{4}''$ x $\frac{7}{8}''$ stock 13–$\frac{1}{2}''$ long.

2. Make a center punch mark in one edge of the material 6'' from one end.

3. Heat to a bright red or yellow heat at punch mark.

4. Dip each end of iron in water, cooling it so that only about $\frac{3}{4}''$ remains heated on each side of the punch mark.

5. Clamp in vise just below heated portion and upset by heavy blows.

(Fig. 193 A.) Work must be done rapidly in order that upsetting heat is not lost before there is opportunity to clamp in vise and strike.

6. Repeat this process until metal is from ⅜″ x ½″ in thickness. Pound on edge on face of anvil to prevent the metal spreading in width. Upset in thickness only.

7. Reheat and place on the face of anvil working, by backing up blows with the pene of hammer, to the shape indicated. (Fig. 193B.) Be careful not to draw the metal in length.

8. Bend over the corner of the anvil with overhanging blows with the upset part at outer corner of the angle. (Fig. 193C.)

9. Complete angle by taking short, high heat at angle, cooling as in four if necessary, and place on anvil with one end butting against the hardie. Pound down on the other end securing a sharp corner at the outside of the angle. (Fig. 193D.)

10. Cut ends to length and forge on chamfer at dull red heat with wet hammer.

11. Lay out positions for holes, center punch, drill with ¼″ drill and countersink.

Job 15.—Wearing Irons and Brace for Road Drag.—Used

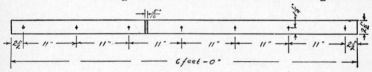

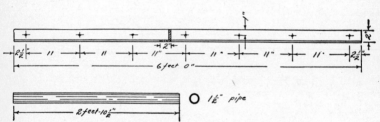

FIG. 194.—Wearing irons and brace for road drag

to hold drag in shape and to protect the scraping and pulverizing edges of the drag (Figs. 173, 174, 177, and 194).

Construction.—1. With hack saw cut a piece of ⁵⁄₁₆″ x 2–½″ material 6″ long.

2. One and one-fourth inches from the lower edge make six center punch marks in line, the two outer ones being 2–½″ from each end and the remainder equally spaced.

3. Drill and countersink for ⅜″ sleigh shoe bolts at these punch marks.

4. In the same manner, cut, layout, center punch, drill and countersink the two by two-inch angle iron used on the pulverizing edge of the drag.

5. Using pipe cutter or hack saw, cut two sections of 1–½″ pipe 2′ 10–½″ long to serve as braces.

15

Job 16.—Welded Eye Bolt and Ring for Road Drag.—Used in road drag to hold parts together and as a means of attaching the team. (Figs. 162, 175, 176, 195, 196 and 197.)

Construction of Ring.—1. Cut 11″ from a piece of ½″ round stock.
2. Take a short high heat on ends and upset. (Fig. 162, A and B.)

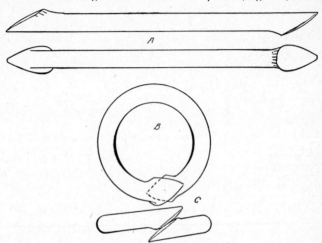

Fig. 195.—Method of making ring.

3. Scarf end as for lap weld. (Fig. 170.)   Make scarfs on opposite sides. (Fig. 195.)
4. Heat one-half of iron to uniform bright red and bend over horn of anvil, working from scarf point back to middle.
5. Repeat with the other end.
6. With ring heated to uniform bright red close the scarfs together by standing on edge of anvil.
7. Maintain uniform heat in ring and work roughly to shape on anvil horn so that scarfed ends are in position for welding. (Fig. 195, B and C.)
8. Apply flux, bring to welding heat and weld on the face of the anvil. Strike one blow to unite pieces and then weld down scarf points. Reheat if necessary to finish weld. Do not attempt to unite by pounding when the iron is below welding heat as it will simply be drawn out.
9. Work weld to square cross section of the size desired, next octagonal and finally finish round by rocking on anvil horn as it is pounded.
10. Shape to true ring by heating to a uniform bright red and working back over anvil horn. Curve can be put in the part desired by cooling part in water that does not require bending.

Construction of Welded Eye Bolt.—1. Cut from ½″ round stock a piece 3′ 8″ long.
2. Heat about 1-½″ of end to bright red and scarf by backing up blows. (Fig. 196 A.)
3. Bend scarf as shown at figure 196B.

4. Mark lightly with center punch 4″ from angle formed by bending scarf.

5. Heat to bright red at punch mark and bend nearly at right-angles by overhanging blows. (Fig. 196C.)

6. Heat the portion of the rod between the punch mark and the

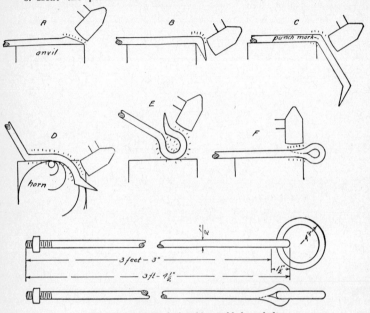

FIG. 196.—Method of making welded eye-bolt.

shoulder of the scarf to a uniform bright red and bend to ring shape over the horn of the anvil. (Fig. 196D.)

7. Maintain ring at bright red heat and close on the face of the anvil forming eye. (Fig. 196E.) Fit scarf to rod.

8. Spread eye over hardie sufficiently to insert ring.

9. Bring to yellow heat, insert ring and again close scarf against rod.

10. Apply flux, bring to welding heat and weld as shown in figure 196F.

11. Cut rod to length required, round up end and thread with ½″ die.

12. Tap blank nut to fit.

13. Construct eye bolt for other end of drag the same way except length. Make length to fit.

Job 17.—**Range Pole Shoe.**—Used as a protection for the lower end of range poles (Figs. 162, 173, 174, 180B, and 197).

Construction.—1. Cut 3″ length of ¾″ round iron.

2. Heat to bright red and upset sufficiently to make light drive fit in ¾″ black iron pipe.

3. Insert in end of pipe. Bring to yellow heat and apply flux freely.

4. Return to fire and heat slowly to welding heat, turning as heating progresses to insure uniform heat throughout.

5. Weld and draw to a square point.

6. Cut off with pipe cutter or hack saw to proper length and finish shoulder square.

7. Mark with center punch, drill small hole and countersink to permit fastening shoe to pole with flush screw.

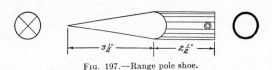

Fig. 197.—Range pole shoe.

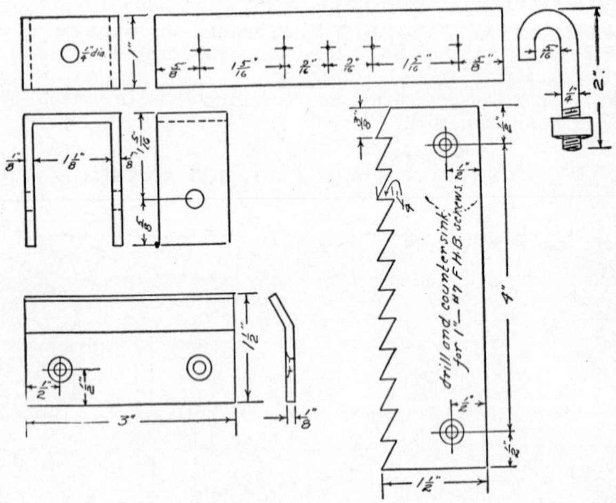

Fig. 198.—Irons for stitching horse.

8. If galvanized iron piping is used the galvanizing must be burned off before welding is attempted as the galvanizing makes the iron slippery at welding heat.

Short range poles can be made complete from ⅜″ or ½″ pipe by making point as directed above.

Job 18.—Irons for Stitching Horse.—Used as a latch, attachment for strap used to close jaws, and fulcrum for treadle on stitching horse (Figs. 173, 174, 175, 176, 178, and 198).

Construction of Stirrup.—1. Cut from a ⅛″ x 1″ piece of band iron, a section 5″ long.

2. Make center punch marks at points shown in drawing and **drill** ¼″ holes at points indicated.

3. Clamp iron in vise and bend cold, at points indicated forming **the** stirrup shown.

Construction of Catch for Side of Leg.—1. With cold chisel cut from ⅛″ x 1-½″ iron, a piece 5″ in length.

2. Clamp in vise and file notches along one edge approximately ¼″ deep x ⅜″ long.

3. Center punch, drill and countersink holes as shown for F. H. B. screws.

4. Smooth up edges with file.

Construction of Plate for Treadle.—1. With cold chisel cut a piece 3″ long from ⅛″ x 1-½″ iron.

2. Center punch, drill and countersink as shown.

3. Clamp the piece in the vise ½″ from the edge and bend to the approximate angle shown in the side view.

4. Round up edges with file.

Construction of Staple Bolt for Treadle.—1. Heat end of ¼″ round mild steel rod to bright red and bend to staple form indicated.

2. Cut to length shown in drawing.

3. Smooth up end with file and cut thread.

4. Tap blank nut to fit.

Job 19.—Making a Chain Link and Repairing a Chain.—

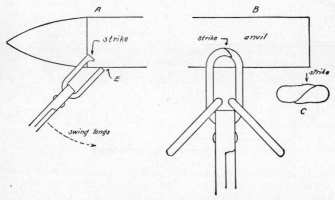

Fig. 199.—Method of making chain link.

A chain link made as described makes a permanent **repair for a** broken chain (Fig. 199).

Construction.—1. Select a piece of round rod the same size **as the** material used in making the chain that is to be repaired.

2. Heat to a bright red at a point in the rod having the distance from the end slightly greater than the length of the link to be made. Do

not attempt to make a link too short as it cannot be handled in welding as easily as a longer one.

3. Bend to a U-shape at this point, making the inside width of the U but slightly wider than the diameter of the rod from which it is made.

4. Reheat to a bright red and cut off both legs of the U to an equal length on the hardie. When cutting material on the hardie finish the cut by shearing, overhanging blows to avoid striking and injuring the edge with the hammer.

5. Heat ends of U to a bright red and scarf for welding by holding as shown at "A" figure 199. Hold the leg E against the side of the anvil with the end of the other leg lying on top as shown. Swing the link about the point E as a fulcrum in the direction of the arrow as it is pounded on the top, drawing it out to a rough point on the inside to the shape shown. The link is then turned over and the other leg scarfed in the same manner.

6. Reheat the scarfed ends to a bright red and bend over the point of the anvil horn until they cross and lie in a position for welding as shown at C.

7. Spread link like a key ring over hardie and insert parts of chain to be united. Again close link to shape shown at C.

8. Heat to welding heat, indicated by white, wet appearance, and weld by holding on anvil in position shown. Be sure to weld down points of scarf first as they are small and quickly cool below the welding heat.

9. Secure round cross section in weld by holding welded portion of link over the point of the horn and rocking it back and forth as it is pounded.

10. If link is spread too wide at the welded end bring it back to shape by heating it and striking diagonally downward as it is held edgewise on top of the anvil. Do not strike straight down on the side of the link or it will make it assume a shape somewhat like a figure 8.

Job 20.—Straight Jaw Tongs.—Straight jaw tongs are used

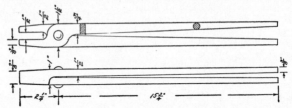

FIG. 200.—Straight jaw tongs.

for handling all common shapes of hot irons while working at the forge and anvil (Figs. 162, 163, 166, 200, and 201).

Construction.—1. Cut a section of ⅞″ x ⅞″ square iron bar 8″ in length. Use Norway iron if obtainable.

2. 1-⅛″ and 2-¼″ from each end make center punch marks.

3. Heat to a bright red at second center punch mark and bend over the edge of the anvil to the angle shown at figure 201A.

4. Heat at the first punch mark and bend this section back parallel with the long part as at figure 201B.

5. Reheat the iron and turning it one-quarter of the way over place it on the anvil as shown at figure 201C. Strike as indicated. This leaves the top surface flat and at the same time forms a shoulder on the under surface where the corner of the anvil cuts up into it.

6. Again bring iron to a working heat and place it on the anvil as shown at figure 201D. Work the jaw down to ½″ thick at the base and ⅜″ thick at the end, working to dimensions shown in detail. (Fig. 210E.)

7. Bring to white heat and punch a ⅜″ hole at the point indicated. The hole should be started from the side of the jaw marked F to permit the jaw to lie flat on the anvil when brought over the pritchel hole to

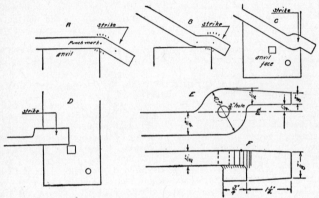

Fig. 201.—Method of making straight jaw tongs.

drive out the pellet from the reverse side, in finishing the hole. The hole should be punched rather than drilled, to secure strength. Make the hole first with a ¼″ punch and enlarge to ⅜″ by stretching. Finish the jaw to shape and size shown in figure 201E and F.

8. In the same way make a jaw on the other end of the bar, making them rights and lefts.

9. Cut the bar in the center and scarf the ends for welding as shown in figure 168, Chapter XIV.

10. Cut two pieces of ½″ round iron 14″ long.

11. Scarf ends for welding as shown in figure 168, Chapter XIV.

12. Heat jaw and handle to welding heat and weld.

13. Heat handles to bright red and taper by drawing out, making them first square, next octagonal and finally round.

14. Cut a piece of ⅜″ rod 1-¼″ long for a rivet. Heat the rivet red and assemble the two sections of the tongs. When finished jaws should work freely. If too tight, heat and work back and forth while heated.

15. Cut handles to length required and smooth up work.

Job 21.—**Cold Chisel.**—The cold chisel is necessary in farm shop work in making repairs to metal. It is used for cutting cold iron and can be made in various shapes for different purposes. The shape shown is the best adapted to general use (Fig. 202).

Construction.—1. At a point 7" from the end of a ¾" octagonal tool steel bar apply heat until red and cut off with sharp hot chisel. Cut in from all sides to the center to preserve a smooth end.

2. Select best end of section to cut off for cutting edge. Heat the top end to bright red and shape as shown in the drawing, making taper first square, next octagonal and finally round. Permit the top to cool slowly to prevent extreme hardness and consequent danger from chips flying from the top when struck with the hammer.

3. Heat cutting end to bright red and forge to wedge shape by drawing out over the base of the horn. (Fig. 163.) Finish on the flat surface of

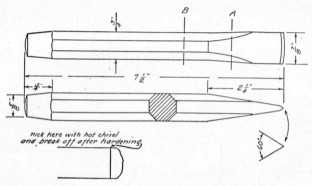

FIG. 202.—Method of making cold chisel.

the anvil. Maintain steel at bright red heat while working. Do not work at dark red heat and do not permit steel to become too hot.

4. When worked to shape desired make a cut across both sides near the end with the hot chisel as shown.

5. Heat cutting end of chisel back to point B slowly to a dull "cherry red" heat, the hardening heat of average steel, and bury it in the ashes in forge to cool slowly. This anneals it, making it soft and ductile, and relieves internal stresses, making the steel tougher and stronger. The annealing may be omitted if desired.

6. When annealing is completed reheat to cherry red or hardening heat to point B and plunge in water to point A. Swing the chisel to and fro and move up and down slightly to prevent sharp division between hardened and unhardened portions which might cause cracking. This treatment makes the lower portion very hard and brittle.

7. Pull the chisel from the water and rap sharply on the anvil to break off the portion below the nick formed with the hot chisel. This leaves good steel for the cutting edge. The extreme end is likely to be injured by too high a heat.

8. Polish the end of the chisel by rubbing on a brick, concrete floor or other means and watch for the band of color, caused by heating, work down from the uncooled section of the chisel between A and B. When the proper color has reached the edge, dark blue for a chisel for general use, plunge the tool in water again, cooling it. If the portion between A and B is still red, cool it slowly to prevent hardness and brittleness at this point.

9. Grind edge to shape and angle shown in drawing.

CHAPTER XVI

THE FARM WATER SUPPLY. INSTALLATION AND REPAIR OF PUMPS. MISCELLANEOUS FARM REPAIRS

WATER for farm use is obtained almost entirely from wells and springs. With the exception of a very few cases, the water is below the point where it is to be used, making pumping necessary, and if

FIG. 203.—Gravity water system. Large attic tank supplied by engine-driven pump drawing water from a well. (Gould Mfg. Co.)

running water is desired in the buildings a system of storage and distribution is required as well.

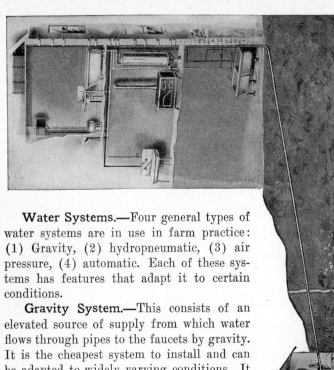

Water Systems.—Four general types of water systems are in use in farm practice: (1) Gravity, (2) hydropneumatic, (3) air pressure, (4) automatic. Each of these systems has features that adapt it to certain conditions.

Gravity System.—This consists of an elevated source of supply from which water flows through pipes to the faucets by gravity. It is the cheapest system to install and can be adapted to widely varying conditions. It may range from a small tank in the attic, supplied by a force pump in the basement or well-house, and furnishing water for the kitchen sink (Fig. 203), to a concrete tank or reservoir on a nearby hill, supplied by a spring or power pump, furnishing water for the entire farmstead.

Limitations.—The attic tank is suitable only for use in connection with the soft water supply. Drinking water in summer becomes warm and brackish when stored so near the roof, unless the tank is supplied direct from a spring or by means of a hydraulic ram (Fig. 204), and the water allowed to flow constantly.

A concrete tank placed on a nearby hill furnishes the best type

Fig. 204.—Simple gravity system. Water supplied by a hydraulic ram operated by discharge from spring. Overflow from tank can be piped to barn and ram permitted to work continuously, maintaining a supply of fresh, cold water for drinking and household use. (Gould Mfg. Co.)

of reservoir for a gravity system. Where the elevation is sufficient to permit burying the tank in the ground cool water is assured for summer, and winter freezing is prevented. Freezing will not be serious, however, as long as the bottom is on the ground, protecting the pipes where they enter the tank. Earth can be graded up about the sides to furnish heat insulation.

Elevation Required.—Where the distance from the supply tank to the point where the water is to be used does not exceed 100 feet, a water level of from 10 to 15 feet above the highest faucet will give a satisfactory flow. As this distance is increased the elevation of the tank should be increased.

The quantity of water used will vary greatly. The season, the weather, the facilities provided for using it, and the kind of work being done by the animals supplied are all influencing factors. Usually the quantity used increases after the installation of a system. The following are fair average daily requirements:

```
Man (bath and all purposes) ................25 gallons
Horse ....................................12   "
Cow .....................................12   "
Sheep ................................... 2   "
Hog ..................................... 2   "
```

Determining the Size of Tank Required.—The necessary capacity in gallons can be determined for any given place from the table. For example, a tank supplying water to a family of six people and to twenty-five head of cattle should have a capacity of at least 450 gallons or 60 cubic feet. One cubic foot is equal to 7½ gallons. Where a windmill is used for power this capacity should be multiplied by three to insure sufficient water to carry over calm periods.

Capacity of Cylindrical Tanks

Diameter in feet	Depth of Tank in Feet								
	4	5	6	7	8	9	10	11	12
	Capacity in Gallons								
4	376	588	846	1152	1504	1904	2350	2844	3384
5	470	735	1058	1439	1880	2380	2938	3555	4230
6	564	881	1269	1727	2256	2855	3525	4265	5076
7	658	1028	1481	2015	2632	3331	4113	4976	5922
8	752	1175	1692	2303	3008	3807	4700	5687	6768
9	846	1322	1904	2591	3384	4283	5288	6398	7614
10	940	1469	2115	2879	3760	4759	5875	7109	8460
11	1034	1616	2327	3167	4132	5235	6463	7820	9306
12	1128	1763	2537	3455	4512	5711	7050	8531	10152

Hydropneumatic System.—In this system the water is pumped into an airtight steel tank. As the water is pumped in, the air is compressed above it, and the resulting pressure is used to force water from the faucets when they are opened. This system is adapted to general farm use where the quantity of water required is not too great. Where large quantities of water are needed it is expensive to install because of the large tank necessary. The tank is usually placed in the basement, insuring cool water in the summer and protecting against freezing in the winter. A hydropneumatic outfit is shown in figure 205.

FIG. 205.—Simple hydropneumatic system. (Kewanee Private Utilities Co.)

Air Pressure System.—In this system an air compressor is used and compressed air only is stored. This is piped to the well where it operates a submerged pump. The pump is automatic, starting when the pressure is released by the opening of a faucet and stopping when the faucet is closed. It pumps water directly from the well, insuring cool water if it is permitted to run long enough to empty the pipe.

This system is adapted to use where it is desired to have both cistern and well water on tap, as the same power plant can operate both pumps. It is also adapted to use where it is desirable to have the power plant at some distance from the well or other source of supply. Figure 206 shows an air pressure system.

Automatic System.—This system (Fig. 207) consists of an electrically-driven pump controlled by a pressure-operated switch. When the pressure is released by the opening of a faucet the pump starts and continues to operate until the pressure is again restored after the faucet is closed. Being electrically driven it is restricted to localities where electric power is available. This may be obtained either from a commercial line or from a home lighting plant. Where battery current from a home lighting plant is used for power an installation of this kind is not advised for stock watering because of the cost of operation. The system is well adapted to household use,

Fig. 206.—Installation of air pressure system. (Milwaukee Air Power Pump Co., Milwaukee, Wis.)

and must be installed where there is no danger of freezing, as a small quantity of water is stored to maintain the pressure.

Choice of System.—Because of its simplicity, ruggedness, low cost and adaptability to widely varying conditions, some form of the gravity system is advised for general farm use. Where the gravity

Fig. 207.—Electrically-driven automatic water system. (Delco Light Co.)

system is used much of the work of installation can be done by the owner and his help, and in many cases existing equipment used.

The Farm Pump.—Practically all of the pumps used in farm practices are of the reciprocating type, and can be divided roughly into two classes: (1) Lift pumps, (2) force pumps.

A simple lift pump is shown in figure 208. Water is raised by a plunger working within the cylinder. With this type of pump water can be lifted only to the spout as the top of the pump is left open. It is adapted to such purposes as watering stock where the water is raised from a comparatively shallow well and discharged

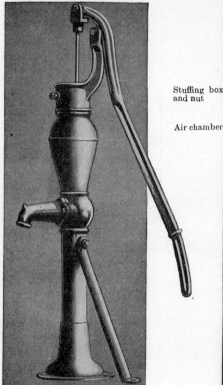

208

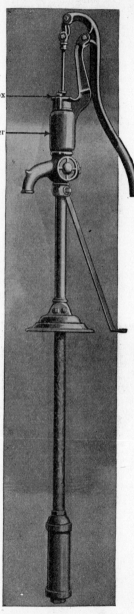

Stuffing box
and nut

Air chamber

FIG. 208.—Simple lift pump. Note the
absence of stuffing nut at the top of the standard where the pump rod comes through, preventing the use of this type of pump where
water has to be forced above the spout of the
pump or against pressure. (Courtesy Red
Jacket Manufacturing Co., Davenport, Iowa.)

FIG. 209.—Simple single-acting force
pump. This pump differs from the lift pump
in that the rod, passes through a gland and
stuffing nut at the top of the air-chamber,
making a water-tight joint which permits using
the pump to force water to an elevated tank or
against pressure. The pump is also provided
with an air-chamber, which tends to relieve
shocks and strains on the pump and equalizes
the flow to some extent.

209

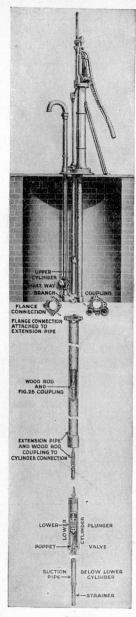

UPPER
CYLINDER
THREE WAY
BRANCH   COUPLING

FLANGE
CONNECTION

FLANGE CONNECTION
ATTACHED TO
EXTENSION PIPE

WOOD ROD
AND
FIG.28 COUPLING

EXTENSION PIPE
AND WOOD ROD
COUPLING TO
CYLINDER CONNECTION

LOWER   LOWER   PLUNGER
        CYLINDER
POPPET   VALVE

SUCTION   BELOW LOWER
PIPE   CYLINDER

STRAINER

210

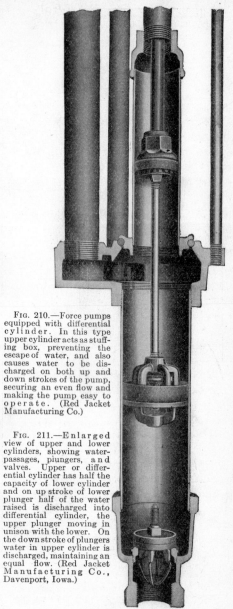

Fig. 210.—Force pumps equipped with differential cylinder. In this type upper cylinder acts as stuffing box, preventing the escape of water, and also causes water to be discharged on both up and down strokes of the pump, securing an even flow and making the pump easy to operate. (Red Jacket Manufacturing Co.)

Fig. 211.—Enlarged view of upper and lower cylinders, showing water-passages, plungers, and valves. Upper or differential cylinder has half the capacity of lower cylinder and on up stroke of lower plunger half of the water raised is discharged into differential cylinder, the upper plunger moving in unison with the lower. On the down stroke of plungers water in upper cylinder is discharged, maintaining an equal flow. (Red Jacket Manufacturing Co., Davenport, Iowa.)

211

into an open trough at or below the level of the spout. It cannot be used to supply an overhead tank or to discharge against pressure.

The force pump shown in figure 209 is similar to the lift pump, but has a closed top, which permits the water to be pumped against pressure. It is also provided with an air chamber which serves to equalize the flow somewhat and to relieve shocks caused by the sudden starting of the water column when the plunger is raised. A differential cylinder is sometimes used to further equalize the flow of water. This is shown in figures 210 and 211. Force pumps, being designed for higher lifts, are usually built stronger than lift pumps and equipped with smaller cylinders, particularly where they are to be hand operated. Both force and lift pumps can be obtained with windmill or power tops which permit their operation by gasoline engine or other power.

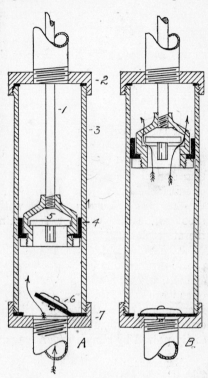

Properties of Air.—Air is compressible, elastic, and has weight. When pressure is brought to bear upon it, it can be crowded into a smaller space, immediately expanding again when the pressure is released. This property is utilized in the air chamber of force pumps as well as in

FIG. 212.—Operation of simple suction or lift pump. In "A" plunger is shown on upstroke. It is drawn up by plunger rod 1, poppet valve 5 in plunger of bucket is seated and partial vacuum is created below plunger because of airtight seal that it makes with cylinder wall because of leather packing 4. Atmospheric pressure on surface of water being greater than pressure below, upward-moving plunger "flap" valve 6 is lifted and water flows upward through it filling the cylinder. On down stroke B, flap valve 6 closes and the water above it, being imprisoned beneath the downward moving plunger, the poppet valve 5 in the plunger is raised and the water escapes to above the plunger. On the next up stroke the process is repeated and the water above the plunger is raised toward the spout.

the storage tanks of air pressure systems and hydropneumatic outfits.

The action of a simple lift pump is shown in figure 212A

16

and B. At A the plunger is shown at the lower end of the cylinder. As it starts upward the air beneath expands, filling the increasing space. As the air expands the pressure is lessened and it soon drops so low that the pressure of the atmosphere on the water of the well (14.7 pounds) is sufficient to force a column of water up the suction pipe and push open the valve at the bottom of the cylinder. The water flows into the cylinder until the weight of the water in the suction pipe plus the remaining air pressure in the cylinder is equal to the outside atmospheric pressure.

In B the plunger is starting on its return trip. The valve in the bottom of the cylinder closes, trapping the water in the cylinder. Water being practically incompressible, cannot be squeezed into a smaller space as air would, and consequently the valve in the plunger is forced open and the water escapes through it as the plunger continues to move downward. When the plunger reaches the bottom of its stroke the process is repeated. As the plunger again starts upward the valve closes and the water above is carried toward the spout while the cylinder is again filled by the pressure of the atmosphere.

Atmospheric Pressure and Suction.—The effect of atmospheric pressure due to the weight of air, *i.e.,* the filling of the pump cylinder when the plunger is pulled upward, is frequently spoken of as " suction " and the pipe leading from the water to the cylinder is commonly called the " suction " pipe. The fact that it is pressure, caused by the weight of air, that is lifting the water can be very easily proved by simple experiments.

Experiment 1.—Fill a bottle with clean water. Insert a short glass tube through a hole in a loosely fitting cork and apply the mouth to the end of the tube and suck. Water will flow up the tube and into the mouth.

Now tightly seal the cork in the bottle with sealing wax or paraffine and again attempt to get water by sucking. This time no water will be obtained. Air must be free to press upon the surface of the water and force it up the tube when the pressure above is reduced by sucking.

Experiment 2.—Place about an inch of water in a square syrup can and bring it to a boil. Let it boil briskly for a few minutes to fill the can with steam and drive out the air. Remove the can from the fire, screw the cover on quickly and tightly and dash cold water over the can to condense the steam contained. As the steam is condensed a vacuum will be drawn inside the can and the weight of the air outside will crush it. (Fig. 213.)

Height to Which Atmospheric Pressure Will Raise Water.—With a perfect vacuum above it a column of water 33.95 feet in height will be supported by the atmosphere at sea level. It cannot be raised above this. As the elevation is increased, this height is reduced until at 10,560 feet it is but 22.82 feet.

Practical Limitations.—A perfect vacuum cannot be obtained with an ordinary pump, and there must also be sufficient difference in pressure to cause a flow of water to the cylinder. Because of these factors a pump cylinder cannot be placed more than twenty to twenty-five feet above the water surface. In mountainous regions this should be reduced to 15 feet. In all cases the cylinder should be placed as near the water as possible. Water can be drawn long distances horizontally where the lift is low and a large pipe is used to avoid friction. Care must be exercised in laying suction pipe to secure tight joints, as a very slight leak will admit enough air to spoil the action of the pump.

Selection of a Pump.—Where the well is shallow and the water is to be discharged at the spout

Fig. 213.—Gallon syrup can crushed by atmospheric pressure. Water was first placed in the can and boiled over the firepot, driving out the air. Top was then quickly screwed in place and steam condensed by plunging can in cold water, creating vacuum inside and causing can to be crushed by weight of outside air as shown.

level, a lift pump fitted with a large diameter cylinder can be used. If the lift is high and the water has to be forced to an elevated tank or against pressure, a force pump with a smaller cylinder should be purchased. For hand use the "double-acting" pump is the best. This, through the action of a differential cylinder, discharges half of its water on the down stroke of the plunger, making the flow more nearly constant and the operation of the pump easier. The following table gives the cylinder size best adapted to various conditions:

Depth of Well.	Cylinder Diameter
30 feet	3–1/2″
30– 75 feet	3″
75–125 feet	2–1/2″
125–200 feet	2″

Types of Cylinders.—Cylinders are obtainable in brass, called brass body, in brass-lined, and in plain cast iron. Of these the brass-lined cylinder is the best (Fig. 214). The cast iron shell gives it the strength of the cast iron cylinder, while the brass lining gives it the smoothness of the brass body cylinder.

Pump troubles can be diagnosed quite closely from the action of the pump.

Indications.	Cause.	Remedy
Pump loses priming, water runs down leaving cylinder empty. Handle rises slowly when pumping stops.	Lower cylinder valve is worn or is held from seat by sand or gravel. Cylinder may leak.	Replace valve or clean seat. Replace lower cylinder head if found cracked.
Pump works easily, frothy water discharged.	Suction pipe leaks air. Low water in well.	Tighten or repair suction pipe. Lower pump below water.
Handle pulls down with rubbery feeling and flies up when released.	Suction pipe choked. Suction pipe too small. Cylinder too high above water level. Strainer at bottom of pipe clogged.	Clean pipe or strainer removing obstruction. Use larger pipe. Lower cylinder.
Pump works hard.	Obstruction in discharge l i n e. T o o small a pipe used. Too large a cylinder used. Plunger leathers too tight.	Remove obstruction. Replace with larger pipe. Replace with smaller cylinder. Fit plunger leathers.
Handle works easily with little or no water pumped.	Sand or gravel under plunger valves. Plunger valve worn out. Plunger leathers worn.	Remove gravel. Repair valve. Replace worn out plunger leathers.
Double acting pump discharging water on down stroke of handle only.	Sand under lower check valve. Lower valve worn out. Upper plunger leathers worn.	Remove sand or gravel. Replace valve. Replace p l u n g e r leathers.

The hydraulic ram is an automatic pump using the energy of falling water to raise a smaller quantity to a height above the source of supply. Under average conditions it will pump about 1/10 of the water passing through it, the exact quantity depending upon the length of the discharge pipe, the height to which the water is raised and other factors. It is useful for pumping water from a spring or stream situated below the buildings where the following conditions exist:

1. The spring must furnish a minimum flow of three gallons per minute.

2. There must be a minimum fall of three feet, *i.e.*, the ram must be at least three feet below the water level in the spring.

3. There must be good drainage below the ram permitting the free discharge of waste water and preventing flooding during periods of high water.

The ram may be used to supply either an elevated tank or a pressure tank. A small tank in the house attic (Fig. 204) is the most common installation; the ram is permitted to work continuously and the overflow led to the barn. This insures a constant supply of fresh, cold water at the house.

Where conditions are right for installing a ram a manufacturer should be consulted and the ram ordered and placed under his instruction. This fixes responsibility for results.

Operation of the Ram.—In figure 215, G is the drive pipe, down which water flows from the spring to the base of the ram, B, and escapes through the impetus valve, F. When sufficient velocity is attained the impetus valve is closed suddenly, stopping the flow of water in the drive pipe and causing it to exert a hammer-like blow upon the water contained in the base of the ram. The check valve, E, is opened by the momentary high pressure and a portion of

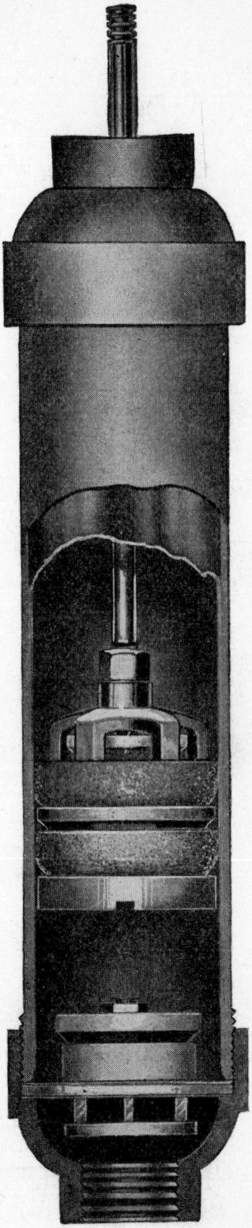

FIG. 214.—Brass-lined cylinder. This type of cylinder is best for general use. The cast-iron shell gives strength and protection against denting while assembling and making repairs, while the brass lining gives all of the smoothness of a brass body cylinder. (Red Jacket Manufacturing Co.)

the water is forced into the air bell, A, compressing the air above it. Compressed air is elastic. Consequently there is a rebound which closes the check valve, E, and causes a slight backward surge in the drive pipe, reducing the pressure in the base. This causes a small quantity of air to enter through the snifting valve, C, and the impetus valve to again drop open. Water now starts flowing down the drive pipe, G, and the process is repeated as long as the ram continues to run. Water entering the air bell, A, is forced up the

Fig. 215.—Hydraulic ram. Useful for pumping water where a spring supplies a flow of at least 3 gallons per minute and a fall of 3 feet is obtainable between the ram and the spring. A. Air-chamber. B. Body. C. Snifting valve. E. Check valve. F. Impetus valve. G. Drive pipe. H. Service pipe, carrying water to buildings or elevated tank. (Gould Manufacturing Co., Seneca Falls, N. Y.)

discharge pipe, H, to the buildings. The air admitted by the snifting valve maintains the supply in the bell, which would otherwise be absorbed by the water.

The ram may be used in connection with springs, streams, or flowing wells. Where a small spring occurs in connection with a stream unfit for drinking a double-acting ram may be installed.

This uses the water of the stream as motive power and pumps the spring water to the buildings.

Pipe Fitting.—A set of pipe tools consisting of ½-inch, ¾-inch, 1, and 1¼-inch dies, a pipe vise, pipe cutter, reamer and two 18-inch Stillson wrenches will be found sufficient for most jobs, as most of the work will consist of cutting, threading and putting pipe together. Pipe is joined by means of threaded sleeves called couplings. Elbows of 45 degrees or 90 degrees are used for making changes in direction. Where a pipe is connected between two other pipes or where it may be desirable to disconnect it without disturbing the remainder of the line, a union is used. A bushing or reducer is used where it is desired to make a change in size. Common pipe fittings are shown in figure 216. Pipe is fitted with a tapered thread, and a pipe cement or lubricant is used when assembling to permit it to be screwed tightly together. It also tends to prevent rusting in the joint, making the pipe easy to take apart later if necessary. Pipe cement should be applied to the

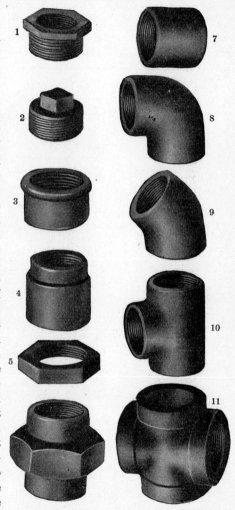

Fig. 216.—Common pipe fittings used in the installation of farm water-works: 1, bushing; 2, plug; 3, cap; 4, reducer; 5, lock nut; 6, union; 7, coupling; 8, 90° elbow; 9, 45° elbow; 10, tee; 11, cross. (Gould Mfg. Co.)

threaded ends of the pipe only. When applied inside the couplings it is likely to obstruct the pipe after hardening. White lead paste is often used as a lubricant and cement in assembling pipe. The addition of graphite improves it.

Size of Pipe to Use.—In farm water installations the factors or causes acting to create a flow of water in the pipes are: (1) Pressure due to pumping, (2) the pull of gravity.

In gravity systems the vertical distance of the source above the point of discharge is called the "head." These two factors, head and pressure, are interchangeable; pressure of one pound per square inch corresponding to a head of 2.3 feet, while a head of one foot is equal to a pressure of .434 pounds per square inch.

There are many factors which act to retard the flow of water in a pipe.

  1. Friction is proportional to the length of the pipe.
  2. Friction increases approximately as the square of the velocity.
  3. Friction varies inversely as the diameter of the pipe; a ½″ pipe offering twice the resistance of a pipe 1″ in diameter.
  4. Friction is increased by roughness, bends, elbows and valves.

From the above it is evident that under conditions of long lines, low heads, or where a large supply of water is desired, a large pipe should be used. ¾″ and 1″ pipes are standard sizes for farm use.

Flow of Water Through Pipes 200 Feet in Length

Diameter of Pipe in Inches	Head in Feet			
	5	10	15	20
	Discharge in Gallons Per Minute			
½″	.68	.98	1.21	1.41
¾″	2.02	2.92	3.61	4.23
1″	3.82	5.49	6.88	8.00
1-¼″	7.92	11.38	14.06	16.32
1-½″	12.82	18.40	22.75	26.40

Soldering.—The use of threaded fittings makes it possible to do almost any job of farm plumbing by the use of pipe tools alone. However, the occasional use of lead pipe and the necessary repairs to metal roofs and tinware makes a knowledge of soldering desirable.

Tools and Equipment Required.—The soldering copper is the most essential tool. With it, solder, and a flux, simple repair work can be done. A heavy copper should be purchased for farm work, as it retains the heat longer. It is also advisable to purchase them in pairs, so that one may be heating while the other is being used. The shape shown in figure 217 is most desirable for general use. The following tools are desirable:

Gasoline fire pot.   ½″ cold chisel.
Snips.   Small punch or nail set.
                       Rivet set.

Essentials of Soldering.—To secure satisfactory work in soldering the following essentials must be secured:

Fig. 217.—Equipment for soldering: 1, gasoline fire-pot tor heating soldering copper; 2, snips for cutting sheet metal; 3, cold chisel; 4, punch; 5, rivet set; 6, soldering copper; 7, sal ammoniac; 8, solder; 9, soldering flux; 10, knife for scraping metal bright; 11, riveting hammer.

1. The soldering copper must be kept hot, clean and have the point well tinned.
2. The metals to be soldered must be scraped thoroughly, securing clean, bright surfaces for uniting.
3. A good flux must be used to keep the metals in this condition and to aid in the flow of the solder.
4. The metals that are being united must be heated above the melting point of the solder used.

Heating the Soldering Iron.—The soldering iron should be placed in the pot so that the flame plays against its base. This protects the tinning on the point of the iron from the flame, keeping it clean and in good condition. Where the soldering iron must be heated in a coal stove it can be protected by using a short length of 1½-inch pipe, 6 to 8 inches long, and heating the iron within it.

Keeping the Iron in Condition.—One of the best arrangements for maintaining the tinning on the iron is the brick soldering " jig " shown in figure 218.   Small pieces of rosin and sal ammoniac are placed in the cavity cut in the brick, and the heated iron cleaned, fluxed and tinned as it is rubbed on the brick in contact with solder.   A few rubs before replacing the iron in the pot for reheating will keep it in excellent working shape.   Should the iron be overheated, file the point smooth before tinning.

Fluxes are used to prevent oxidation and aid in the flow of the

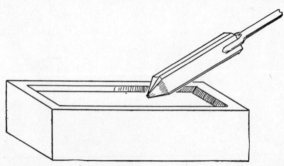

Fig. 218.—"Soldering jig" made from soft brick. Top is dug out with cold chisel and rosin, sal ammoniac and solder placed in the cavity so formed. Heated iron is rubbed in this to clean and "tin" it.

melted solder.   They consist of a liquid, paste or powder that is applied to the surfaces after scraping.   The following materials are used as fluxes :

Chloride of zinc (liquid).   Tallow.
Commercial flux (paste).   Hydrochloric acid.
Rosin (paste, powder or liquid).

Chloride of zinc is the most generally used flux in rough repair work.   It is prepared from hydrochloric acid and zinc, as directed in Job 6.   It is satisfactory for use on tin, galvanized iron, copper and general work.   When used on galvanized iron, hydrochloric acid is sometimes added.   This acts on the galvanizing and should be washed off when the work is completed to prevent further action.

Rosin is used in soldering tin, copper, galvanized iron and lead. It is prepared for use by pulverizing and applying as a powder, by mixing to a paste with tallow or by forming a thin varnish by dissolving in alcohol.

Commercial fluxes are largely made in the form of pastes because of convenience. They are satisfactory and can usually be obtained at hardware stores or dealers in electrical equipment.

Tallow is used in its original condition when soldering lead. It is smeared over the freshly shaved surfaces and protects them from oxidation.

Job 1.—**Cutting and Threading Pipe.**—Pipe is obtainable in lengths of about 20 feet. Where greater or lesser lengths are

219   220

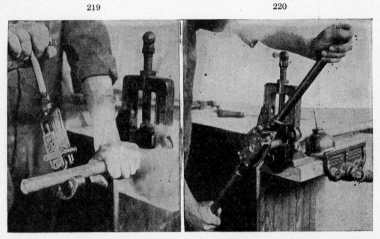

Fig. 219.—Cutting pipe. The pipe is secured in the vise and cut by rotating the cutter back and forth, giving the handle about ¼ turn to the right to force the cutters into the work at every push forward.

Fig. 220.—Threading pipe. Pipe is gripped in vise and dies turned on until pipe projects about two threads through die. Use considerable pressure when starting die to insure its getting a start on the end of the pipe.

required the pipe must be cut and threaded for joining up in the length desired.

Method of Work.—1. Determine and mark point at which it is desired to cut pipe.

2. Place in pipe vise with marked point about 6″ from vise.

3. Adjust cutter to pipe, turn down tightly, apply lard oil and move handle sufficiently to make a mark clear around the pipe. With 3-wheel type of cutter a half revolution is sufficient. (Fig. 219.)

4. Tighten one-fourth turn and repeat. Repeat this process until pipe is cut off. Use plenty of oil.

5. Insert pipe die of the size described in stock. See that guide bushing in stock corresponds to size of pipe being threaded.

6. With file remove burr from end of pipe so that guide bushing will slip over it easily.

7. Apply lard oil to dies and pushing guide over the end of the pipe turn stock to the right at the same time using considerable pressure. (Fig.

220.) When dies engage pipe pressure can be discontinued as they will feed themselves on. Strive to engage dies at once. Otherwise a rounded pipe end results which is hard to join.

8. Continue threading until pipe end projects two to three threads through dies.

9. Back off dies by turning to left. Remove chips by rapping and remove burr on inside of pipe with reamer.

Job 2.—**Threading a Nipple.**—Short pieces of pipe are known

FIG. 221.—Threading a nipple in a jig. The end of a pipe is threaded, cut to the length required, and turned into coupling B, which is turned onto a length of pipe carried in the vise. The nipple A may be shorter than shown by using a guide bushing in the die stock that will pass over the coupling.

as nipples. Because of their short length a special means of threading is resorted to.

Method of Work.—1. Thread one end of pipe as described under Job 1.

2. Cut nipple to length desired as described under Job 1.

3. Thread a second pipe of the same diameter with a long thread the thread being sufficiently long to permit a coupling to be screwed on to within about ½″ of its entire length.

4. Screw on coupling.

5. Screw threaded end of nipple into exposed end of coupling and thread as before. Where nipple is extremely short, termed a "close nipple," use a guide bushing in the stock that will fit over the coupling. In this way the thread can be cut clear up to the coupling. (Fig. 221.)

6. Use reamer to remove inside burr.

7. Remove finished nipple from coupling which has served as holding chuck.

Job 3.—Repairing Leaky Compression Faucet or Bibb.—

Compression faucets (Fig. 222) are in general use as water outlets in farm water systems. They open by lifting a rubber or fiber disc from the pipe opening by means of a screw connected with the handle. Through use this disc becomes worn and leaks, making repair or replacement necessary.

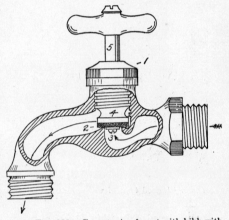

Method of Making Repair.—1. Close shut-off cock in supply line shutting off water supply.

2. Adjust wrench to fit cap, and remove, being careful not to injure nickle plated brass cap with wrench. Use cloth inside of wrench jaws.

3. Unscrew inside portion of faucet, removing it and exposing disc.

4. See if there is obstruction between disc and seat, if so remove it and reassemble faucet.

FIG. 222.—Compression faucet with bibb with side cut away, showing interior parts and water-passages. Faucet is opened by turning threaded portion 4 to left, raising fiber disk 2 from its seat. Nut 1, acts as compression nut to packing of candle-wicking about stem 5, making a water-tight joint. Faucet is repaired when worn by removing cap 1, unscrewing threaded portion 4, and replacing fiber disk 2, by removal of screw 3.

5. If disc is frayed or grooved take out screw holding it and replace with new disc. Faucet discs or washers can be obtained at hardware store for a small sum. Discs cut from rubber or leather are unsatisfactory because too soft. Usual size of faucet is ¾″.

6. If packing between inside part of faucet and top is destroyed so that faucet leaks around stem, slide cap to top of stem and wind a few turns of oiled candle wicking about stem.

7. Screw disc down on seat and turn cap in place. Test faucet to see that it works freely. Close faucet.

8. Turn on water at shut-off and test for leaks.

Job 4.—**Installing a Farm Pump.**—Practically all farm water supplies are obtained from wells, cisterns, or springs whose level is below that of the point at which the water is used, making the use of a pump necessary.

Method of Work.—1. Examine situation and determine type of pump required.

2. Determine proper size of cylinder to use by reference to page 243.

3. Measure depth of well and determine length of pipe and pump rod required. Pipe should reach nearly but not quite to well bottom. Cylin-

Fig. 223.—A good type of well-covering. Note concrete trough for carrying away waste water.

der must be placed within 25 feet of permanent water level and the nearer it can be placed the better. Best results are secured when lower cylinder is submerged. Sufficient pump rod must be purchased to reach from top of pump to bottom of cylinder.

4. Purchase pump and piping.

5. Examine valves and see that they seat properly. Remove any metal chips or other obstruction that might hold them from seat.

6. Soak valves and plunger leathers in luke warm water until soft.

7. Assemble pump. Use pipe cement on joints and draw up tightly to prevent air leaks below cylinder. If well is shallow, pump may be assembled complete on surface and then lowered into well. In this case secure all measurements for pipe lengths and begin assembling at pump and work downward. With deep well lower a length of pipe into the well and hold by means of chains, clamps or wrenches while the length above is screwed into place. Cut and thread pump rod so that the joints come a little above the pipe joints when the plunger is at the bottom of cylinder. This permits installation or removal of pump in sections.

8. In case of double acting force pump place upper cylinder six to eight feet below well covering and drill small hole, ⅛″ in discharge pipe just

above level of upper cylinder to prevent freezing. Pump drains down to this point when pumping ceases.

9. Fasten base of pump to water-tight platform, concrete preferred. (Fig. 223.)

10. Arrange means to carry waste water away from well, preventing surface wash from getting back into well.

11. If power is used, select pulleys giving the pump a speed of not greater than 40 strokes per minute and adjust stroke to as long as can be used without plunger hitting at top or bottom of cylinder. Test pump

FIG. 224.—Lifting pump by means of two levers and chains.

by hand before applying power to avoid possible breakage. A slow speed with long stroke is best for power work.

Job 5.—Repairing the Farm Pump. Putting in a New Plunger Leather.—The pump will eventually fail through wear. The ability to locate the trouble and remedy it is an advantage to the farmer living at a considerable distance from the plumber.

Method of Work.—1. Determine probable source of trouble by noting action of pump. In this case a worn plunger leather or defective plunger valve is assumed.

2. Provide materials indicated as being necessary to make repair.

3. Take pump from well. Pump may be lifted by means of two levers and chains as shown in figure 224. Two chains are used giving each a slip hitch about the pipe. One lever supports the pump while the other is raised to secure a new grip. This process is repeated until a joint appears at the surface when it is taken apart. Continue until the cylinder is reached. If well is shallow entire pump can be raised and taken apart on the surface.

4. When cylinder is reached support pipe beneath cylinder to prevent pipe slipping into well and remove upper cylinder head. Take out plunger.

5. Fasten upper part of plunger in vise and remove lower part by turning. Lower part is usually slotted making it possible to fit and use a piece of flat iron like a large screw driver if special tool is not available. It may also be turned by means of a punch or dull cold chisel and hammer. If it resists turning tap lightly around circumference to loosen thread. If this fails apply heat and soak in kerosene.

6. Clean metal faces of plunger by scraping and fit new leather which has been previously soaked.

7. Assemble plunger using grease and graphite on thread to prevent rust and permit easy removal in the future.

8. Examine pump for other possible defects before reassembling, making repairs where needed.

9. Reassemble pump, beginning at the cylinder and working upward, lowering pump into well as the work progresses.

10. Fasten to platform and test.

Job 6.—Making a Zinc Chloride Flux.

—A flux is used in soldering to lessen the oxidation of the metals and to aid in securing a flow of solder into the joint. A zinc chloride flux is easily prepared, and is well adapted to general repair work.

Method of Work.—1. Secure at the hardware store a pint of commercial hydrochloric acid and place in a quart glass fruit jar.

2. Secure a quantity of scrap zinc, cut it into small pieces with the snips and add slowly to the acid. Add sufficient zinc to neutralize the acid. This condition can be told by pieces left undissolved in the bottom of the jar after the bubbling action has ceased. Zinc taken from discarded dry cells, if scraped clean, makes a good flux because of its purity.

3. When action has ceased pour off the clear liquid and add an equal quantity of clean soft water.

4. Place a lump of sal ammoniac in a strong cloth and pound to a powder with a hammer. Add two teaspoonfuls of this sal ammoniac powder to the quart of liquid. Keep this as a stock solution in the glass jar, pouring out a small quantity in a jelly tumbler for use. Discard and obtain a fresh supply when it becomes dirty.

Do not store this flux near tools as the fumes from it cause them to rust.

Job 7.—Tinning the Soldering Iron.

—To have the molten solder flow freely from the point of the iron it must be coated with a film of solder. The process of applying this solder is called " tinning " the iron, and a soldering copper so treated is said to be " tinned."

Method of Work.—1. Clean the iron with a flat file, making the four sides of the point clean and bright.

2. Heat in fire pot or by other means until copper will melt solder freely upon touching it. Do not heat hotter than required to do this.

3. Take from fire and if dirty wipe on damp rag or waste.

4. Plunge point into glass of soldering flux as prepared in Job 6.

This cleans point and makes it bright. Other fluxes may be used for the purpose as well.

5. Rub the point of the cleaned and heated iron in solder. (Fig. 225). The melted solder should flow over the entire point covering it with a bright coating of tin like silver. The iron must be kept in this condition to do satisfactory work. The use of the "jig" (Fig. 218), will keep the point bright and clean unless the tinning is burned off by overheating.

Job 8.—Soldering Leaky Buckets.—Buckets frequently develop leaks through jams caused by rough handling or seams are

225   226

FIG. 225.—"Tinning the iron." The iron is filed to a smooth point, heated, dipped in flux, and rubbed in melted solder. Applying an even coat to the point. In this illustration melted solder is held in hollow in block of sal ammoniac, which of itself acts as a flux.

FIG. 226.—Picking up solder with point of hot iron. Solder is supported on bench top and a supply of solder obtained on iron by holding hot iron in contact with solder.

opened by water freezing in them. In most cases repairs can be quickly made by soldering.

Method of Work.—1. Scrape surface to be soldered absolutely clean and bright. The success of the soldering depends largely upon the thoroughness with which the material is scraped. Scrape with an old pocket knife or mowing machine section.

2. With wooden mallet and block return bucket to as near original shape as possible, bringing the surfaces together that are to be soldered.

3. Apply flux to the surfaces to be united. Flux can be applied by means of a small stick with the end pounded forming a small stiff brush.

4. Heat soldering copper, placing in fire so that flame does not play on point. Copper is to be previously tinned as directed in Job 7. As experience is gained copper can be placed in pot to heat while work is being prepared for soldering.

5. When copper has heated sufficiently to melt solder quickly remove from fire pot and wiping quickly on damp rag or waste, plunge point into flux.

6. Pick up solder with heated iron (Fig. 226) and apply to place to be soldered. Move soldering iron slowly enough to permit material to be heated above the melting point of solder, about 370 degrees F. Heavy

17

material requires a hotter iron and slower movement than light metal. Hold surfaces being soldered in close contact until solder solidifies. Tilt bucket so that melted solder will flow along seam to the point desired. If the heat is right, the surface clean and properly fluxed, and the iron is clean and well tinned, solder will flow along it as ink after a pen. When solder begins to build up under the iron and appear rough and dull in color it indicates that the iron is getting too cold and it should be reheated. Solder flows freely from a hot iron and hardens smoothly. An overheated iron is indicated by the tinning on the point changing to a bronze color. When overheated it must be retinned. Where more solder is required, as in filling a seam, than can be picked up by the iron (Fig. 226), hold the solder above the iron and melt off the quantity desired.

7. Again scrape and apply flux to any places to which solder fails to adhere. Excess solder can be removed by a sharp rap while still in molten state.

8. Smooth up work and test with hot water for leaks.

Job 9.—Replacing a Broken Ear on a Galvanized Iron Pail.

—Pails, otherwise good, are frequently discarded because of a broken ear. When a pail fails from this cause the rivets holding the ear usually pull out due to the metal of the pail rusting about them.

Method of Work.—1. Cut from light galvanized iron, with the snips, a piece about 3" square. Cut off lower corners about ¼" and bend to fit curvature of pail.

2. Fit patch centrally over place where ear has been removed and with upper edge pushed well up under rim of pail.

3. While held in this position punch holes with nail set or small punch in each corner of patch supporting the inside of the pail on the end of a block of hard wood while so doing. (Fig. 227.)

4. Light pot and heat soldering iron.

5. Remove patch, and with old pocket knife or discarded mower section, thoroughly clean both the edges of the patch and the portion of the pail met by it. Scrape until absolutely clean and bright.

6. Put patch in position and rivet in place with small tinned or copper rivets. Support the inside of the pail on the horn of the anvil while doing this, and finish rivet heads smooth with rivet set.

7. Scrape the ear of the pail clean; clean the portion of the patch upon which it is to be placed; punch the holes and rivet in position.

8. Clean the portion of the patch appearing through the hole in the pail, and the surface of the pail around the holes where the old rivets rusted out. Scrape out all rust down to a bright surface.

9. Apply zinc chloride flux to the cleaned surfaces, using a little extra hydrochloric acid if obtainable.

10. Remove hot copper from fire pot, dip point in flux and apply solder as when making repair to tin bucket. Use copper very hot and work back and forth in melted solder until work is thoroughly heated.

11. Wipe melted solder quickly with waste. This removes some of the galvanizing permitting the next solder that is applied to get down to the metal beneath the galvanizing. Solder applied to the surface of galvanizing with a moderately hot iron does not make a permanent repair. Sufficient heat must be used to remove some of it and let the solder get down to the metal beneath.

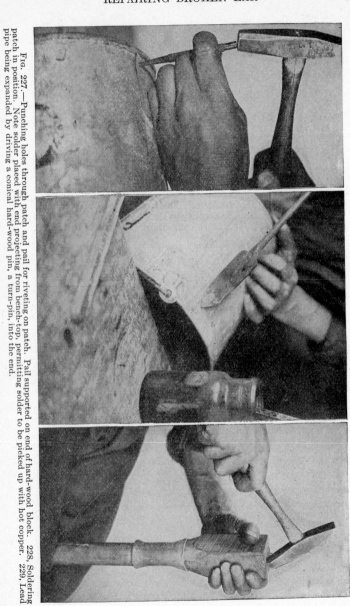

Fig. 227   Fig. 228   Fig. 229

Fig. 227.—Punching holes through patch and pail for riveting on patch. Pail supported on end of hard-wood block. 228, Soldering patch in position. Note solder placed with end projecting from bench-top, permitting solder to be picked up with hot copper. 229, Lead pipe being expanded by driving a conical hard-wood pin, a turn-pin, into the end.

12. Again apply flux and solder as before. Tilt work so that solder flows into seams. Use plenty of flux and heat the material thoroughly. The result should be a smooth, tight job. (Fig. 228.)

Job 10.—Joining Lead Pipe.—Lead pipe is sometimes used in plumbing where bends make it difficult to use galvanized iron fittings. The joint described is easily made and is tight.

Method of Work.—1. Extend end of pipe into which water flows with turn pin. (Fig. 229.)
2. With a knife shave the inside portion of the bell-shaped end so formed until bright and immediately smear with tallow to prevent oxidation.
3. With the rasp taper the end of the other pipe to fit into the bell just formed. Shave this end bright and coat with tallow.
4. Heat the soldering copper and prepare for soldering by dipping point in flux as in Jobs 8 and 9.
5. Insert spigot end in bell end, hold upright and melt in solder with hot iron. Heat solder until thoroughly liquefied but be careful not to melt pipe. Resin can be used as flux in connection with tallow if desired.

Nominal Dimensions and Weight of Galvanized Steel Pipe[1]

Pipe size nominal dia.	Internal dia. actual size	Outside dia. actual size	Weight per foot in pounds
¼″	.364	.540	.424
½″	.622	.840	.850
¾″	.824	1.050	1.130
1″	1.049	1.315	1.678
1½″	1.610	1.900	2.787
2″	2.067	2.375	3.652

Correct Length of Pipe Thread.[1]—The following table gives the correct length of thread to fill the pipe fittings properly.

Size of pipe	Total length of thread	Length of thread used by fitting	Threads per inch
¼″	9⁄16″ plus	7⁄16″	18
½″	11⁄16″ plus	9⁄16″	14
¾″	¾″ plus	9⁄16″	14
1″	15⁄16″ plus	11⁄16″	11.5
1½″	1″ minus	11⁄16″	11.5
2″	1″ plus	12⁄16″	11.5

Rules for Obtaining Lengths to Cut Common Sizes of Pipe

1. Measure distance between faces of fittings and add length of thread as shown in column 3, for each thread to be cut.
2. Measure center to center distance between pipes to be connected, subtract one half the length of each fitting and add length of thread as shown in column 3, for each thread to be cut.

[1] From *National Pipe Standards*, published by the National Tube Company, Pittsburgh, Pa

CHAPTER XVII

CARE AND REPAIR OF HARNESS

To BE kept in condition, harness must be cleaned and oiled periodically and repaired when necessary. A few stitches taken at the beginning of a rip will frequently save expensive repairs.

Methods of Harness Repair.—Leather is commonly joined by two methods; sewing and riveting. Sewing is usually the better

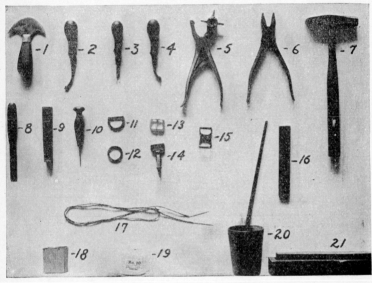

FIG. 230.—Tools and material used in harness-repairing: 1, round knife; 2, finishing wheel; 3, edger; 4, creasing tool; 5, revolving turret head punch; 6, pliers; 7, riveting hammer; 8, leather knife; 9, rivet set; 10, awl; 11, D; 12, ring; 13, buckle; 14, snap; 15, Conway loop; 16, two-foot rule; 17, waxed thread with needles; 18, copper rivets; 19, linen thread No. 10; 20, edge blacking; 21, oil-stone.

method, making a stronger, neater and more flexible union. Riveting is quicker, being more in the nature of a temporary repair. Except in places where metal is being joined to leather or other exceptional cases, stitching should be used.

Tools and Equipment Required.—Repair work can be done with a pocket-knife, kneedles, awl, thread, and wax, but a few simple tools help very much in making a satisfactory repair. These are shown in figure 230.

261

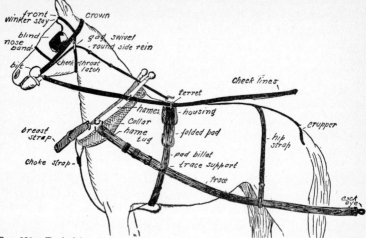

FIG. 231.—Typical farm harness without breeching, showing name and location of parts.

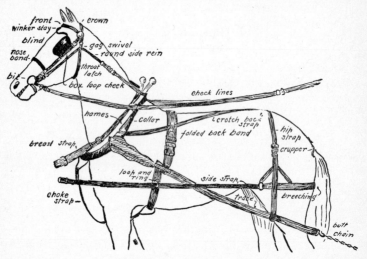

FIG. 232.—Typical farm harness with breeching, showing name and location of parts.

A good quality of harness leather should be used in making repairs. Straps cut from spongy flank and belly pieces of the hide are worthless. Harness leather can be purchased by the pound or side, and should be secured from a reputable dealer who can guarantee the quality.

The thread used in stitching leather is made from flax fiber. The size known as No. 10 is in general use for the purpose. It is unwound from the inside, and is best kept in a tin or cardboard box with the end projecting through a hole in the cover to prevent tangling.

Black wax used for coating the thread is obtainable in two grades; summer and winter. The winter wax is softer than the summer grade, and can be used in a colder temperature. Both must be used where it is warm, or they will chip from the thread.

Harness needles differ from ordinary sewing needles in that they are coarser and have round points. The size known as number 5 is suitable.

The finishing wheel is used for smoothing out the stitching, and making it appear uniform after completion. It can also be used to mark the position of the stitches before sewing is begun. A size marking six stitches to the inch is good for general use.

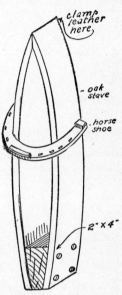

Waxed End.—The thread used in harness repairing consists of a number of linen threads twisted together, forming a cord about 5 feet in length with tapered ends. The wax protects it from moisture, makes a very strong and durable thread, and holds it from pulling out of the stitching. The number of threads used in making a waxed end will vary from 3 to 7, depending upon the nature of the work.

Fig. 233.—Stitching clamp made from two oak barrel staves held together by means of horseshoe or ring pushed down over the top. In use the clamp is held between the knees while stitching.

Stitching Clamp.—A stitching horse is the best arrangement for holding the work while stitching, but a clamp made from two oak barrel staves can be used (Fig. 233).

Washing and Oiling Harness.—For washing, warm soft water should be used in connection with some pure soap such as castile. To dislodge hardened grease a fairly stiff brush may be used or it may be scraped off with a dull knife, taking care not to injure the stitching. For oiling heavy harness, *U. S. Farmers' Bulletin 1183* recommends either a mixture of tallow and cod oil or tallow and neat's foot oil, or a mixture of all can be used. The use of a grease containing mineral acids or oxalic acid is detrimental.

Job 1.—Making a Six-thread Waxed End.—A waxed thread is used for making repairs to harness. It resists pulling from the awl holes and is waterproof, due to its waxed coating.

Method of Work.—1. Pull from the center of a ball of linen shoe thread a piece about five feet in length. A longer thread cannot be handled conveniently in stitching.

2. Hold the thread between the thumb and finger of the left hand and roll down the right leg under the palm of the right hand until the twist

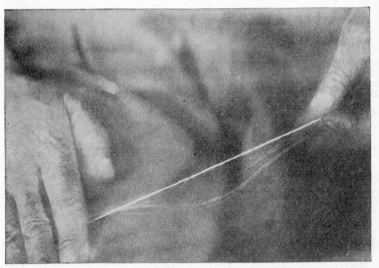

FIG. 234.—Separating the fibers of the thread, preparatory to breaking by rolling it down the leg against the twist until all twist is removed from the thread.

is removed from the fibers composing the thread and they lie straight. (Fig. 234.)

3. Separate the thread at this point by grasping between the thumbs and fingers on each side of the untwisted portion and twitching lightly. Be careful to secure a long tapering break.

4. Prepare five other threads in the same manner laying them separately on the bench top as they are separated from the ball.

5. Lay the threads side by side with the ends uneven. This will give a long tapering end when they are twisted and waxed.

6. Place some shoemaker's wax on a piece of leather and warm it slightly.

7. Loop the assembled threads over a hook or nail and holding them about 6″ from the end with the left hand, wax the ends as shown in figure 235.

8. Hold one end of the thread in the left hand, between the thumb and finger and roll the other end down the right leg under the palm of the right hand (Fig. 236). Hold with the left hand in returning the

235   236

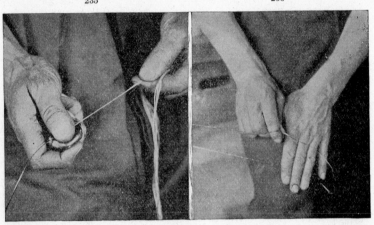

FIG. 235.—Waxing the ends of the thread to hold it together preparatory to twisting.
FIG. 236.—Twisting thread by rolling it down the leg.

FIG. 237.—Waxing the thread. The thread is looped over a nail or other support. The free ends held in the left hand by twisting them around the fingers and wax applied and evenly rubbed in.

thread to the top of the leg to prevent untwisting. When sufficient twist has been put in one end repeat with the other end.

9. Equalize twist in ends by seizing one end in each hand and pulling back and forth a few times through hook over which it is hung.

10. Wind one end of the twisted thread a few times around the fore-finger of the left hand and the other end around the second finger in the same way and wax thread by rubbing with waxed pad described in

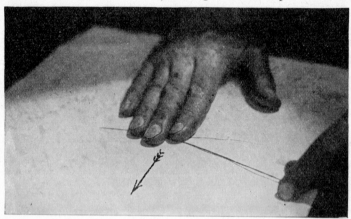

FIG. 238.—Twisting thread into needle by rolling on clean bench-top.

number 7 (Fig. 237). Smooth thread by rubbing between thumb and finger of right hand.

11. Draw tapered end of thread through needle as far as it will go. It should lap back on thread for a distance of 2–½″ to 3″. Draw thread

FIG. 239.—Beveling straps with round knife for splicing. Straps are beveled on the flesh side to conserve strength as the hair side is the stronger.

smoothly back by pulling between finger and thumb and twist around main part of thread by rolling under palm of the hand on clean bench top. (Fig. 238.) Again smooth thread by pulling between thumb and finger. The thread where joined to the needle should be no larger than the remainder of the thread and should be smooth and round.

12. Attach needle to other end in same way. Keep waxed thread in a warm place during use. If it snarls in use rub with bee's wax.

Job 2.—Splicing a Strap.—Straps can be repaired by stitching or riveting or by use of a Conway loop. Stitching makes the best repair.

Method of Work.—1. Bevel off straps on *flesh* side for a distance of from 2-½″ to 3″. Cut ends off square. Beveling or "skiving" can be done with the round knife or sharp plane. (Fig. 239.) It is done on flesh side of leather because the strap is weakened less by keeping the hair side intact.

2. Lay the straps on a board with the hair sides up, lapping them somewhat more than the amount of beveling. Lay a rule or short straight edge along one side and fasten splice temporarily by means of small nail at each end.

3. Using the finger as a guide run the finishing wheel or pricking wheel along each side of the splice marking the location of the awl holes. Awl holes can be located with a rule if wheel is not available. Locating the awl holes insures uniform stitches.

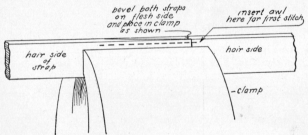

FIG. 240.—Splice in clamp in position for stitching, hair side of both straps to the right and strap nearest the workman on the outside.

4. Place work in stitching clamp with hair side of straps to the right as shown in figure 240.

5. Holding the awl horizontally push it through the leather from the hair side making the first hole just beyond the beveled end of the right hand strap.

6. Withdraw the awl and insert needle. Pull thread through until half is on each side of the strap.

7. Make second hole with awl through straps in place marked. Insert left needle and pull through about 3″ to 4″ with thumb and finger of right hand. Catch thread with hand and pull it through for a foot or so.

8. Insert right hand needle. As it is pushed through hole pull left hand thread back a little. This prevents needle from going through thread. Pull needle through far enough to grasp with hand. Loop right and left hand threads about the hands and pull up snug (Fig. 241).

9. Repeat the above process until stitching is carried as far as desired.

10. When stitching is finished place the left needle in the hole and pull through as usual. Push right needle through and give left thread a turn

through the loop formed in right hand thread. Put the needle from the left back through strap and pull up, and cut off the threads on the flesh

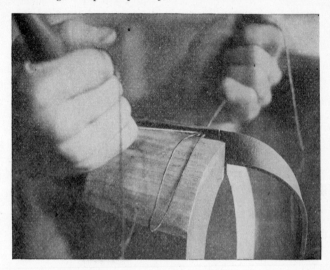

FIG. 241.—Leather stitching, pulling up the threads.

side. This locks the stitch and leaves the face of the strap smooth (A, Fig. 242).

11. Finish other side of splice in same way. If necessary make third row of stitching in center.

12. Place hair side on smooth surface as flat iron and pound flesh side

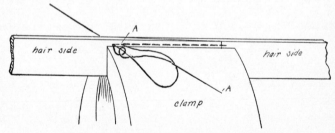

FIG. 242.—Method of locking stitch. Needle from the flesh side of the strap is put through the loop in the right-hand thread and is given a turn about it. Needle A is then put back through the strap at A and both threads cut off on the flesh side.

lightly with smooth-faced hammer imbedding the stitch.

13. Run finishing wheel over stitching on hair side. This makes stitches appear uniform.

14. Apply edge black to splice and polish.

Job 3.—**Attaching a Buckle and Keeper by Stitching.**—One of the weakest parts in a harness is the point where a buckle is attached. It is also one of the points receiving the greatest wear, and is therefore most frequently broken.

Method of Work.—1. Remove old buckle and pick out stitching with awl or knife point.

2. Cut end of strap off square and bevel flesh side back for 2–½″ with round knife or sharp plane. (Fig. 243.)

3. Punch two holes in the center of the strap 3″ and 4″ from the end respectively.

4. With sharp knife cut out leather between the holes forming a slot for buckle tongue.

5. Cut strap for keeper from light material sufficiently long to fold

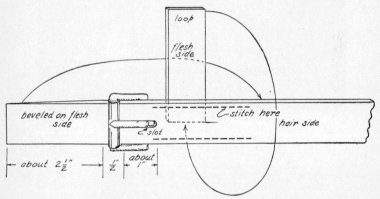

Fig. 243.—Method of preparing strap for attachment of buckle and keeper loop. Beveled end is folded around in direction of arrow and stitched down, keeper loop being folded about and end placed beneath splice before stitching down.

around two thicknesses of the strap with the ends meeting. Crease the edges with the creasing tool.

6. Place buckle on strap with tongue opening toward hair side of strap. Fold beveled end of strap back on flesh side of strap.

7. Mark strap for stitching with pricking or finishing wheels.

8. Insert strap forming keeper loop at right-angles to strap as shown in figure 243.

9. Fasten in stitching clamp, make awl hole, draw thread through half way and continue stitching as directed for splicing in Job 2. This stitches across one end of strap used to form keeper.

10. Remove work from clamp and insert other end of keeper into the splice until the ends meet at center of strap.

11. Replace in clamp and start stitching. When keeper loop is reached insert awl at an angle (Fig. 244) and continue stitching in this way until stitching is carried half way through loop. When mid point is reached insert awl from other side making one long stitch which is hidden within keeper loop.

12. Lock stitch at the end of splice and cut off thread. Block up keeper to shape by making wooden wedge of the width and thickness of the strap used, inserting it in the keeper and pounding lightly with the hammer.

Fig. 244.—Stitching through a loop. Strap fastened in clamp and awl inserted through loop at an angle. When half way through insert awl from the other side as indicated by arrow.

13. Smooth up work with the hammer and finishing wheel as directed in Job 2.

14. Apply edge black and polish.

Job 4.—**Cleaning and Oiling Harness.**—A harness, well cared

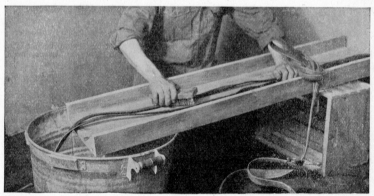

Fig. 245.—Cleaning harness preparatory to oiling. Bottom of trough makes good scrubbing-board and returns soapsuds to tub. (Cornell lesson leaflet, 160, Rural Engineering Series.)

for, kept clean and oiled with suitable oils, has a long period of usefulness. Leather may be preserved and protected from wear by cleaning and oiling at frequent intervals.

Method of Work.—1. Take harness apart and examine for wear and breaks. Repair rips and breaks and put harness in condition.

2. Wash harness thoroughly in warm soft water using a mild soap and stiff brush to remove grease. (Fig. 245.) Caked grease and sweat can be scraped off with dull knife. Rinse in clear water.

3. Hang harness up in warm room and dry until water disappears from surface, but apply oil while leather is still damp.

4. When dried sufficiently, no water on surface but leather still damp, apply warm oil. Rub it well into the leather working it and kneading it in the hands until a good penetration is secured. Use oil as directed p. 263.

5. After harness has hung over night in a warm room, to secure further absorption of oil, wipe off excess with dry cloth and reassemble. Leave hanging in warm room for a sufficient length of time after this to have all grease disappear from surface.

Suggested Harness Jobs

1. Attach a new cockeye to a tug.
2. Attach a set of heel chains.
3. Splice a broken tug with mending plate and rivets.
4. Attach a buckle with rivets.
5. Replace a broken hame staple.
6. Replace a broken hame bottom loop.
7. Make a riveted halter.

Selection and Care of Harness

1. Select simple, heavy harness well made from firm, plump leather.
2. Avoid over-ornamented harness for work purposes.
3. Avoid new harness in which the leather shows minute cracks on the grain side when sharply bent.
4. Clean and oil frequently (see job 4). Avoid hot water, harsh soaps, and rapid drying.
5. Hang in well-ventilated room away from stable fumes.
6. Inspect frequently and keep small breaks repaired: "A stitch in time saves nine."
7. If possible, change adjustment frequently so that buckle wear does not come constantly at one point. Do not do this at the expense of harness fit, however.

QUESTIONS AND EXERCISES

1. What methods are in common use for splicing leather? For what condition is each method best suited?
2. When splicing leather which side of the strap should be beveled? Why?
3. What common farm tools can be used to bevel the end of a strap?
4. When purchasing leather for harness upkeep and repair what portion of the hide would you select? Why?
5. If you had several hides to choose from how would you make your selection?
6. When making a harness repair how can a piece of heavy leather be reduced to the required thickness with common farm tools?

CHAPTER XVIII

ROPE AND ITS USE ON THE FARM

THE American farmer is a heavy user of rope and cordage, making a knowledge of the selection, use and care of rope together with skill in making splices and certain knots and hitches of value to him.

Materials from Which Rope is Made.—Rope is made from a variety of vegetable fibers as manila, sisal, cotton, jute and coir.

FIG. 246.—Rope-end (1); unlaid, showing strands (2); yarns (3); and fibers (4).

Practically all of the rope and cordage used in farm practice is made from either manila or sisal fiber or a combination of the two.

Manila fiber is taken from the outer layers of the Abaca plant, which closely resembles that of the banana. The world's supply comes from the Philippine Islands, and is shipped from the port of Manila, hence the name.

Sisal Fiber.—The sisal plant is called by the natives "henequen," and is grown in huge plantations in Yucatan. The leaves are harvested and the fiber removed by modern methods. The fiber secured is inferior to the better grades of manila, being heavier, stiffer, coarser, and weaker.

Manufacture of Rope.—The fiber is oiled, straightened, and spun with a right-hand twist, into yarn. A number of yarns are then put together and twisted to the left, forming a strand. Three or four of these strands are then twisted together to the right to form a rope (Fig. 246). This twisting, although necessary to join the fibers, which average only about six feet in length, greatly

272

reduces the strength. Excessive twist weakens a rope, increases the weight per foot, makes the rope stiff and rigid, subject to kinking, internal chafing and wear, and hard to splice and tie.

For general farm use rope is available in three different styles, 3-strand, 4-strand, and hawser-laid (Fig. 247).

Selection of Rope.— The choice of a rope depends largely upon the service to which it is to be put. Where it is used over pulleys of proper size there is little outside wear, the greater wear coming on the interior, due to chafing as the rope bends. Such a condition is found in horse fork service, and a medium lay manila rope should be used for this purpose. Sizes 3/4-inch and 7/8-inch are in common use. For well-drilling, land-clearing, etc., a hawser-laid cable should be used. This, because of its hard exterior, resists outside wear well, and will give the best service under these conditions. Halter ties should be made of a very

FIG. 247.—Common types of rope: 1, four-strand with heart; 2, four-strand without heart; 3, well-driller's cable (hawser-laid); 4, three-strand rope.

soft lay rope because of its flexibility, softness, and freedom from kinking. Cotton rope is much used for cattle halters.

Three-strand rope is in most general use, and is lighter and stronger than corresponding grades and sizes in 4-strand, but does not run so freely through pulleys, being more subject to kinking. It is obtainable in soft, medium or hard twist or " lay." For general use the medium lay should be chosen.

Four-strand rope is made with or without a heart. The rope containing a heart is usually made with a firmer lay than the "no-heart" rope, which is laid up soft. Four-strand rope is round in cross-section (Fig. 247), and runs through pulleys freely. For these reasons it is sometimes used in horse fork work, although its greater cost usually prevents such use. It runs 6 per cent heavier, and sells for one cent more per pound than ordinary three-strand rope.

Hawser-laid rope is used for well-drilling and similar work, where there is great outside wear. It is made from three small ropes twisted to the left to form one large one, and presents a hard exterior, which resists outside wear.

Strength of Rope.—Manila fiber has great strength, resisting a pull of about 30,000 pounds per square inch of cross-section before breaking. Various formulas are in use for computing the breaking strength of new manila rope. The Whitlock Cordage Company gives the following formula: $D \times D \times 7500$ equals breaking strength in pounds. D equals diameter of rope in inches.

Example: What is the breaking strength of a new manila rope 1″ in diameter?
Solution: $1 \times 1 \times 7500$ equals 7500, pounds breaking strength.

Sisal rope has only about three-fourths the strength of manila.

Yardage, Breaking Strength and Safe Load of New Three-strand Manila Rope

Diameter Inches	Length per lb. Feet	Inches	Breaking Strength	Safe Load	Pulley Diameter in Inches
			lbs.	lbs.	
¼″	33	4	400	55	2
⁵/₁₆″	25	0	630	90	2–½
⅜″	20	0	900	130	3
⁷/₁₆″	16	8	1240	175	3–½
½″	13	0	1620	230	4
⅝″	7	6	2880	410	5
¾″	6	1	3640	520	6
⅞″	4	3	5440	775	7
1 ″	3	6	6480	925	8
1–⅛″	2	7	8820	1260	9
1–¼″	2	2	10120	1445	10

Rope is sold by the pound, but is used by the foot. Cheap rope is usually made of an inferior fiber or loaded during the process of making so that it is either weaker and shorter lived or it is heavier per 100 feet than rope made from first quality manila. Sisal fiber is one of the most common adulterants. Its presence makes a rope rough and unpleasant to handle. Rope should be kept dry, as water injures the fibers from which it is made. If wet it should be dried

FIG. 248.—Inspecting a rope for wear. The rope is grasped in both hands and untwisted and the conditions of the interior observed.

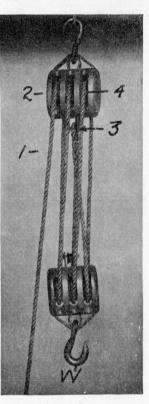

FIG. 249.—Blocks and tackle: 1, fall rope to which pull is applied; 2, fall block, the block from which the fall rope runs; 3, becket, ring to which rope is attached; 4, sheave, grooved wheel over which the rope runs; W, point at which weight is attached for lifting.

in the sun before coiling. Turn rope clockwise when coiling, and when uncoiling pull from the center of the coil or from the end first laid down to avoid kinking. Where used on a horse fork avoid driving over the rope with the wagon or horses, as this might result in external injury. Turn to the left at one end of the travel and to the right at the other to keep the rope in its original condition and to avoid kinking.

Inspection.—The outside appearance of a rope used with pulleys is little indication of its true condition, as the wear is largely inside. To inspect the rope, grasp it firmly in both hands and untwist it (Fig. 248). If it shows considerable wear on the inside the load should be lessened, and if there is considerable powder and short pieces of broken fiber the rope should be discarded or put to use where its failure will do no damage. Such a rope is likely to break under a very light load.

Block and Tackle.—One or more grooved wheels mounted within a suitable frame is called a block. Two of these blocks with a rope properly attached and threaded through them constitute a tackle. The different parts of a set of tackle and their names are shown in figure 249. The sheaves should be kept well oiled to lessen friction.

Lifting Force of Tackle.—The advantage secured by the use of tackle depends upon the number of parts of rope supporting the load, and the way in which the pulleys are attached. The common rule for determining the mechanical advantage secured follows:

Multiply the pull in pounds by the number of ropes supporting the load. This gives the theoretical weight that can be supported.

Due to friction in the rope and blocks, it is never possible to lift as much as computed by the theoretical rule given. The following table, originally arranged by J. B. Frear, from the *American Civil Engineers Pocket Book,* gives the ratio existing between weight lifted and pull on fall rope, with the number of sheaves and size rope indicated:

| Number of Sheaves | | Diameter of Rope in Inches | | | | |
Fall Block	Movable Block	3/4 "	7/8 "	1 "	1-1/4 "	1-1/2 "
1	1	1.93	1.92	1.93	1.92	1.91
2	1	2.73	2.68	2.74	2.68	2.67
2	2	3.48	3.37	3.50	3.37	3.36
3	2	4.12	3.95	4.16	3.95	3.93

Example: What weight can be lifted by a tackle using 3/4 " rope and having three sheaves in the fall block and two in the movable block if a pull of 100 pounds is applied to the fall rope?

Solution: Looking under column of table 3/4 " rope we find opposite the number of sheaves given 4.12. Multiplying the pull in pounds, 100 by this ratio factor gives 412 pounds as the weight that could be lifted with this tackle and force acting as described. If the question were: how great a force would be required to raise a weight of 412 pounds with this tackle, the process would be reversed and the weight divided by this factor.

Job 1.—Finishing the End of Halter Lead Rope.—To prevent the end from becoming frayed through use and to permit its being passed through hole in manger for tying.

I. Wiring.—1. Cut a piece of galvanized iron wire three times the diameter of the rope in length and bend wire to ring shape.

2. Slip ring over rope about 1/2 " from end and pound down with hammer or tighten with pliers.

II. Whipping.—1. Cut strong cord about four feet in length.   Waxed harness thread or hardware twine is good.

2. Pass this beneath a strand of the rope about one turn from the

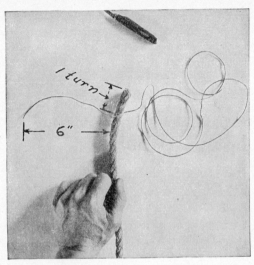

FIG. 250.—Placing the cord in position for whipping.

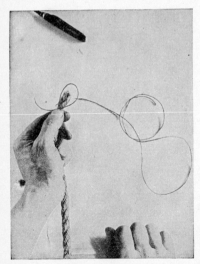

FIG. 251.—Short end of cord folded back.

FIG. 252.—End of halter lead rope whipped to prevent untying.

rope's end. Pull through until the cord projects about 6" to the left. (Fig. 250.)

3. Take a turn about the rope with the long end of cord and fold short end over so that it lies along the rope toward the end.

4. Wrap the long end of cord tightly about the rope, keeping turns

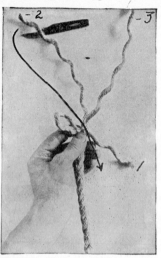

FIG. 253.—Fold strand 1 over 2 and 3.

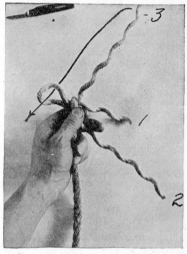

FIG. 254.—Fold strand 2 down by 3.

FIG. 255.—Pull up tight.

close together but avoiding their crossing. Continue this until whipping is about half completed.

5. Fold short end of cord back in a loop with end of loop projecting to the end of rope or slightly beyond. (Fig. 251.) Place this loop in groove between strands of rope and continue whipping as before.

6. Continue whipping to within about ½" of the end of rope. Pass the end of the cord with which whipping is being done through loop in

other end of cord and pull the loop beneath the whipping with the free end. Cut off projecting ends. Finished whipping is shown in figure 252. Whipping must be tight and smooth. If cord is allowed to cross itself it soon wears off where it crosses destroying the whipping.

III. Crowning.—1. Unlay rope five to six turns and spread as for wall knot.

2. Fold strand one over between two and three leaving small loop projecting to left. (Fig. 253.)

3. Fold strand two down between three and loop formed in one as shown in figure 254.

4. Pass end of strand three through loop in one as shown by arrow

FIG. 256.—Crown tied and each strand given one tuck.

FIG. 257.—End of halter lead rope finished by crowning.

(Fig. 254), and pull up tight. Rope will appear as in figure 255.

5. Raise strand on rope with marline spike and tuck strand one under, pull up tight.

6. Revolve rope one-third turn to the left and repeat with strand two.

7. Repeat with strand three. Rope should now appear as in figure 256.

8. Beginning with strand one again, tuck each strand as before, crossing over one strand and going under the next and continue doing this until each strand has been tucked three times.

9. Divide strands and continue tucking with half of each strand for three or four times, giving each strand but one tuck at a time. Pull up tight as tucking proceeds.

10. Roll on the floor under the foot and cut off loose ends leaving about ½″ until rope has been used for awhile when it may be trimmed closer. Finished crown is shown in figure 257. Tucking must show a regular basket weave, over one strand and under the next.

Job 2.—**Tying Two Ropes Together.**—It is sometimes necessary to attach two ropes together temporarily to secure sufficient length.

I. Square Knot.—1. Cross the ropes as in figure 258, with the end of the left-hand rope on top.

2. With the right hand give the end of the left-hand rope a turn about the right-hand rope. (Fig. 259.)

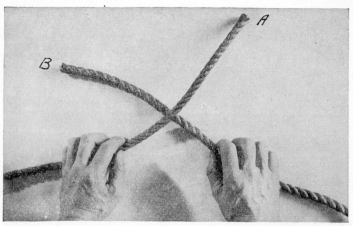

FIG. 258.—Ropes crossed for tying square knot. End of left rope on top.

FIG. 259.—Left-hand rope given one turn about right-hand rope.

3. Again cross the ends as in figure 260, and give A a turn about B.

4. Grasp the rope as in figure 261, and pull up tight.

II. Weaver's Knot.—1. Cross ropes as for square knot. (Fig. 262.)

FIG. 260.—Completing square knot.

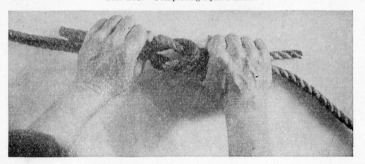

FIG. 261.—Pulling square knot up.

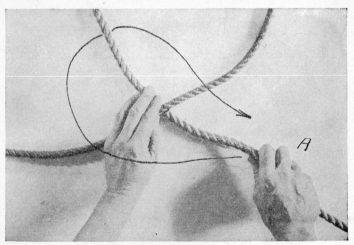

FIG. 262.—Ropes in position to join by weaver's knot.

2. Grasp standing part of rope A with right hand and give it a turn beneath its own end. (Fig. 262.)

3. Fold end of B back through turn in A as shown by arrow in figure 263.

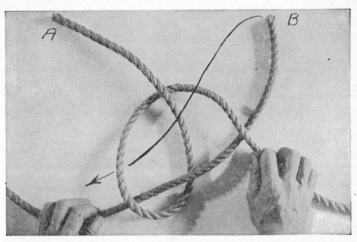

Fig. 263.—Standing part of rope given a turn beneath its own end.

4. Hold rope as shown in figure 264 and tighten knot by pulling with right hand. Finished knot is shown in figure 265. This is an excellent

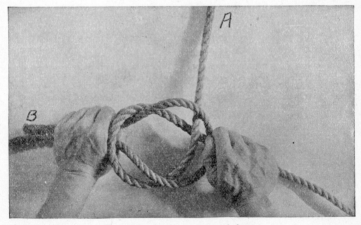

Fig. 264.—Setting up weaver's knot.

knot for tying broken binder twine as it will pass through the tying mechanism without catching. Also adapts itself well to making temporary repair on broken strap. Easily untied when pull is released.

Job. 3.—**Attaching Hay Fork Rope to Evener.**—A non-slipping loop in the end of a rope that may be quickly attached to an evener, and easily untied, is required.

I. **Bowline Knot.**—1. Pick up the end of the rope and place it on the left leg in the position shown in figure 266.

2. Give the standing part a turn around this free end in the direction of the arrow.

3. Pass the free end beneath the standing part and back through the turn in direction of arrow. (Fig. 267.)   Completed knot is shown in figure 268.

Pass end of loop so formed up through the "D" on evener and fasten with toggle. (Fig. 269.)   The bowline is the best non-slipping loop made.

FIG. 265.—Ropes joined by weaver's knot.

It can be adapted to many purposes other than the one mentioned. It will not slip in service and as soon as the load is released it can be very easily untied, even when wet.

Job. 4.—**Taking up Slack in a Hay Fork Rope.**—Where a long hauling rope is used it is sometimes desirable to shorten it temporarily without cutting.

I. **Sheepshank.**—1. Form a double bight in the rope as in figure 270 to take up the slack.   This must be placed near evener as it will not run through pulleys.

2. Form a turn in the standing part of the rope and push A through it. (Fig. 271.)

3. Do the same with B.

4. Completed sheepshank should appear as in figure 272.   It is made more secure by the use of a toggle at each end as shown in figure 273, although it will hold so long as a load is on it without the use of toggles.

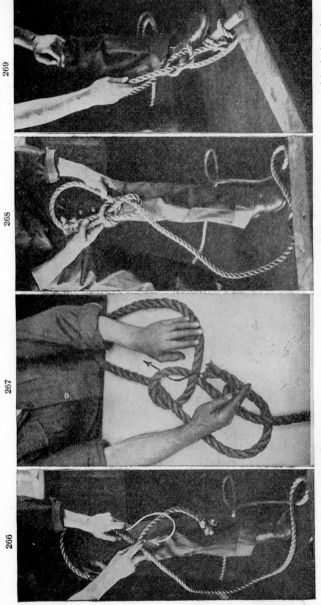

FIG. 266.—Starting the bowline, hitching hay fork rope to evener.   FIG. 267.—Bowline knot.   Free end being passed back through turn in standing part of rope.   FIG. 268.—Completed bowline.   FIG. 269.—Rope attached to evener by means of bowline and toggle.

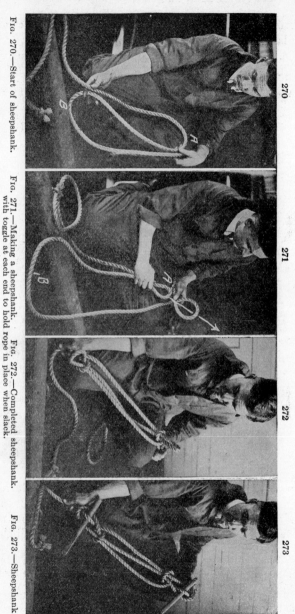

Fig. 270.—Start of sheepshank.   Fig. 271.—Making a sheepshank, with toggle at each end to hold rope in place when slack.   Fig. 272.—Completed sheepshank.   Fig. 273.—Sheepshank

Job 5.—Attaching a Guy Rope to a Post.—It is often desirable in building to quickly and securely attach a guy rope to a post or stake. The hitch, though temporary, should be secure, easily made and easily undone.

Clove Hitch, Sailor's Method.—1. Pull the rope taut with the left hand.

2. Form a turn in the rope with the right hand and slip it over the top of the post while keeping the rope taut with the left. (Fig. 274.)

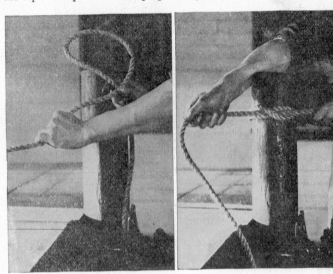

FIG. 274.—Making clove hitch "sailor's method."　　　FIG. 275.—Completed clove hitch.

3. Make a second turn in the rope and drop it over the top of the post.

4. Pull up tight. Finished hitch appears as in figure 275. Useful for hitching a rope upon which the pull must be sustained while hitching.

Job 6.—Lifting Timbers to Upper Part of Barn When Building.—When building, a secure hitch that is quickly made and undone is needed by which timbers may be attached to a rope and lifted to the upper part of the building. The timber hitch is used for this purpose.

Timber Hitch.—1. Wrap rope about timber, take a turn about standing part of the rope and tuck the free end twice beneath the rope where it goes around the timber. Tighten by pulling on standing part. Complete hitch is shown in figure 276.

Job 7.—**Hitching to a Timber That is to be Hauled Lengthwise.**—When pulling a log or timber along the ground a hitch should be used that will grip the stick and prevent slipping over the end.

Timber Hitch and Half Hitch Combined.—1. Make a timber hitch

FIG. 276.—Finished timber hitch, will resist pull in direction of arrow.

FIG. 277.—Timber hitch and half hitch combined.

about the timber two or three feet from the end as directed in Job 6. (Fig. 276.)

2. Take a turn in the standing part of the rope and slip it over the end of the stick. Tighten by pulling on standing part in the direction of the arrow. The complete hitch is shown in figure 277.

Job 8.—**Raising Barn Rafters.**—To raise rafters to position and hold them while they are being stayed.

Rafter Raising Hitch.—1. Secure a light stiff pole 15 to 20 feet long.

2. Tie an overhand knot or wall knot in each end of a piece of ½″ rope about 8′ long.

3. Double this rope in the middle and lash securely to the top end of the pole at such a point that the top of the loop will swing easily over the end of the pole when extended.   (Fig. 278.)

4. Place pole beneath rafter to be raised with rope over the upper

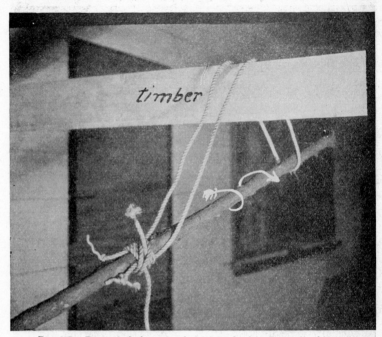

Fig. 278.—Rope attached to top end of pole, and pole and rope placed in position on timber for tightening preparatory to raising timber. Hitch is tightened by twisting to right in direction of arrow.

side of rafter. Loop rope over end of pole and tighten hitch by twisting pole to right.   (Fig. 279.)

5. Push rafter into position with pole secured by rope. Rafter may be held in position while being stayed as push or pull can be exerted on pole equally well.

6. When rafter is stayed release hitch by turning pole to left until loose.

Job 9.—Hitching Rope to Well Pipe to Lift Pump from Well.

Taut Line Hitch.—1. Take two turns about the pipe above the point where the standing part of the rope first crosses it.   (Fig. 280.)

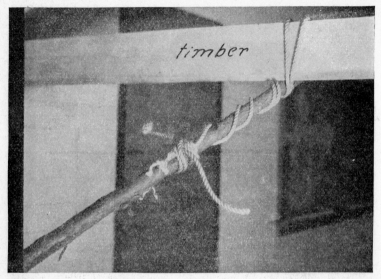

FIG. 279.—Rafter raising hitch in position and tightened by twisting. Hitch is released by untwisting to left and pulling on pole.

280   281   282

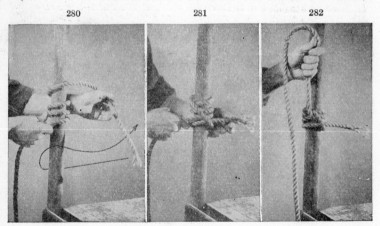

FIG. 280.—Free end being final turn around pipe below standing part.
FIG. 281.—Completed taut line hitch.
FIG. 282.—Taut line hitch pulled up.

2. Cross the free end over and take one more turn below the standing part of the rope. Insert free end through beneath this turn as shown in figures 280 and 281.

3. Pull hitch up tight. Completed hitch should appear as in figure

19

282. This hitch will resist a pull without slipping. Useful to attach to other smooth objects. May be tied to a rope that is already taut under a load.

Job 10.—Hitching a Horse to a Hitching Post.—To tie an animal with a secure knot that is easily undone when desired.

Hitching Tie.—1. Pass halter rope around post from right to left forming a bight.

2. Cross free end beneath standing part and bend back over to the left forming turn around standing part. (Fig. 283.)

3. Pull bight of rope up through this turn, figure 284, and tighten

283　　　　　　284　　　　　　285

Fig. 283.—Start of halter tie.
Fig. 284.—Bight of rope pulled up through turn.
Fig. 285.—Completed halter tie.

knot. Put free end through loop to prevent untying. Completed knot is shown in figure 285.

4. To untie, take free end from loop and pull. This knot may be used about a post, through a ring or through a hole in the manger for stable tying. When tied around a post care should be taken to pull it up snug preventing it from slipping down the post.

Job 11.—Splicing a Leading Rope into a Halter Head.— Used to fasten the rope securely and permanently to the halter head.

I. Eye Splice.—1. Unlay the rope from five to six turns. Pass through ring in halter head and arrange the strands as shown in figure 286.

2. Raise a strand on the standing part of the leading rope and tuck strand one beneath it. (Fig. 287.)

3. Insert the marline spike on the under side of the rope with the point toward the body. Strand two should be tucked in the direction of the arrow, going under one strand and coming out of the rope where strand one entered it. (Fig. 288.)

4. Strand three is inserted where one comes out of the rope and comes out where two enters it. Each strand should now come out of the rope at a different point.

5. Cross over one strand with each of the strands, and tuck as in " crowning." (Job 2.)

6. When each strand has been tucked three times divide it and continue tucking with the remaining half.

7. When through tucking roll under foot and cut off free ends leaving ½″ projecting until halter has been used for some time. Strands should be pulled up tightly in tucking and untwisted so that fibers composing them will lie down flat and make a smooth job. Finished eye splice is

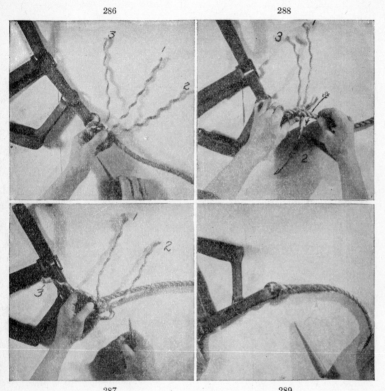

Figs. 286, 287, 288, and 289.—Lead rope spliced to halter head by eye splice.

shown in figure 289. Useful for forming eye at end of rope or for splicing one rope into the side of another.

Job 12.—**Splicing a Hay Sling.**—Used to make a secure and permanent fastening in a rope that does not have to run through pulleys.

Short Splice.—1. Unlay the end of each rope seven to eight turns.

2. Place the ends of the ropes together with the strands of one alternating with the strands of the other. (Fig. 290.)

3. Tie an overhand knot in the strands A and B, strand A from the left-hand rope being between the body and the other strand when the knot is started.

4. Do the same with the other two pairs of strands.

5. Pull each knot up tight working them up a little at a time until all are uniformly tight. (Fig. 291.)

6. Cross one strand beyond the knot and raise a strand with the marline spike. Tuck the free end of the loose strand under in the direction

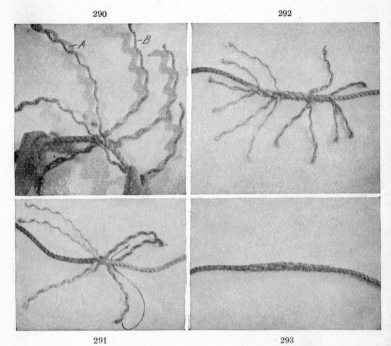

290   292

291   293

FIG. 290.—Ends interlaced in position to tie overhand knots joining strands
FIG. 291.—Each pair of strands tied by overhand knot. Arrow shows point at which to raise strand to start tucking.
FIG. 292.—Strands divided to taper off splice. FIG. 293.—Completed short splice.

of the arrow in figure 291, and pull up tight. Untwist strand as it is pulled up so that yarns will lie down well.

7. Repeat with the other two strands.

8. Do the same with the strands at the other side of the splice.

9. Repeat this operation until each strand has been tucked three times. Give each strand but one tuck at a time.

10. Divide the strands and continue tucking with one-half of each to taper off the splice gradually. (Fig. 292.)

11. Cut off projecting ends and roll under foot to finish splice. Do not cut strands too close as they may pull out when the splice stretches in use. Figure 293 shows completed splice.

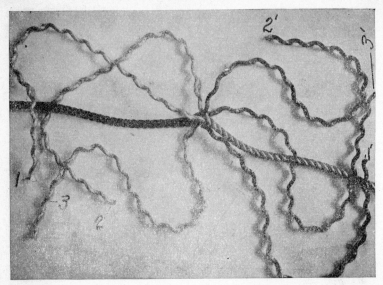

FIG. 294.—Ropes unlaid 16 to 18 turns and put together with strands alternating as for short splice. Arrange strands in pairs.

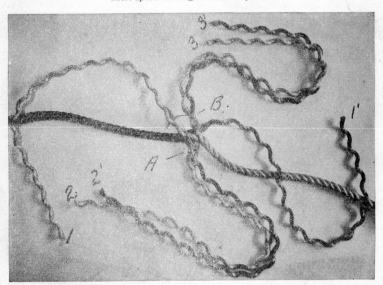

FIG. 295.—Corresponding strands selected and two pairs, *A* and *B*, tied.

Job 13.—**Splicing a Hay Rope.**—Used to make a secure and permanent splice which will pass through pulleys easily.

Long Splice.—1. Cut the ends of the rope off square and unlay each end an equal distance, 3′, or 16 to 18 turns.

2. Put the ends of the ropes together with the strands alternating as in figure 294.

3. Select the pairs and tie two pairs together as at A and B, figure 295, leaving the third pair to work with.

4. Unlay one strand of the third pair one turn to the right and lay

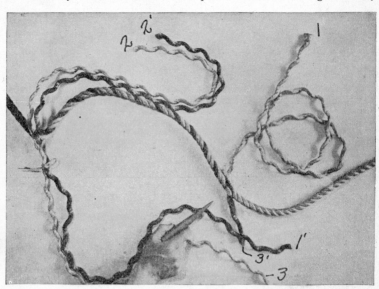

Fig. 296.—Overhand knot tied in first pair of strands, 1 and 1′, tied with strand from left between body and strand from right, pulling down smoothly into rope.

the left hand strand in its place. Twist the strand up tight as it is laid in place so that it lays down smoothly into the rope.

5. Continue this until but about 6″ of the left hand strand remains.

6. Cross the strands with the one from the left on top and tie in an overhand knot. If knot is tied correctly it will pull down into the rope smoothly. (Fig. 296.)

7. Cut the string from a second pair of strands and unlay and splice in to the left as directed four, five and six. (Fig. 297.)

8. Cut the string from the third pair of strands and tie in an overhand knot in the middle of the splice.

9. Cut the free ends of all strands about 6″ long. (Fig. 298.)

10. Tuck these ends as in short splice until three tucks have been made by each strand on each side of overhand knots. Untwist strands as they are tucked so that they will lie down flat in the rope and enlarge it the least amount possible.

11. Roll the splice under the foot to smooth it and reduce it in size and cut off projecting ends. Do not trim ends closely until rope has been put in service and has been stretched up or the strands may pull out.

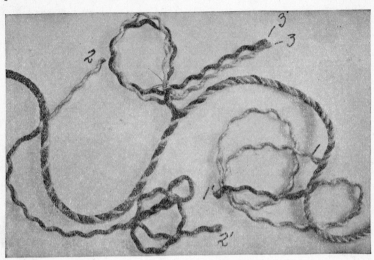

FIG. 297.—Cut the strings from a second pair of strands and unlay and splice in to the left as directed 4, 5, and 6.

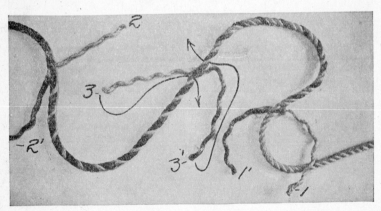

FIG. 298.—Strands cut to about 6 inches long after tying. Ready for tucking. Tuck all strands as indicated by arrows for 3 and 3'. Give three tucks each.

Finished splice should appear as in figure 299. Other sizes are unlayed and shortened a proportionate amount in splicing. Four strand rope is spliced in the same way except that it should be unlaid farther, about four feet, and the two pairs of center strands are spliced, one to the right

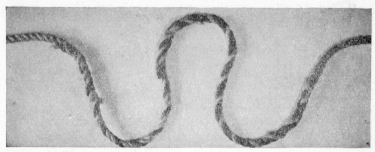

FIG. 299.—Finished long splice.

300   302

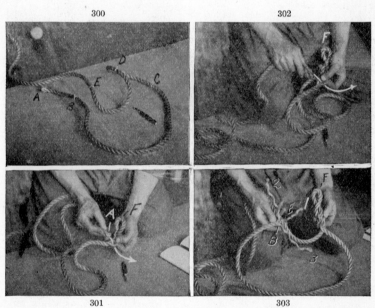

301   303

FIG. 300.—Rope with measurements laid off for construction of rope halter.
FIG. 301.—Forming loop in rope halter. End *A* is being tucked back through the rope in direction of arrow.
FIG. 302.—Construction of rope halter, long end of rope being tucked beneath 1 strand in loop *F*.
FIG. 303.—Construction of rope halter. Loop *F* is completed and end *A* is unlaid back to *B* and spliced into rope at *E* either by means of eye splice, Job 13, or strand 1 can be folded back and tucked beneath strands of rope held in right hand while strands 1 and 2 are tucked to the right and left as indicated.

and the other to the left until the knots used in joining the ends of the strands are equally spaced. Where a four strand rope is laid up with a heart, the cord forming the core or heart is cut and the ends simply butted up together.

Job 14.—**Making a Rope Halter.**—Used to make a cheap and secure fastening for tying or leading animals.

Method.—1. Cut a piece of ½″ rope 13′ long. Finish one end by whipping, wiring or crowning as directed in Job 2.

2. From the other end lay off distances A–B 5″, B–C 32″, C–D 12″ and E–D 13″ as shown in figure 300. Tie strings about rope to mark location of these points.

3. Bend the rope so that points C and D lie side by side. (Fig. 300.)

4. Raise a strand of the rope with the marline spike near the bottom of the loop F and pull the end A through under it. (Fig. 301.) The eye formed at F should be about ¾″ inside diameter.

5. Raise a second strand half way between the first crossing and D and pass the end A back through under it, as indicated by the arrow. (Fig. 302.)

6. Raise a strand at C and pull the long end of the rope through under it. (Fig. 303.) Pull up tight.

7. Unlay the end of the rope to the point B.

FIG. 304.—Completed rope halter.

8. Grasp the rope at B and turn two or three times to the right to take the twists out and to make the halter head more flexible and of better shape.

9. While held in this position raise a strand of the rope at E and pass the middle unlaid strand under it. Pass the other two strands through the rope as shown in figures 286, 287, 288 and 289, Job 11.

10. Pass the leading rope through the eye formed between C and D and pull up to the size desired. Figure 304 shows the completed halter.

11. Halter as described is for a medium sized cow. Measurements may be taken directly from the head of an animal to get exact lengths. Boiling the rope before making the halter makes it more flexible and easily handled. If desired rope may be colored where halter is to be used for exhibition animals. Cotton rope makes the most flexible halter.

QUESTIONS AND EXERCISES

1. What characteristics does manila fiber possess that make it superior for rope making?

2. When selecting rope what are some of the things that you would look for as indications of long-fiber, first-quality manila rope?

3. When offered rope at an exceptionally low price what things should be investigated before purchase?

4. Compute the approximate cost of enough ¾″, 3-strand manila rope for the horse fork on your farm. Compute the cost of the same amount of 4-strand rope.

5. For what purposes have you seen rope used on the farm? What would you estimate as the quantity of rope in use on your farm at one time?

6. What type of rope would you select for use in a horse fork?

CHAPTER XIX

CONCRETE IN FARM PRACTICE

WITHIN recent years the use of concrete in farm practice has become extensive. Sanitary education has pointed out the necessity of non-absorbent, easily cleaned floors in dairy stables and other

FIG. 305.—Interior of sanitary barn. Concrete floor and mangers. (Portland Cement Association.)

farm buildings where human food is produced. At the same time the increasing cost of lumber and its susceptibility to decay have shown the need of a more permanent building material where conditions of wear or dampness occur. Concrete best meets these conditions, and can be largely made from local materials by farm labor (Fig. 305).

Concrete is an artificial stone resulting from an intimate mixture of cement with inert materials as sand, gravel and water.

298

When first mixed it is plastic, and may be given any shape desired by the use of suitable forms or molds. In about a week's time it becomes hard, dense, wear-resistant and permanent. These qualities gradually increase with age.

Cement is the active ingredient of concrete. It is made by combining two materials, one rich in lime and the other carrying a high percentage of clay, as limestone and shale, in certain definite proportions. The materials are pulverized and burned at a high heat, and the resulting clinker ground to a flour-like fineness, forming the light gray powder known as Portland cement. The name " Portland " was given to cement manufactured by this process because of the resemblance of concrete made from it to building stone quarried on the island of Portland, near England. A standard brand of Portland cement is a uniform, reliable product, and may be depended upon to give satisfactory results when properly used.

Natural cement is made from rock which contains the necessary ingredients naturally combined in approximately correct proportions. It lacks the extreme strength and uniformity of cement made by the Portland process.

Method of Packing.—Portland cement is marketed in paper sacks or cloth bags, containing approximately one cubic foot each and weighing 94 pounds net. Four of these units constitute a barrel containing 376 pounds of cement, the unit by which it is usually sold. For farm use the cloth sack container is preferable, as there is less waste through tearing. The sacks are charged to the consumer when the cement is bought, but are redeemable at their purchase price when empty and returned to the dealer in good order.

Storing Cement.—Cement should be stored in a dry place. If stored on an earth or concrete floor planks should first be laid down and covered with tarred paper to prevent the passage of moisture to the cement. Where moisture laden air is likely to blow over the pile of cement cover it with a tarpaulin or building paper.

Aggregates are materials mixed with cement to give bulk to the resulting concrete. Sand and gravel or crushed rock are the aggregates in most common use. Sand is usually spoken of as " fine aggregate," and includes all particles from the finest up to those that will just pass through a $\frac{1}{4}$-inch mesh screen. Screened gravel or crushed stone is called " coarse aggregate," and includes all stone ranging from $\frac{1}{4}$-inch up. The maximum size of coarse aggregate should not exceed in diameter one-third of the thickness of the work in which it is placed. The strength of concrete depends largely upon the proper selection and combination of the aggregate.

Sand should be clean, coarse, hard, and bright with particles well graded in size from 1/4 inch down. There should be no clay, loam or vegetable matter present, as it weakens the concrete. Loam may be injurious either chemically or mechanically. An acid may be present which will retard the setting of the cement, or it may coat the sand grains and prevent the cement from adhering to them.

Bank run gravel is the most frequently used farm aggregate. It should be clean, free from clay, loam and vegetable matter, and

FIG. 306.—Gravel bank or pit, showing top soil falling down and mixing with aggregate. Soil should be "stripped" before gravel is taken for concrete work. (Portland Cement Association, 111 West Washington Street, Chicago.)

should contain a large amount of hard, well-rounded pebbles, ranging in size from 1/4 inch up to 1 1/2 or 2 inches. Gravel or stone containing many flat pieces should not be used, as they tend to bridge over, forming "stone pockets" in the concrete. Care should be taken in getting the gravel from the bank to strip back the top soil, preventing it from mixing with the gravel (Fig. 306). When properly used, gravel forms an ideal aggregate.

Screening Gravel.—Bank run gravel almost invariably contains too much sand, and, in addition, is usually arranged in strata so that it is not uniform in sand and pebble content. The use of gravel without screening results in one of two things:

1. An inferior grade of concrete will be produced, or
2. If concrete of maximum strength is made more cement will be used than would be otherwise necessary.

Before use, gravel should be passed over a ¼-inch mesh screen, and the portion passing the screen considered as sand. The sand and pebbles can then be recombined in the proportions desired.

Proportioning a Concrete Mixture.—To obtain a hard, dense concrete certain rules must be followed in proportioning. Gravel or stone carries a certain percentage of voids, as may readily be proved by adding water to a pail filled with stone.

The exact percentage of the voids will vary with the character of the stone. Stone that is rounded in shape and well graduated in size will show less void space than will a stone that is uniform in size.

While not so easily demonstrated, the same is true of sand. In general these spaces will approximate 30 to 50 per cent of the whole. It is common practice to arbitrarily assume the void spaces in gravel to be 50 per cent, and to use half as much sand as gravel for the purpose of filling them. Enough cement is added to thoroughly coat each sand particle, and to fill the spaces existing between them (Fig. 307). With

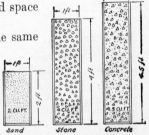

Fig. 307.—Proportioning concrete. Volume resulting from mixing 1 cu. ft. cement, 2 cu. ft. sand, and 4 cu. ft. stone. Cement and sand fill void spaces in stone without increasing the volume materially. (Portland Cement Association.)

these void spaces in mind, Taylor and Thompson, in "Concrete, Plain and Reinforced," have established four arbitrary proportions covering, with slight modifications, the range of work ordinarily found. Their recommendations, with modifications adapting them to farm use, follow:

1. **Rich Mixture.**—1: 1-½: 3, or one sack of cement, 1-½ cubic feet of sand and three cubic feet of crushed stone or screened gravel. Used where a very dense strong concrete is required as in concrete fence posts, supporting columns and thin reinforced walls that must be exceptionally strong and water-tight.

2. **Standard Mixture.**—1: 2: 4, or one sack of cement, two cubic feet of sand and four cubic feet of crushed stone or screened gravel. Used for reinforced floors, monolithic silo walls, corner posts and columns of larger cross section, cisterns, watering troughs and machine foundations.

3. **Medium Mixture.**—1: 2-½: 5, or one bag of cement, 2-½ cubic feet of sand and five cubic feet of crushed stone or screened gravel. Used for barn floors, feeding floors, barnyard pavements, sidewalks, foundation walls above ground and retaining walls.

4. **Lean Mixture.**—1: 3: 6, or one bag of cement, three cubic feet of sand and six cubic feet of crushed stone or screened gravel. Used for footings and foundation walls below ground, heavy walls and similar work.

Determining Quantity of Materials Required.—The following table, arranged from data secured from Taylor and Thompson's "Concrete, Plain and Reinforced," gives the quantities of cement, sand and screened gravel required for 100 cubic feet of concrete when mixed in the proportions noted.

Mixture			Cement (Bags)	Sand, Cubic Feet	Screened Gravel, Cubic Feet
1:	1-½ :	3	27.08	41	81
1:	2 :	4	21.31	43	85
1:	2-½ :	5	17.46	44	87
1:	3 :	6	14.95	45	90

As an example of the use of the above table, suppose it is desired to obtain the quantities of cement, sand and gravel needed for a barn floor 36' x 100', if laid 4" thick using a 1: 2-½: 5 mixture.

Solution:

36' x 100' x ⅓' = 1200 cubic feet.

Referring to the table we find that for every 100 cubic feet of concrete, when a 1: 2-½: 5 mixture is used, 87 cubic feet of gravel, 44 cubic feet of sand and 17.46 bags of cement are needed

Therefore:

$$1200 \div 100 \times 87 = 1044 \text{ cubic feet of gravel.}$$
$$1200 \div 100 \times 44 = 528 \text{ cubic feet of sand.}$$
$$1200 \div 100 \times 17.46 = 210 \text{ bags of cement.}$$

As a rough estimate, it is safe to consider the coarse aggregate required as being nine-tenths of the volume of the concrete. This will usually provide for waste in handling as well.

A wagon bed 16 inches x 3 feet x 12 feet, inside measurement, will hold about 50 cubic feet of gravel when rounded up. It is usually assumed that a team will draw a yard and one-half at a load.

A mortar composed of cement and sand alone is sometimes used for facing concrete work, the object being to secure a hard, dense wearing surface. The following table taken from Taylor and Thompson gives the quantity of mortar that may be expected from a bag of cement when mixed in the proportions noted.

Proportions	Clean, Coarse Sand	Mortar
1:1	1 cubic foot	1.38 cubic feet
1:2	2 cubic feet	2.11 cubic feet
1:3	3 cubic feet	2.83 cubic feet

Thorough mixing is essential to successful concrete work. Machine mixing is preferable to hand mixing, as good concrete can be secured more cheaply by this method. Small mixers are now on the market, capable of handling a one-bag batch, that are a useful part of farm equipment.

For small jobs a mixing box about 3½ feet x 10 inches x 6 feet, made with a tight, smooth bottom makes the most convenient arrangement for combining the cement and aggregate.

FIG. 308.—Tools used in mixing and laying concrete: *A*, gravel screen; *B*, trowel; *C*, water barrel for cleaning tools; *D*, hoe for mixing; *E*, shovel for placing concrete; *F*, garden rake for settling concrete in place; *G*, hatchet for sharpening stakes and setting forms; *H*, wood float for finishing; *I*, tamper for preparing cinder or gravel foundation; *J*, mixing box; *K*, straight edge.

It can be easily moved about, keeping it next to the work, and the concrete shoveled directly into the forms. Figure 308 shows equipment commonly used in mixing and placing concrete.

Clean water should be used in mixing concrete. Impure water may retard or prevent setting. The quantity of water used in mixing the first batch should be measured and the same amount used in each subsequent batch, making the concrete uniform in consistency.

Measuring the Materials.—To secure a uniform concrete, the materials must be measured. This is most conveniently done by preparing a bottomless box (Fig. 309) of a size sufficient to hold the fine aggregate, filling it once with the sand and twice with the stone. The table given below shows the sizes of measuring boxes for one bag batches of the proportions listed.

Proportions	Capacity of Measuring Box, Cubic Feet	Length	Inside Dimensions, Width	Depth
1 : 1–½ : 3	1–½	2′	1′	9″
1 : 2 : 4	2	2′	1′–4″	9″
1 : 2–½ : 5	2–½	2′	1′–8″	9″
1 : 3 : 6	3	3′	2′	9″

Consistency.—In general use concrete has about the consistency of a mud pie (Fig. 310). It will stand in a mound, but when

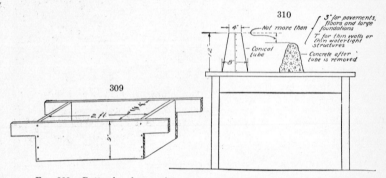

FIG. 309.—Bottomless box used to measure coarse and fine aggregate (stone and sand) when mixing concrete. Box shown designed for one bag batch mixed in proportion of 1: 2: 4. Box should have capacity equal to quantity of sand in mixture.

FIG. 310.—"Slump" test for determining proper amount of water to use in mixing concrete to obtain practical maximum strength. Concrete is packed in bottomless conical tube on bench-top. Tube is then lifted and amount of settlement determined after setting 1 to 2 minutes. Settlement should not be more than noted for best results. (Portland Cement Association.)

patted water will rise to the surface and the mass will quake or shake like jelly. This is called a " quaking " mixture, and is easily compacted into forms. Where thin walls are being " poured," stones are to be imbedded, or reinforcement used, a wetter mixture may be necessary. Use the driest mixture possible with character of the work being done to secure greatest strength.

Placing the Concrete.—Concrete should be placed in the forms promptly when thoroughly mixed. It begins setting within about thirty minutes after the addition of water, and should not be disturbed afterward, as its strength is lowered by so doing. When placed in the form it should be spaded or rammed to compact it.

Working a spade between the concrete and forms (Fig. 311) forces the larger pieces of stone back and brings the mortar to the outside, insuring a smooth surface.

Concrete should be placed in layers not exceeding 6 inches in depth, and the work of placing made continuous if possible. New concrete does not unite well with old. Where work must be stopped, imbed stones in the upper surface of the wall with their tops projecting, forming a lock joint with the concrete placed when work recommences (Fig. 312). When work is resumed the old surface should be carefully cleaned, the surface wetted and covered with a paste which is made from cement and water, before fresh concrete is added. Where a floor is being laid the work

Fig. 311.—Spading concrete back from forms to insure smooth surface. (Portland Cement Association.)

should be brought to a square edge when stopped for a time.

Care must be taken to prevent dirt from rattling down into

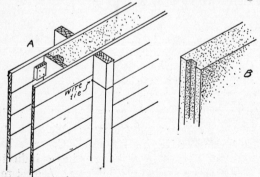

Fig. 312.—Method of making a vertical joint in a foundation wall where necessary. A. Temporary stop nailed in form. B. Appearance of wall after stop is removed. (Portland Cement Association.)

20

the concrete when placed directly in a trench as in building foundations.

Rubble Concrete.—When placed in masses, up to 50 per cent of hard, round field stone can be added to concrete as it is placed. This results in a considerable saving of cement. The concrete must be worked compactly around the stones, avoiding open places in the wall.

Finishing.—A wood float gives the most satisfactory finish for general farm use. A floor or walk, finished with a wood float is less slippery and better wearing than one troweled with a metal trowel. A pleasing finish for walls may be secured by applying cement and water, mixed to the consistency of cream, as quickly as the forms can be removed. Apply with a whitewash brush.

The strength of concrete is dependent upon a number of factors. Chief among these are:

1. Quality and character of the aggregate used.
2. Proportion of cement used in the mixture.
3. Care used in mixing and placing the concrete.

Taylor and Thompson give the following as safe loading to apply steadily to concrete that has been properly placed, and has thoroughly hardened.

Proportions	Pounds per square inch
1:1-½:3	500
1:2 :4	450
1:2-½:5	400
1:3 :6	360

Necessity of Reinforcing Concrete.—Concrete is strong in compression but is relatively easy to pull apart. This makes it necessary to use a reinforcing material high in tensile strength when it is required to withstand a pull. Mesh reinforcement is frequently used where the concrete is placed in slabs and has to withstand temperature changes. Due to expansion and contraction, cracks may develop without its use.

A beam supported as in figure 313 tends to bend under a load applied at the middle. As it bends the material in the bottom of the beam is under tension or is being stretched. Concrete being relatively weak in tensile strength, fails by breaking as indicated unless provision is made to care for the tensile stress. A steel rod imbedded as shown in figure 314 will care for the tension on the under side of the beam.

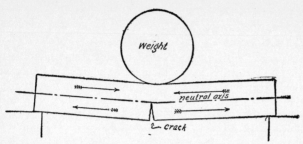

Fig. 313.—Stresses in a loaded concrete beam. Direction of stresses is shown by the arrows. The neutral axis represents the point in the cross-section of the beam where the stress changes from a push to a pull, compression to tension. In a beam loaded as above the upper half is under a compressive stress while the lower half is under tension. Concrete being very strong under compression will fail on the tension side as indicated unless reinforced with steel.

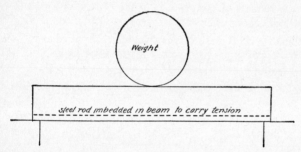

Fig. 314.—Beam shown in Fig. 313 reinforced with steel rod to carry tensile stresses in beam. Steel is strong under tension, makes a good bond with concrete, and expands at practically the same rate when heat is applied.

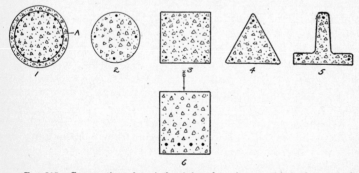

Fig. 315.—Cross-section of typical reinforced work met with in farm practice. 1. Column supporting load at the top. A. Spiral hoop, reinforcement used to prevent bursting. 2, 3, 4, 5. Fence-posts reinforced to care for loads from all sides. 6. Concrete beam loaded as indicated by the arrow and supported at both ends. If supported at one end only— a cantilever beam—reinforcement should be placed in the loaded side, as this side would be in tension. (Portland Cement Association.)

A general rule for placing reinforcement is: Place reinforcement in the side of the concrete that would be stretched should the piece bend under a load. It should be near the surface with only sufficient concrete covering it to protect it. Figure 315 shows position of reinforcement in typical cases.

Material to Use for Reinforcement.—Steel is the material used in reinforcing concrete. (1) It has great tensile strength, being strong where concrete is weak. (2) It makes a good bond with concrete, permitting the concrete to obtain a firm grip upon its surface. (3) It has practically the same coefficient of expansion as concrete, shrinking and elongating to the same extent under ordinary changes in temperature.

Steel rods are made for this purpose in various sizes. Ordinary steel rods obtained from the local blacksmith shop should not be used as they stretch slightly under tension.

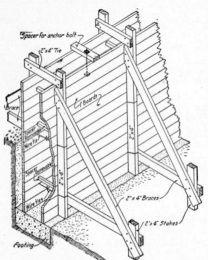

FIG. 316.—Typical wall form, showing braces, spacing blocks, and tie wires. (Portland Cement Association.)

For most farm uses woven wire fencing makes a most satisfactory reinforcing material, but it is difficult to keep in position while placing the concrete.

Forms.—Concrete when first mixed, must be supported by forms until it has hardened sufficiently to retain its shape.

Forms for Wall Building.—Unseasoned pine or spruce shiplaps make the best materials for form building. They do not swell and warp when wet concrete is placed in contact with them, and are more readily fitted together than is matched material. For an exposed surface the form material should be planed, resulting in a smooth surface on the concrete, but where appearance is not essential any rough materials may be used that will retain it.

Wet concrete is extremely heavy. Unless securely stayed, the forms will be sprung out of shape, resulting in a crooked wall of uneven thickness. For ordinary walls a 2-inch by 4-inch upright placed about every 3 feet, with 1-inch boarding applied horizontally, will give sufficient strength if well braced. To prevent spreading, the uprights are wired together as shown in figure 316. Spacing blocks are used to keep the form walls at the proper distance apart, the forms being pulled up against them by inserting a short rod through the wire and twisting.

Floor forms are usually made from 2-inch x 4-inch material placed edgewise, resulting in a floor 4 inches in thickness. The pieces used should be straight and surfaced on the upper edge, making a guide for a straight edge in striking off the surplus material. The supporting stakes are placed on the outside of the forms and the nails driven from the outside, permitting their easy

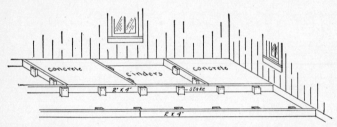

FIG. 317.—Typical arrangement of forms for floor construction. Floor laid in alternating squares approximately 5′ x 5′.

removal when the concrete is placed. The forms should be placed flush with the desired floor surface, and alternate squares laid. The arrangement of a form for floor laying is shown in figure 317.

Handling Concrete in Cold Weather.—Concrete can be successfully used during freezing weather by heating the aggregate, water, and cement, and protecting the concrete after placing to conserve this heat. Gravel and sand are most easily heated by making a sheet-iron arch on which the materials are piled, and maintaining a fire in the arch. Carefully protect the placed concrete by using straw, canvas, blankets, or sacks. Do not use manure, because of a possible chemical effect on the green concrete.

Job 1.—**Mixing a One-bag Batch of 1:2:4 Concrete.**—To secure a uniform mixture of cement, sand, stone, and water of the consistency and proportions desired.

Method of Work.—1. Run gravel over a ¼″ mesh screen. Consider portion passing through the screen as sand and the portion passing over it as stone.

2. Place mixing box in convenient location near work and measure into it two cubic feet of sand.

3. Spread the sand and empty on a sack of cement.

4. Turn cement and sand with square pointed shovel until the mixture has a uniform color free from streaks or bands.

5. Spread the mixture of cement and sand and add four cubic feet of stone.

6. Turn cement sand and stone several times until uniformly mixed.

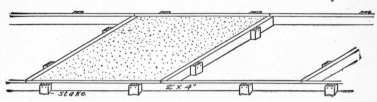

Fig. 318.—Typical form for concrete walk construction. Form is placed on prepared bed of tamped cinders or gravel and walk laid in alternate squares. When squares first laid have hardened remaining squares are laid.

7. Open shallow crater in top of pile and add water. Mix as water is added until a quaking, jelly-like mass is secured. Add water slowly and in known quantities so that an equal quantity can be used in subsequent batches.

8. Shovel wet concrete into forms and place immediately.

Fig. 319.—Striking off surplus concrete with straight edge.

Job 2.—**Laying a 3½-foot Concrete Walk.**—To provide a smooth, durable walk with a non-slipping surface.

Method of Work.—1. Stretch lines 3' 6" apart between points it is desired to connect with walk.

2. Excavate between the lines 6" deep and fill in with cinders or gravel. This may be omitted if solid, well drained foundation is provided by ground surface.

3. Wet gravel or cinders and tamp to a firm, even surface.

4. Use straight 2″ x 4″ scantlings with dressed edges, and fasten to stakes as shown in figure 318, making form for outside edge of walk. Use a line in setting these forms, placing them straight and at a uniform slope. They should be level crosswise at any point and 3′ 6″ apart inside.

5. Cut cross piece 3′ 6″ long and nail in place to form first block. Make blocks 4′ long.

6. Mix concrete as directed in Job 1, using a 1: 2–½: 5 mixture.

7. Shovel mixed concrete directly from mixing box into forms, compacting it by spading and ramming. Use slightly more concrete than is

FIG. 320.—Markers in place, ready to cut across surface of walk, separating it into blocks.

required to fill forms and strike off surplus with straight edge used across forms with a sawing motion. (Fig. 319.)

8. Float surface lightly with wooden float, pushing all pebbles beneath surface.

9. Cover block with canvas or old sacks to prevent too rapid setting in hot weather.

10. Mark position of edge of cross piece next to concrete on side forms. Carefully remove piece and set in place for second block. Lay second block as directed for block one.

11. When first block laid has stiffened slightly lay straight edge across forms at marks made and divide first block from second by cutting along straight edge with the trowel. (Fig. 320.) Cut clear through to the base.

12. Run groover along this cut, finishing the ends of the blocks with rounded edges. Finish edges in same manner by use of edger.

13. Lay and finish successive blocks in the manner described for first block. If desired blocks may be laid alternately as indicated in figure 318.

Job 3.—Making a Concrete Gate Post 1 foot x 1 foot x 5 feet High.

Method of Work.—1. Make a form of planed lumber 1′ x 1′ inside cross-section, 8′ in height. (Fig. 321.) Form can best be assembled with screws.

2. Dig hole 4′ deep and 2′ square where it is proposed to locate the gate post.

3. Set up form, plumb it up and brace rigidly in place with 5′ of its length projecting above ground surface.

4. Bore holes in form and insert hinges for gate and staples for holding ¾″ rod to which fence is attached.

5. Cut four ⅜″ steel rods 8′ 11″ long and fasten in corners of post form 1-½″ from each side in cross-section. (Fig. 322.)

6. Mix concrete as directed in Job 1, using proportions of one part cement, two parts sand and four parts stone.

7. Shovel concrete into form and compact it by tamping with a rod. Be careful to avoid misplacing reinforcing bars.

8. When concrete reaches ground surface be careful to work pebbles back and to bring mortar to the surface, giving a smooth finish, by spading between the form and the concrete with a long, narrow board sharpened to a long wedge at the lower end.

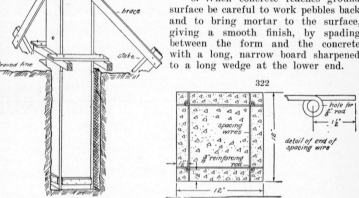

Fig. 321.—Form for concrete gate-post. Where soil is firm form may be set on top of ground and the hole used as form for bottom part of post. Form must be well supported as at *A* to prevent bulging when concrete is tamped in place and securely braced to keep an upright position. Reinforcing rods should extend clear to the bottom, as greatest stress is at ground-line. Insert greased wood pins to provide holes for hinges.

Fig. 322.—Cross-section of concrete gate-post, showing reinforcing rods and spacing wires used to hold rods in position while filling form.

9. When filled to the top make pyramidical top by using a stiff mortar mixed in the proportion of one part cement to two parts clean coarse sand. Build top up with trowel.

10. As soon as top sets sufficiently to prevent marring, cover with damp sacks and keep protected in this way to prevent too rapid drying.

11. Remove form in one week and protect post with damp sacks to retard drying.

12. Tamp dirt firmly about the base of the post to ground level to insure firm setting. Do not attach fence or gate until the post has stood at least thirty days, to be sure that post has reached its full strength. Figure 323 shows the post in use.

Job 4.—**Making a Concrete Water Trough 3 feet x 2 feet x 8 feet,** to provide a permanent and sanitary place from which cattle may drink.

Method of Work.—1. Stake out location of tank and excavate to

Fig. 323.—Farm gate with poured concrete posts. (Portland Cement Association.)

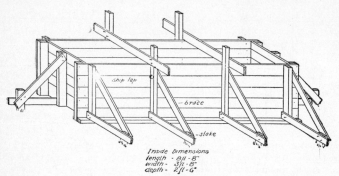

ship lap

brace

stake

Inside Dimensions
length - 8ft - 8"
width - 3ft - 8"
depth - 2ft - 6"

Fig. 324.—Outside form for watering-trough. Form is set up over foundation and thoroughly braced and staked in position to prevent springing when concrete is placed.

the depth of 3′ to 4′. Fill pit with field stones to give drainage beneath tank and to prevent heaving.

2. Spread cinders or gravel on top of stones, wet down and tamp thoroughly to make foundation upon which to lay concrete.

3. Build outer form of planed ship-lap, 2′ 6″ high x 3′ 8″ wide x 8′ 8″ long inside. (Fig. 324.)

4. Place outer form in position on base. Square and level it up and brace rigidly in position to stakes driven solidly into the ground.

5. Construct inner form as shown in figure 325. Round off all corners making inner corners of trough round.

6. Prepare seven ¼″ round bars 12′ 6″ in length. Bend at right-angles

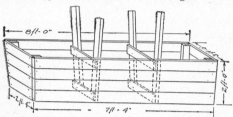

FIG. 325.—Inner form for concrete watering-trough; cross-bracing is shown by dotted lines. Corners are rounded and side-walls are given a slant or "batter" of 1 inch per foot.

2′ 1″ from each end. These form longitudinal reinforcement for the bottom and vertical reinforcement for the ends. (Fig. 326.)

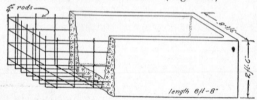

FIG. 326.—Section of trough removed to show arrangement of reinforcing rods. Note: rounded outer corners can be secured by plastering inside corners of outer form with clay, or by nailing a curved strip of tin in the corners.

7. Prepare nine ¼″ round rods 7′ 6″ long. Bend at right-angles 2′ 1″ from each end. These form crosswise reinforcement of the bottom and vertical reinforcement for the sides.

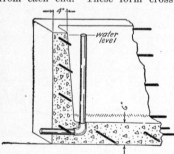

FIG. 327.—Section of corner of trough, showing detail of overflow and drain-pipe and reinforcing rods.

8. Mix concrete as directed in Job 1, using one part of cement, two parts sand and four parts screened gravel.

9. Place 3″ of concrete in the bottom of the form working it firmly into place.

10. Place the reinforcing rods on this concrete, spacing them equally.

11. Wire four ¼″ rods around this vertical reinforcement to form longitudinal reinforcement for the sides and ends. Be careful to have rods overlap well where spliced together.

12. Cut a piece of 1-¼″ pipe 12″ long. Thread it and affix an elbow. Place in concrete so that pipe will project at one end of trough and elbow will be flush with finished floor surface. Hold in this position by hole bored in end of form. A 2′ length of pipe screwed into this forms an overflow while the removal of the length permits the draining of the tank. (Fig. 327.)

13. Place the remainder of the floor to the 6″ line.

14. Place the inside form immediately and fasten in place by means of stays nailed across the top. (Fig. 328.)

15. Mix and place concrete in side walls. Spade thoroughly to compact

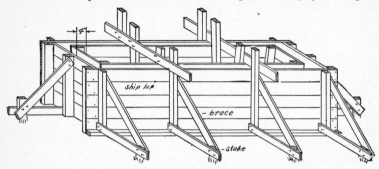

FIG. 328.—Inside form in position with stays nailed across top to support it. Stays shown across top in figure 328 are not nailed in place until inner form has been set.

it, force pebbles back and bring mortar to the surface, insuring a dense, smooth wall.

16. When full, smooth off top edge with float and when concrete has set

FIG. 329.—Concrete watering-trough. (Portland Cement Association.)

sufficiently run edger around outer and inner edge of top, forming rounded edges.

17. Remove forms carefully as soon as concrete has become sufficiently hard and paint the surface with cement and water mixed to a cream-like consistency. Apply with white wash brush.

18. Protect with sacks or canvas to prevent too rapid drying. Figure 329 shows such a trough in use.

CHAPTER XX

GAS ENGINES—INSTALLATION AND CARE

DEVELOPMENT of the internal combustion motor and its application to agricultural uses have made it a leading farm power. The tractor is used in heavy field operations of plowing, seeding, and harvesting, where its immunity to heat and fatigue make it superior to animal power; marketing facilities are increased by the long hauling radius of the truck and automobile, and much of the chore work is done by the small stationary engine. Its automatic features, convenience, and low cost of operation make it particularly desirable for this work.

The Internal Combustion Motor.—Gasoline and oil engines are heat engines, known as internal combustion motors. They are so called because the fuel is burned within the cylinder directly behind the piston.

Principle of Operation.—The operation of an internal combustion motor may be compared to the loading and firing of a gun. A charge of highly combustible fuel is ignited and burned behind the piston. The resulting expansion forces the piston outward, in the same way that the bullet is expelled from the gun barrel.

This provides for one outward stroke of the piston only. To make the operation continuous, the burned gases must be forced from the cylinder, fresh gases admitted, the piston returned to its original position, and the fresh gases ignited. The above events are performed automatically and constitute the gas engine cycle.

A cycle is a chain of events that is completed in regular order, returning to the point of beginning. For example, the regular recurrence of spring, summer, fall, and winter make up a seasonal cycle.

Operation of a Four-cycle Engine.—The common farm engine requires two complete revolutions of the crank-shaft, necessitating four strokes of the piston, two outward and two inward, to complete the cycle. It is therefore called a four-stroke cycle. An engine operating in this way is commonly called a "four-cycle engine." The four strokes of the cycle are:

1. Suction or admission.
2. Compression.
3. Power.
4. Exhaust.

316

1. Suction or Admission Stroke.—The fly-wheel is revolved in the direction of the arrow (Fig. 330) by momentum or some external force. This results in pulling the piston out from the closed end of the cylinder, and creates a partial vacuum behind it. Air, under atmospheric pressure, rushes in through the admission

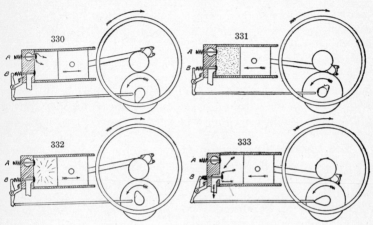

Fig. 330.—Diagram of suction or intake stroke of a four-cycle gas-engine. Piston is moved forward and partial vacuum created behind it in the cylinder. Admission valve A opens under outside pressure and air rushes through intake passages into cylinder, picking up a charge of atomized fuel as it does so, as it passes through the mixing chamber. Exhaust valve B is closed.

Fig. 331.—Compression stroke. Both valves are closed. Piston is forced back into the cylinder by the momentum of the fly-wheel and the imprisoned gases are compressed in the combustion chamber. The piston does not go clear to the head but leaves a space equal to about ⅕ of the contents of the engine cylinder, compressing the gases to about five times atmospheric pressure when the engine is working at full throttle.

Fig. 332.—Power stroke. Near the end of the compression stroke the spark occurs which ignites the compressed gases, causing an explosion or very rapid burning within the cylinder. The resulting high pressure forces the piston out on the power stroke. Both valves, A and B, being closed, the pressure acting against the piston, forcing it outward, and through the medium of the crank and connecting rod, produces the turning effort.

Fig. 333.—Near the end of the power stroke the exhaust valve B is opened by the action of the cam on the half-time gears transmitted through the push rod and rocker arm. The piston, as it is forced back by the momentum of the fly-wheel, forces the burned gases out through the exhaust valve passage.

valve A to relieve this vacuum, and in so doing picks up a spray of fuel from the needle valve orifice, filling the cylinder with a highly combustible vapor mixed with air.

2. Compression Stroke.—The admission valve is now closed and the piston forced back into the cylinder by the revolution of the fly-wheel (Fig. 331), compressing the gases into about one-fifth of their original volume in the closed end of the cylinder. This results in greater power when the gases are ignited.

3. Power Stroke.—Just before the piston reaches the inner end of its travel in the compression stroke, the gases are ignited by an electric spark within the cylinder. The resulting quick combustion produces a high degree of heat and consequent pressure in the confined gases, forcing the piston outward and producing the power stroke (Fig. 332).

4. Exhaust Stroke.—Near the end of the outward travel of the piston on the power stroke the exhaust valve is opened and the

Fig. 334.—Sectional view of semi-Diesel farm engine. This engine has no ignition devices and ignites its fuel by the heat of compression. (Sears Roebuck and Co.)

piston returning to the closed end of the cylinder pushes the burned gases out (Fig. 333).

This completes the cycle. On the next forward stroke of the piston a charge of gases is drawn into the cylinder and the cycle of events continued. A power impulse is received only once in every two revolutions. Where but a single cylinder is used power for completing the other three strokes of the cycle, as well as for driving the machinery in use must be obtained from the momentum of the fly-wheel.

The two-cycle engine performs the operations of admission, compression, combustion, and exhaust in two strokes of the piston or one revolution of the engine. It is little used in farm practice.

Engines of the semi-Diesel type in which the liquid fuel is fed to the cylinder by gravity are now being made for farm use (Fig. 334). They are simple, have neither carburetor nor electrical ignition devices, as fuel is ignited by the high compression. Due to the high compression carried these are economical in operation, burning the low grade fuel oils satisfactorily.

Gas Engine Timing.—The opening and closing of admission and exhaust valves and the production of the spark within the cylinder are termed " events " in the gas engine's cycle. In order

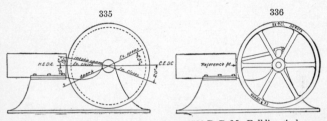

Fig. 335.—Timing of farm engine running at 500 R. P. M. Full line circle represents first revolution of cycle. Broken line represents second revolution of cycle. Diagonal lines represent position of center line of crank when events listed should occur. Intake valve should open 6-10° past *H E D C* and close 10-40° after *C E D C* has been passed. Points of opening and closing cannot be definitely controlled with automatic valves. Ignition takes place 25° before *H E D C* is reached. If oscillating magneto is used, give 10° to 15° more advance. Exhaust closes at *H E D C* or a little beyond and opens 25° before *C E D C* is reached.

Fig. 336.—Diagram of engine with timing marks on fly-wheel. The engine can be timed by bringing any point on the fly-wheel to coincide with reference point on frame, adjusting the engine so that the event desired takes place at this point.

that the engine may deliver maximum power with minimum fuel consumption, proper timing of valves is necessary.

The Exhaust Valve.—The exhaust valve is set to open before the end of the power stroke is reached. The exact point of opening depends upon engine speed and design. Figure 335 shows the point in the revolution at which the exhaust valve should open on an engine running at 500 R. P. M. The exhaust valve should close at the head end dead center (H.E.D.C.) or slightly beyond it.

The admission valve should open from 6 to 10 degrees after the crank has passed the H.E.D.C. and should remain open until the crank has passed slightly beyond the crank end dead center (C.E.D.C.). The point of closing should vary with the speed and design of the engine, and will range from 10 to 40 degrees after C.E.D.C. has been reached.

Stationary farm engines are usually equipped with automatic inlet valves which do not permit timing, opening under atmospheric pressure and closing by the tension of a spring. The spring should be only sufficiently strong to prevent chattering, giving the earliest opening and the latest closing possible. Valves may be timed by changing the length of the push rod. Lengthening the rod gives an early opening and late closing, and shortening the rod gives the reverse of this effect. Valve timing can also be changed by shifting the meshing of the timing gears one or more teeth forward or back.

Ignition Timing.—An appreciable length of time is required for the flame to spread through the gases after the spark is produced. To secure the greatest energy from the fuel it is necessary to have it all burning and ready to exert its greatest pressure on the piston when it starts forward on the power stroke. The spark, therefore, must be set to occur before H.E.D.C. is reached. The exact amount of advance is dependent upon engine speed and design, and the character of the fuel used.

Rule for Spark Setting.—A general rule for spark setting is to give an advance of five degrees for every 100 R.P.M. made by the engine. This is sometimes increased to 8 degrees per 100 R.P.M. in the case of a make-and-break ignition system. Where an oscillating magneto is used 12 to 15 degrees should be added to the computed setting to provide time for the tripping mechanism to operate.

Setting the Valves and Spark.—Manufacturers commonly place timing marks on their engines (Fig. 336), making it necessary only to bring the proper mark on the fly-wheel to correspond to the reference mark on the frame and when in this position to set the engine by adjusting the length of the push rod operating the ignitor or the valve being set.

Where there are no timing marks the engine should be timed to the closing of the exhaust valve. The time of closing of this valve is least affected by conditions of speed and design of any of the events of the cycle. The engine is set on H.E.D.C. on the exhaust stroke and the exhaust valve adjusted to close at this point. The exact closing point of the valve is determined by inserting a piece of thin, tough paper between the rocker arm and the valve stem (Fig. 337). The paper will be pinched between them as long as the valve is held open, but will be released when it seats. With the valve set to close at the proper point the shape of the operating cam will usually cause it to open where it should. The point of opening can be checked by noting when the paper begins to be pinched as the fly-wheel is turned forward.

Establishing H.E.D.C. and C.E.D.C. by the Tram Method.— These points can be most accurately determined by the "tram" method. A simple tram is made as shown in figure 338.

To use the tram the engine is turned forward until it has com-

Fig. 337.—Holding paper between valve rocker arm and valve to determine closing point. When the paper is released the valve is closed.

pleted from two-thirds to three-fourths of its outward stroke and the distance from the piston to the open end of the cylinder carefully measured. With the engine in this position the tram is set up and a mark made on the chalked surface of the fly-wheel (Fig. 338).

The engine is now turned slowly forward until the piston has reached the same point on its inward travel that it had on its outward travel when the first tram point was located. When the engine has been brought to the proper point, again set the tram up and mark "tram point No. 2" on the face of the wheel.

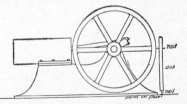

Fig. 338.—Construction of simple tram and method of using it to mark fly-wheel. In illustration tram is being used to locate tram point No. 1. Dead center will be midway between tram points No. 1 and No. 2.

With the tape carefully measure the distance between tram

21

points 1 and 2, and locate a point midway between them. Mark this point C.E.D.C. When the engine is turned forward until this mark coincides with the point of the tram it will be on the C.E.D.C. Head end dead center can be located and marked by carefully measuring around the wheel with the tape half of the circumference from the C.E.D.C. When the point so marked is brought to coincide with the point of the tram when held as before the engine will be on H.E.D.C.

The above applies to horizontal engines with open outer cylinder ends and crank case, a common farm type. When the engine has more than one cylinder, as in the case of a tractor, No. 1 cylinder only is timed. Timing No. 1 automatically times the remaining cylinders.

An event is said to have "lead" when it occurs before the dead center to which it is timed is reached. When it occurs after the dead center is passed it is said to have "lag."

The length of a degree in inches is found by dividing the circumference of the flywheel in inches by 360.

Fig. 339.—Make and break ignitor. 1. Insulated electrode. 2. Ignitor points. 3. Movable electrode. 4. Gasket. 5. Outside ignitor trip.

Rules.—For " lead " and " advance " lay off the required degrees from the proper dead center point in the direction of rotation.

For " lag " lay off the required distance from the proper dead center mark in a direction opposite to rotation.

Exhaust valve closing, intake valve opening and spark are timed from the H.E.D.C.

Exhaust valve opening and intake valve closing are timed from the C.E.D.C.

Ignition Systems.—Two general types of ignition systems are in common use on farm engines: (1) the make-and-break or low tension system, and (2) the jump spark or high tension system.

The make-and-break or low tension system uses a low voltage current. It is not capable of jumping across a fixed gap and consequently the ignitor is designed with one movable electrode (Fig. 339). The fixed electrode is insulated from the block by a mica bushing, while the movable electrode is grounded to the engine permitting the engine to be used as one side of the ignition circuit. A spark coil is introduced into the circuit to induce a current of sufficient pressure to arc across the gap when the circuit is broken and ignite the gas about the points. Figure 340 shows the method of wiring a typical make-and-break system.

The jump spark or high tension system uses a spark plug with a small fixed gap, across which the electric current is forced to jump. The resulting spark ignites the charge. Air under pressure, as it is in the gas engine cylinder, offers great resistance to electrical flow. This makes a high voltage current necessary to jump the gap.

The induction coil is used to step up the low pressure battery current to the voltage required. It consists of two windings, primary and secondary, about an iron core. The primary winding consists of a few turns of comparatively coarse, insulated copper wire through which the battery current flows, and is provided with a vibrator and a condenser. The secondary winding, composed of

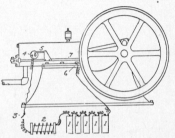

FIG. 340.—Method of wiring engine equipped with battery ignition and make-and-break ignitor. 1. Dry cells connected in series, zinc to carbon. 2. Spark coil or "kick coil," consisting of insulated copper wire wound about a soft iron core. 3. Switch for turning current off and on. 4. Insulated electrode on ignitor block. 5. Movable electrode on ignitor block operated by trip on push rod. 6. One side of battery circuit grounded to metallic part of engine frame. 7. Push rod operating exhaust valve and ignitor.

many turns of very fine insulated copper wire, is wound over the primary winding (Fig. 341). The condenser serves to absorb and equalize electrical shocks and tends to prevent sparking at the vibrator's points. The coil and wiring must be kept dry. The vibrator points should be kept flat with a magneto file, insuring that they meet squarely and so adjusted that they give a sharp, snappy buzz. A typical jump spark system is shown in figure 342.

Sources of Current.—Batteries and magnetos are the sources of current commonly used in farm practice. The magneto is higher in first cost but has a longer life and gives a more uniform and dependable spark.

The battery usually used is made up of No. 6 dry cells, from 4 to 6 cells being wired up in series as shown in figures 340 and 342. A 4-cell battery connected up in this way should furnish a current of about 6 volts and 25 to 30 amperes. A cell that tests less than 10 amperes should be discarded.

Magnetos may be divided into two general classes (1) rotary and (2) oscillating. The rotary magneto has a revolving inner part or armature which may or may not carry a winding, depending upon the design. A common type has a soft iron core shaped like a shuttle (Fig. 343), and carries a winding of insulated copper

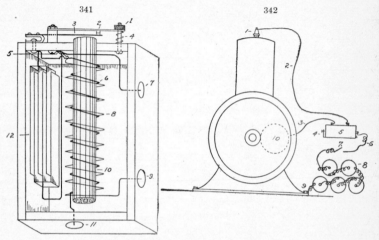

Fig. 341.—Sectional view of induction coil. 1. Vibrator adjusting nut. 2. Vibrator points. 3. Contact spring. 4. Spring. 5. Junction of primary and secondary windings permitting terminal 7 to be used by both coils. 6. Primary winding. 7. Primary contact terminal. 8. Secondary winding. 9. Secondary (high-tension) terminal. 10. Soft iron core. 11. Primary contact terminal. 12. Condenser.

Fig. 342.—Diagram of high-tension wiring. 1. Spark plug. 2. Secondary wiring or "high-tension" cable. 3. Primary wire to timing mechanism. 4. Vibrator on coil. 5. Induction coil. 6. Primary wire to battery. 7. Switch. 8. Battery. 9. Wire from battery grounded to engine. 10. Timer.

wire. This revolves between the poles of a strong permanent magnet, inducing a flow of electricity in the winding, which is collected by suitable rings and brushes and led to the ignition device.

Cooling System.—The burning of the fuel within the cylinder of an internal combustion motor produces great heat. Only about 20 per cent. can be utilized in running the engine. This makes it necessary to provide a means of cooling the engine, as otherwise it would become so hot it would be destroyed. Two general methods are employed for controlling the temperature of farm engines, (1) air cooling, (2) liquid cooling.

Air Cooling.—In an air cooling system a fan, driven by the engine, is employed to force an air blast over the cylinder. The

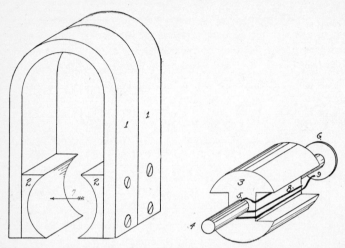

Fig. 343.—Diagrammatic representation of simple magneto. 1. Permanent field magnets. 2. Iron pole shoes with curved surfaces bringing poles of magnets close to armature. 3. Soft iron cylindrical armature with slot cut lengthwise to receive winding of insulated wire. 4. Armature shaft. 5. End of winding grounded to armature shaft. 6. Collector ring or disc insulated from armature shaft. 7. Arrow indicating direction of flow of magnetic force from pole through armature. 8. Armature winding of insulated wire, one end grounded to armature shaft at 5, the other attached to insulated collector ring or disc at 9, from which the current is taken off by a suitable brush. 9. Point of attachment of winding to collector ring.

Fig. 344.—Air-cooled farm engine. 1. Flanges on cylinder to increase heat-radiating surface. 2. Fan driven by fly-wheel to increase air circulation over cylinder.

cylinder is flanged (Fig. 344) to increase the area in contact with the cooling blast of air as much as possible. This system of cooling is adapted to small farm engines used in intermittent service or running under light load; larger, slow moving, heavily loaded engines require liquid cooling.

Liquid Cooling.—In this type of cooling system a jacket or hollow wall is cast about the cylinder, permitting the circulation of a liquid, usually water, about the heated parts of the motor.

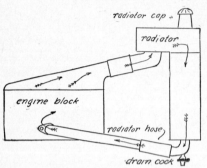

Thermo-siphon System.—A cooling system in which the water is circulated by heat is known as a thermo-siphon system. The water about the cylinder becomes heated and expands, making it lighter; the cooler water in the remainder of the system flows in, displacing it and forcing it to the top (Fig. 345).

FIG. 345.—Thermo-siphon cooling system. The circulation is maintained by the difference in weight between the heated water in the upper part of the cylinder jackets and the colder water in the lower part of the radiator. Water-passages must be large and free from such obstructions as ragged hose-linings, etc.

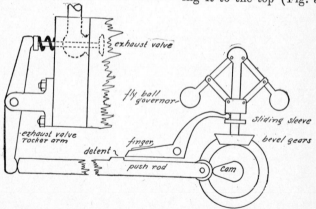

FIG. 346.—Diagram of mechanism of simple hit-or-miss governor. As the speed of the engine rises above normal, the weight of the governor, which is caused to revolve by the bevel gears fly outward, causing the sliding sleeve to be pulled upward and the movable finger to be depressed. This causes it to engage with the detent on the push rod, locking the exhaust valve open and preventing a new charge from being drawn in until the valve is released by the governor.

Hopper Cooling System.—The cylinder jacket is left open at the top, forming a tank or hopper.

Governors.—Two general methods of controlling the speed of the farm engine are in use: (1) hit-or-miss governor, (2) throttling governor. Both of these governors use the principle of centrifugal force.

The hit-or-miss governor acts on the exhaust valve, admission valve and ignition. As long as the engine runs at or below normal speed it is inoperative, but as soon as the speed reaches a point above normal it locks open the exhaust valve, locks the intake valve closed and prevents the ignition device from making contact (Fig. 346).

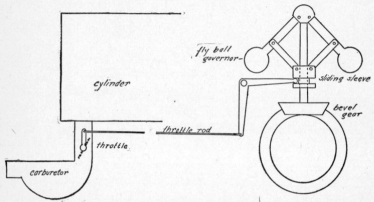

Fig. 347.—Diagram of throttling governor. As speed increases, fly balls swing outward, lifting the sliding sleeve and closing the throttle, lessening the quantity of fuel mixture admitted to the cylinder.

This prevents the engine from making another power stroke until the speed has again fallen, and they are released. This system is adapted for use on single cylinder engines, where a perfectly uniform speed is not essential, and where gasoline is used for fuel.

The throttling governor controls the speed of the engine by lessening the quantity of fuel mixture admitted to the cylinder when the speed increases under the influence of a light load. This is accomplished by means of a butterfly valve, similar to the damper used in a stovepipe, placed in the intake passage between the carburetor and the cylinder, and controlled by the action of the governor weights (Fig. 347). When parallel with the intake passage a full quantity of vaporized fuel and air is admitted to the cylinder. As the speed increases the valve is gradually swung at right angles to the passage by the governor until very little fuel is admitted.

Fuels.—Gasoline vaporizes easily, is highly inflammable, and burns cleanly. Although higher in first cost than kerosene, it is recommended for small engines, particularly where they are used indoors or for intermittent service.

Kerosene contains more energy than gasoline, but due to its heavier nature, does not atomize as freely, and is seldom so completely utilized by the engine. It has a tendency to work down past the piston rings into the crank case, diluting the oil and causing lubricating difficulties. Its lower cost adapts it to use in large engines operating continuously throughout the day. Many tractor owners, however, use gasoline for all work during the cold months because of starting and lubricating advantages.

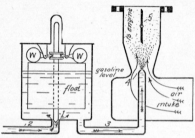

FIG. 348.—Diagrammatic representation of float feed carburetor. 1. Valve controlled by float and weights, *W*, maintaining a constant gasoline level. 2. Pipe leading from gasoline tank to float-controlled valve, 1. 3. Pipe leading from float bowl to jet, 4. 4. Atomizing jet. Liquid gasoline is atomized at this point by rapid passage of air over it. 5. Throttle or damper controlling amount of atomized fuel and air admitted to engine.

Carburetors.—To prepare the liquid fuel for the almost instantaneous burning necessary in the engine cylinder, it must be atomized and mixed with a large volume of air. This is done by the carburetor or mixing valve. Figure 348 is a diagrammatic representation of the principle of a simple float feed carburetor. The air rushing through the passage to the cylinder of the engine on the intake stroke, picks up a quantity of fuel from the orifice and atomizes it, the action being exactly the same as that of the common hand cattle sprayer. The gasoline level at the orifice is maintained by the supply in the float chamber which is connected to the tank and controlled by a float and needle valve 1.

Methods of Lubrication.—A common type of lubricator used on stationary gas engines is the slight feed gravity oiler shown in figure 349. This should be adjusted to feed from 6 to 15 drops per minute on the usual farm engine. The exact amount cannot be given, as the size of the drops vary with the temperature and the character of the oil used. Sufficient oil should be used to give a slight trace of bluish smoke at the exhaust.

For tractors, the constant level splash system is almost universally used. In this method of oiling (Fig. 350) shallow troughs

Fig. 349.—Sight feed gravity oiler. 1. Oiler. 2. Hopper cooling system. 3. Fly-wheel. 4. Governor weight. 5. Governing device. 6. Governor spring. 7. Magneto.

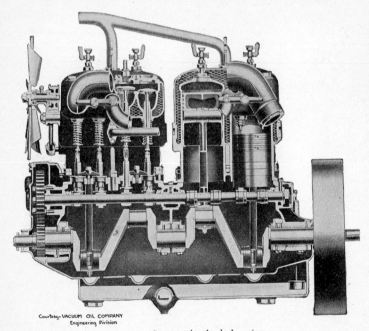

Courtesy-VACUUM OIL COMPANY
Engineering Division

Fig. 350.—Constant level splash system.

are provided in the crank case into which the connecting rods dip
at each revolution, throwing a spray of oil to all interior parts of the
engine. The oil level in the troughs is maintained by a pump which
circulates it from a sump or oil reservoir, the oil being used over
and over. Oil must be added at intervals, and the crank case should
be drained and the oil completely changed at periods averaging
from 30 to 50 hours' service with kerosene or 40 to 75 hours' work
where gasoline is used as a fuel. The directions of the manufacturer should be carefully followed in this.

Common Gas Engine Troubles.—Some of the more common
gas engine troubles with their remedies are given in the following
trouble chart. Special troubles can best be located and corrected
by following the directions given by the manufacturer. When
hunting the source of trouble do not take things apart indiscriminately but rather follow one line of possible trouble through,
making sure that all is right before attempting another adjustment.

Trouble	Probable Reason	Indications	Remedy
Engine will not start.	1. Ignition switch not closed.	1. Engine dead. Fuel appears at admission valve.	1. Close switch.
	2. Fuel not turned on, tank empty or needle valve closed with dirt.	2. Engine dead. No fuel dripping from intake valve when choke is closed and engine cranked.	2. Open fuel valve, or supply fuel.
	3. Engine not choked sufficiently.	3. Little or no sucking sound when engine is cranked. No fuel appears at admission valve.	3. Hold hand over intake or choke in manner provided.
	4. Engine too cold.	4. Engine cold. Fuel appearing at intake and hot blue spark produced when ignitor is snapped but still no explosion.	4. Use high test fuel for starting or warm engine.

Trouble	Probable Reason	Indications	Remedy
Engine will not start.	5. Engine too hot. (flooded)	5. Engine hot. Fuel dripping from carburetor and good spark but engine fails to explode.	5. Hold exhaust valve open and crank engine to clear cylinder.
Engine stops suddenly.	1. Electrical circuit broken.	1. Engine stops without warning.	1. Repair break in wiring.
	2. Fuel exhausted or supply stopped.	2. Engine gives several preliminary pops through carburetor line before stopping.	2. Replenish fuel or repair fuel line.
Engine runs intermittently.	1. Water in fuel.	1. Popping back through carburetor.	1. Drain tank and carburetor bowl and refill.
	2. Insulation worn from wiring resulting in short circuit when wires touch metal or engine.	2. Sparks - Engine will operate when wires are moved about destroying short circuit.	2. Repair insulation with tape.
	3. Loose wiring.		3. Tighten connections.
Engine runs but lacks power.	1. Leaky valves. Valve push rod too long or carbon under valve.	1. Hissing through exhaust or intake passages when engine is turned over by hand.	1. Grind valve or adjust push rods.
	2. Worn and leaky rings.	2. Hissing at open end of cylinder. Smoke issuing at open end when engine is running accompanied by coughing sound.	

Trouble	Probable Reason	Indications	Remedy
Engine runs but lacks power.	3. Lack of lubrication.	3. Coughing a n d smoke from open end o f cylinder while engine i s running. Turns hard.	3. Adjust lubricator to feed more freely. Supply oil.
	4. Valves o r ignition spark out of time.	4. Overheating of engine.	4. Check timing.
	5. Mixture t o o rich.	5. Black smoke from exhaust. Engine hot.	5. Turn d o w n needle valve reducing quantity o f fuel used.

Power Transmission.—The farm gas engine is usually used for a variety of work, making necessary some means of harnessing it to the different machines employed. A system consisting of a line shaft equipped with belt pulleys, connected to the machines by belting is used for this purpose.

Shafting.—Cold rolled steel shafting of the size known as 1½-inch is most satisfactory for farm use. This is finished all over, permitting the placing of a pulley or bearing at any point along its length. A line shaft should be supported parallel with the crank shaft of the engine driving it. The method of doing this is described in Job 7. To prevent springing, bearings should be placed not more than 8 or 10 feet apart.

Pulleys in common use are made of wood and are known as split pulleys, being made in halves and fastened together with bolts. This permits their application to a shaft at any point without its removal from the bearings. In ordering specify diameter, width of face, whether crowned or flat, and the diameter of the shaft upon which it is to be used.

Shaft Hangers and Bearings.—Adjustable shaft hangers with self-aligning bearings lined with babbitt metal may be purchased for supporting the line shaft, but supports can be made that will answer every purpose. A bearing made from hard maple soaked in oil will last indefinitely in farm service.

Belting is available for farm use in canvas, rubber, leather and balata. Of these rubber and canvas seem to best meet the demands of farm service, the rubber for indoor work in dairies where dampness is encountered, and the canvas for silo filling, threshing and other hard service.

Width of Belt Required.—A belt transmits power by friction; its resistance to slipping on the pulley surface. The greater the power to be transmitted the wider the belt must be if conditions of belt speed, pulley surface and belt tension remain the same. A common mistake is to use too narrow a belt and then run it too taut

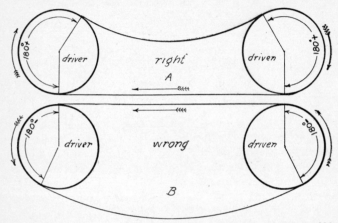

Fig. 351.—Right and wrong way of running belt. Where possible belt should be run horizontally with under side doing the driving. This increases the arc of contact and the tractive effort that the belt will transmit. Belt run as shown in *B* must be run much tighter to carry the same power.

in the effort to prevent slipping. Such treatment results in short belt life and increased wear on the bearings of the machine.

A common rule for determining necessary belt width is based on the assumption that a belt 1 inch wide will transmit 1 horsepower when running at a speed of 800 feet per minute. As the belt speed is increased the power transmitting ability of the belt increases also.

Rule 1. Horse power to be transmitted divided by belt speed in feet per minute over 800 equals width of belt required in inches.

Rule 2. Belt speed in feet per minute equals diameter of pulley in feet times 3.1416 times revolutions made per minute.

Arc of Contact.—The portion of the pulley coming in contact with the belt is known as the arc of contact. Other things being equal, the greater the arc of contact the less the tendency to slip. With pulleys of equal size the arc of contact is approximately 180 degrees, or half the circumference of the pulley. Where one pulley is larger than the other the arc of contact is greater on the larger pulley.

Where possible the belt should run in a horizontal position with the under side of the belt doing the driving (Fig. 351). Running a crossed belt reverses the motion and increases the arc of contact between belt and pulley. It wears the belt, however, consumes power, and should be avoided where possible.

Fitting Belts.— The simplest way of obtaining the proper length of a belt is to place a steel tape about the pulleys in the position the belt is to occupy, and obtain the measurement direct. If the tape is not available a firm, non-stretching cord can be used for the same purpose. Where it is necessary to order belting before the pulleys are in place, a close approximation

FIG. 352.—Types of belt fasteners: 1, alligator belt fastener; 2, clipper belt fastener; 3, crescent belt plates with rivets; 4, belt hooks; 5, leather lacing.

of the length can be obtained by the following rule:

Rule.—Add the diameters of the driving and driven pulleys in feet. Divide this sum by two and multiply the result by 3.1416. Add to this product two times the distance separating the centers of the pulleys. The result is the length of belt required.

Joining the Ends.—Belts are joined by cementing, lacing, riveting, and by means of many types of patent fasteners (Fig. 352). Lacing with a rawhide thong is a suitable method for use in farm practice. To make a good joint the ends of the belt must be cut off square, and the lace holes spaced and punched accurately. A common mistake is the use of too wide a lacing thong and the use of too few holes in the belt ends.

Lacing for Belts of Different Widths.

Belts up to	Size of lace hole	Width of lace	Distance of first row of holes from end of belt	Distance of 2nd row of holes from end of belt	Distance of holes from edge of belt	Space between holes
3″ wide	$5/32$″	¼″	½″	1 ″	3/8″	¾″
3″ to 6″ wide..	$3/16$″	3/8″	¾″	1–½″	3/8″	1″ to 1–¼″
6″ to 12″ wide..	¼″	3/8″	1″	2 ″	½″	1–½″
Over 12″........	$5/16$″	½″	1–¼″	2–½″	1″	1–¾″

Belts up to 3 inches wide may be laced with but one row of holes.

Determining Pulley Speed.—Every farm machine has a proper speed for operation, and in driving it from an engine or line shaft it is necessary to determine the proper pulley size to give the machine the best operating speed. As a general rule it may be stated that in belting from one pulley to another the speed will vary inversely as the diameters of the pulleys, that is, if a pulley two feet in diameter is belted to one having a diameter of but one foot the speed of the smaller pulley will be twice that of the larger. Problems of this kind fall under the following cases:

Case 1.—To determine the diameter of pulley required for a driven machine to give a certain speed (R.P.M.) when the diameter and speed of the driving pulley are known.

Rule.— the diameter of the driving pulley in inches by the speed (R.P.M.) and divide by the required speed of the driven pulley.

Case 2.—To determine the necessary diameter of driving pulley when the speed is known, to give the required speed to a driven pulley whose diameter is given.

Rule.—Multiply the diameter of the driven pulley in inches by its speed (R. P. M.) and divide the product by the speed at which the driving pulley runs. The result will be the required diameter of the driving pulley.

Care of Belts.—Belts should be kept clean and free from grease. Should a rubber belt of sufficient width for the load imposed upon it persist in slipping, apply a few drops of boiled linseed oil to the pulley side, or use a belt dressing recommended by the belt maker. Do not use soap, rosin or tar to make the belt hold, as they will ruin it.

Job 1.—**Cleaning, Testing and Adjusting a Spark Plug.**— To detect faulty plugs and to so adjust the plug that a strong, hot spark is obtained within the cylinder.

Operations.—1. Remove suspected plug from cylinder with spark plug wrench being careful to avoid cracking porcelain. Preliminary tests can be made by grounding central electrode of plug to engine with screw driver.

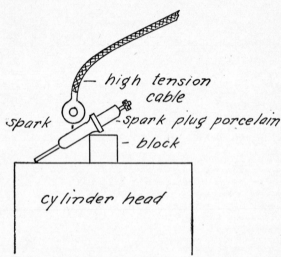

Fig. 353.—Testing a spark plug porcelain for flaws. The porcelain is supported on the cylinder head by a block so that the central electrode is grounded. The high-tension cable is then moved along the porcelain or other insulator. A spark jumping across as shown in the sketch represents an electrical leak or a cracked porcelain.

2. Clean the carbon carefully from the plug by scraping, taking the plug apart for this purpose if the construction permits.

3. If plug is taken apart place the porcelain core on engine with central electrode making contact with metal. (Fig. 353.)

4. With ignition switch on turn engine until coil buzzes and spark is produced at end of high tension wire leading to the plug being tested when wire is brought in contact with metal part of engine. If magneto is used as source of ignition current engine will have to be cranked in single cylinder.

5. Hold end of wire against porcelain core, moving it along the surface. (Fig. 353.) Cracks or electrical leaks in the porcelain are indicated by the spark jumping from the wire to the porcelain. If the core is perfect no spark will pass. This is an excellent method for testing out oil soaked mica core plugs.

6. If the construction of the plug does not permit taking apart, test it by placing several thicknesses of dry paper between the points to increase the resistance. Arrange spark plug with metal shell in contact with metal of engine (grounded), and bring high tension cable to top con-

nection of plug. A spark jumping to the top of the plug indicates a leak in the porcelain core unless it is seen to pass between the points of the plug.

7. If the plug has been taken apart, reassemble it and by careful bending adjust the points to the proper distance apart, using a worn dime as a thickness gauge if no other gauge is available.

8. Bend outside electrode as shown in figure 354 so that oil drops will be led to one side instead of bridging across the gap.

9. Replace in engine and connect up.

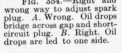

Job 2.—Testing and Adjusting a Make-and-break Ignitor.—To detect trouble and to secure a fat, hot spark for ignition purposes.

FIG. 354.—Right and wrong way to adjust spark plug. *A.* Wrong. Oil drops bridge across gap and short-circuit plug. *B.* Right. Oil drops are led to one side.

Operations.—1. Remove ignition wire from insulated electrode of ignitor block and snap it against clean metal part of engine frame with ignition current turned on. If magneto is used as source of ignition current, engine will have to be cranked while making test. Failure to secure a spark indicates a break in the ignition circuit, a disconnected wire or a dead battery. Test wiring and connections.

2. Turn engine so that ignitor points within the cylinder are separated. They can be held in this position while cranking by removing ignitor trip if it is necessary to crank engine because of use of magneto. Snap ignition wire on insulated electrode. No spark should result. A spark indicates defective insulation about stationary electrode.

3. Again turn the engine so that the ignitor points are forced together and snap ignition wire on stationary electrode. A spark should result. No spark indicates that scale, corrosion or wear is preventing the points from making electrical contact as they should.

4. When trouble is located remove the ignitor block from the engine and correct trouble by cleaning or adjustment. If points are badly scaled or pitted clean by scraping or by use of magneto file. Do not use sand paper.

Job 3.—Cleaning Carbon from an Engine Cylinder.—
Through continued use, poor fuel adjustment or the use of poor lubricating oil, a carbon deposit will form in the cylinder, causing overheating and pre-ignition, indicated by a sharp metallic pound when the engine is working hard.

Operations.—1. Remove the bolts securing the cylinder head. Also remove such other parts of the engine as may be necessary to permit removal of the head. Use perfect fitting socket wrenches for the purpose if obtainable.

2. Remove the head. If cylinder head sticks rap lightly with a mallet and bunt engine back against compression to loosen it.

3. With sharp putty knife, mowing machine section or similar tool scrape all traces of carbon from the inside faces of the head and combustion chamber, leaving the surfaces clean and bright.

4. Wipe out carefully with clean oil moistened cloth.

22

5. Examine valves. If in poor condition fit by grinding. Valves should show a bright ring all around and should not have grooves or shoulders worn in them. If shouldered or blackened indicating the escape of gases, grind as directed in Job 4. If in good condition cut gasket and replace head as directed in Job 5.

Job 4.—**Grinding Valves.**—The valves of an engine should make a perfect fit with their seat. Through use and wear they may develop leaks and must be ground to a gas-tight fit to hold the compression pressure. Leaky valves are indicated by a hissing noise

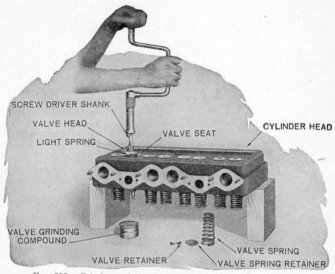

Fig. 355.—Grinding valves. (J. I. Case Threshing Machine Co.)

at the exhaust or intake passages when the engine is turned over against compression.

Operations.—1. Remove head as directed in Job 3.

2. Remove pins and springs holding valves to their seats. Examine valves and seats. If badly pitted or grooved use valve tools to cut new seat and surface valve. If only trouble is a groove cut around the valve by the seat forming a shoulder, it may be removed by careful filing, preserving the original angle of the valve.

3. Apply a small quantity of valve grinding paste to the meeting surfaces of the valve and seat.

4. Insert valve in place with a light coil spring under it to lift it from its seat when the pressure of the valve grinding tool is released. The spring from the intake valve, if of the automatic type, may be used for this purpose.

5. With a valve grinding tool made to fit the openings in the valve

head turn the valve back and forth on its seat, grinding it. The valve should not be turned through a full revolution and care should be taken to stop and start at a different point each time when the motion is reversed. (Fig. 355.)

6. When valve paste ceases to "bite" take the tool from the valve letting it lift from the seat. Apply fresh grinding compound and grind as before, starting with the valve in a new position.

7. Continue grinding in this way until the valve and seat show clean bright meeting surfaces clear around.

8. Wipe valve and seat clean, being careful to get every particle of the grinding material cleaned from the valve and seat.

9. Test grinding by making a series of pencil marks across the face of the meeting surfaces of both valve and seat with a lead pencil. The marks should extend parallel with the stem. Place valve in position and turn a part of a revolution back and forth. If valve fits perfectly the marks on both valve head and seat will be erased. Any marks remaining indicate the need of further grinding.

10. Replace valves and springs in cylinder head, being careful to get them in their proper seats and making sure that the exhaust valve spring is placed on the exhaust valve. Com-

FIG. 356.—Cutting a gasket from sheet asbestos packing.

press springs and insert pins through stems making sure that they are securely locked by the retaining washer or other means provided for the purpose.

11. Cut and apply gasket and head as directed in Job 5.

Job 5.—Cutting and Applying a Cylinder Head Gasket; Replacing Cylinder Head.

—Gas engines are provided with a fireproof gasket between the machined meeting surfaces of the head and cylinder castings to insure a gas-tight fit. When head is removed for cleaning or valve grinding the gasket is frequently destroyed, necessitating the cutting of a new one.

Operations.—1 Clean the meeting surfaces thoroughly by scraping with a putty knife to remove all traces of old gasket material.

2. Lay a sheet of tough hard paper over the inside surface of the cylinder head, hold firmly in position and tap lightly with hammer or smooth mallet around all edges of openings, cutting the paper through.   Fig. 356.)

3. Place this pattern on sheet asbestos gasket material, mark a b o u t openings, and cut out gasket. Make openings for stud bolts with hollow punch of the proper size if available. Gasket when finished should fit freely and lie perfectly flat against the finished surfaces.

4. Apply cup grease or cylinder oil to both sides of gasket. Put gasket in place on end of cylinder and put cylinder head in position.

5. See that the head seats perfectly against the gasket and tighten up the cylinder h e a d

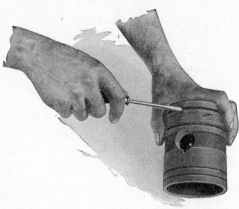

FIG. 357.—Cleaning carbon from piston ring grooves with screw-driver. (J. I. Case Threshing Machine Co.)

bolts carefully and uniformly. Bolts are tightened by turning each up a little at a time, working around and around the head until all are uniformly tight. Drawing a single bolt up tight may result in breaking the bolt or distortion of the head.

6. After engine has run and become heated again tighten up cylinder head bolts. If shellac is used on gasket shellac one side only, greasing the other, permitting easy removal for cleaning purposes.

Job 6.—Fitting Piston Rings.—A piston is fitted with rings to provide a gas-tight fit between the piston and the cylinder walls, and at the

FIG. 358.—Fitting ring to piston. Ring should roll freely in the groove clear around piston, but should fit groove closely. (J. I. Case Threshing Machine Co.)

same time to provide for some expansion due to heat.   Through use and abuse they become carbonized, worn or lose their elasticity, so that they no longer hug the walls, making their replacement necessary.

Operations.—1. Test engine by turning over against compression when well warmed up and lubricated. A hissing sound at the open end of the cylinder or breather pipe indicates leaking rings. Smoke issuing from the open end of cylinder accompanied by a coughing sound when the engine is running also indicate compression escaping by the rings.

2. If leaky rings are indicated, disconnect the connecting rod from crank and pull the piston from the cylinder. Retain bearing shims in their original position and mark the bearing cap so that it may be returned in the position in which found.

3. Remove rings by carefully working three pieces of hack saw blade or other thin steel beneath the ring at the joint and working them about until approximately equally spaced. This lifts the ring from its groove and permits sliding it from the piston. Hang rings as removed on a nail so that they may be returned to original position if found to be all right when piston and rings are cleaned of carbon. Examine for fit with cylinder walls by looking for black spots

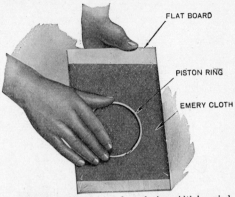

FLAT BOARD

PISTON RING

EMERY CLOTH

FIG. 359.—Fitting rings by reducing width by grinding lightly on emery cloth supported by smooth board. Ring should be supported at as many points as possible by the fingers, and the position changed often to insure even grinding. (J. I. Case Threshing Machine Co.)

on circumference of ring. A black spot indicates escape of gasses at this point. Parts of the ring in contact with cylinder walls are worn bright. Examine ring for wear by inserting it in cylinder and noting gap between ends. Gap should be about one-thousandth of an inch for each inch of cylinder diameter. See whether ring springs out against walls tightly indicating that it has retained its tension.

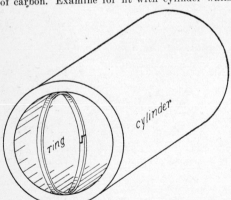

FIG. 360.—Method of inserting ring into cylinder for fitting.

4. Discard rings found to be faulty by above tests.

5. Clean ring grooves in piston carefully scraping out every particle of carbon and charred oil. (Fig. 357.)

6. Fit new rings to piston by placing them in grooves they are to occupy and rolling them about piston. They should fit perfectly clear

around but at the same time freely, rolling around in all parts of the groove without binding. (Fig. 358.) Should the ring be too thick grind on a sheet of fine emery cloth tacked to flat surface. Support ring uniformly with fingers. (Fig. 359.) Test frequently and change position of finger tips often to insure grinding a perfectly flat surface. When fitted clean ring and groove thoroughly.

7. When fitted to piston, place ring in cylinder, figure 360, and turn it about in the position it is to occupy, noting the width of the gap. Gap between ends should be as described in three to provide for expansion due to heat. If ring is too tight fit ends by removing ring and filing carefully between the ends.

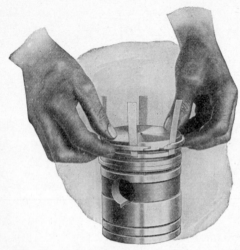

8. Place rings in position on piston by sliding them down over pieces of hack saw blade figure 361, placing the lower ring on first. Place each ring in the groove to which it was fitted.

9. Coat outside of piston and rings with cylinder oil and replace in cylinder. Rings may be compressed and held in position by means of stove pipe wire twisted about them. See that piston is returned in original position so that oil holes will register and any fit, due to wearing in, will be maintained.

FIG. 361.—Putting rings on piston. Rings are slipped down over grooves by means of pieces of hack saw blades or other thin pieces of steel. (J. I. Case Threshing Machine Co.)

10. Attach connecting rod to crank taking care that all shims are replaced in original position and that their edges do not scrape on crank, removing oil film. If bearing is too loose adjust by removing shims of equal thickness from both sides until bearing fits properly when nuts are drawn up tight.

11. Insert cotter pins or wire, locking nuts.

Job 7.—Putting up a Line Shaft.—Where more than one

machine is driven from a single engine a line shaft is required. By a proper selection of pulleys it permits driving a group of machines from the same engine, and at the same time gives each its proper operating speed.

Operations.—1. Hold a straight edge against the finished surface of the balance wheel as shown in figure 362.

2. Drop a plumb bob from each end, marking points A and B on the floor directly beneath each end of the straight edge.

3. With a chalk line strike a line through these points, making a line on the floor at right-angles to the crank shaft of the engine.

4. Mark a point C, in this line at the distance it is desired to locate the shaft from the engine.

5. With this point as a center and a radius of eight feet strike an arc D E as shown.

6. Measure six feet along the line first made from the point C and locate F.

7. With F as a center and a radius of 10′ describe an arc, G H, intersecting arc D E at I.

8. Strike a chalk line through C and I. This will be parallel to the

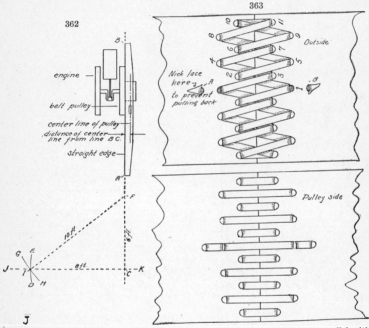

FIG. 362.—Method of laying out center line, J–K, to insure line shaft being parallel with crank shaft of engine.

FIG. 363.—Method of lacing 6-inch belt. Lacing thong is inserted from pulley side of belt up through 1, down through 2, up through 3, down through 4, and so on until outside edge is reached. Lacing is then carried back to middle, first going down through 10 and up through 11, a second time, then down through 8, up through 9, down through 6, and so on until lace is pulled up through A and a nick cut in it to prevent it from pulling out. The other side is laced in the same way with the other half of the lace.

engine crank shaft and represents the center line of the line shaft.

9. Transfer this line to the ceiling by suspending a plumb bob over each end from the ceiling and moving it about until the point of the bob is directly over the line. Mark these points on the ceiling calling them J′ and K′

10. In the same way transfer point C to the ceiling calling it C′.

11. Measure horizontal distance from center of engine belt pulley face to line B A F C.

12. Lay off same distance in same direction from point C′ on ceiling marking the proper location of center of driven pulley face on line shaft.

13. By means of steel square locate positions of hangers supporting shaft at right-angles to line J′K′ and bolt hangers in position so that plumb line dropped from line J′K′ on the ceiling will cut the center of the bearing.

14. Insert shafting in place and adjust to level position by means of

Fig. 364.—Using dividers to space lace holes evenly.

adjustment provided. Where home-made hangers and bearings are used they may be adjusted closely by stretching up a line in the position the

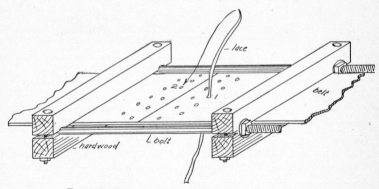

Fig. 365.—Home-made belt clamp applied to belt for lacing.

shaft is to occupy and adjusting the bearings to it. Shims may be used beneath them to bring them to the point desired.

15. When shaft is level adjust top half of bearings.

16. Place pulleys of size required to drive machines at proper speed at points desired.

17. By means of plumb bob and line transfer center line of each pulley face to the floor and by method previously outlined strike a line through

this point at right-angles to line J K, to be used as a guide in setting the machines.

18. Set driven machines parallel to these lines with center lines of pulley faces coinciding with them.

.Job 8.—**Fitting and Lacing a Six-inch Belt.**—A belt is used to connect a motor to a driven machine. Unless ordered endless the ends must be joined by some means that will be strong and will run

Fig. 366.—Lacing a belt. Note use of belt awl for making lace holes in canvas belt.

smoothly over the pulley. Lacing with a leather thong is quickly done and is satisfactory for most farm uses.

Operations.—1. Determine width of belt required to transmit power by method given on page 333. In this case assume 6″ as width found.

2. Measure length of belt required and purchase required amount.

3. Square and cut off each end with sharp knife or chisel.

4. Determine size, spacing and number of holes required in each end of belt from table, page 335. In case of 6″ belt place first row of holes ¾″ from end of belt with holes in end of row ⅜″ from edge of belt. Use six holes ³/₁₆″ diameter spaced 1-¹/₁₆″ apart in the first row. Second row contains five holes placed 1-½″ from the belt end with same spacing as front row, the holes being located midway between those in the first row. (Fig. 363.)

5. When spacing is determined mark and punch holes for lacing thong. (Fig. 364.) Use dividers and square to get holes located accurately. Make holes with punch of size required. With canvas belt use belt awl.

6. If belt clamp is available, figure 365, place belt on pulleys, apply clamp and draw belt ends squarely up together. If no clamp is available lace as shown in figures 363 and 366.

7. Select lacing of proper width, point the end and wet and singe it with match to make it horn-like for lacing.

8. Push end of lace up through hole. Pull half its length through hole and turn so that hair side of lace will lie next to pulley.

9. Push end of lace down through two, up through three, down through four, figure 363, and so on until outside hole is reached. The lace should then go down through ten, up through eleven, down through ten again, and again up through eleven when it goes back down through eight up through nine and so on back to the center.

10. Lace the other side in the same way.

11. When both lace ends have been returned to the center put them up through holes A and B, punched for the purpose and fasten by cutting into one side forming a barb. (Fig. 363.) The lace may be cut off on the outside of the belt. Should a lacing thong be too short it may be spliced by cutting a slit in the end of each piece and pulling each through the other.

Suggested Gas Engine Jobs and Repairs

1. Hunt and locate ignition trouble.
2. Repair wiring.
3. Install new wiring.
4. Clean and adjust breaker points.
5. Adjust governor to higher speed.
6. Adjust governor to lower speed.
7. Clean sticking governor.
8. Replace broken timing gear.
9. Hunt fuel trouble.
10. Repair leaking fuel line.
11. Test fuel line for stoppage.
12. Clean carburetor bowl and jets.
13. Adjust engine to proper idling speed.
14. Oil engine and fill and turn down grease cups.
15. Clean sticking valves.
16. Install new fan belt.
17. Clean cooling system and fill with anti-freeze mixture.
18. Repair leaky radiator.
19. Fit crankshaft bearing.
20. Fit connecting rod bearing.

INDEX

23